# Man, Nature and History

# W. M. S. Russell

# Man, Nature and History

## Controlling the Environment

Nature and Science Library

published for

The American Museum of Natural History

by The Natural History Press/Garden City, New York

The Natural History Press, publishers for The
American Museum of Natural History, is a division
of Doubleday & Company, Inc. The Press is
directed by an editorial board made up of
members of the staff of both the Museum and
Doubleday. The Natural History Press has its
editorial offices at The American Museum of
Natural History, Central Park West at 79th Street,
New York, New York 10024, and its business offices
at 501 Franklin Avenue, Garden City, New York

First published in the United States of America in 1969 by
The Natural History Press, Garden City, New York
in association with Aldus Books Limited
Library of Congress Catalog Card Number 69—17354
© Aldus Books Limited, London, 1967

Printed in Italy by Arnoldo Mondadori, Verona

# Contents

# 1 Man and Nature

In ancient times, so Greek poets tell us, there lived two brothers, Prometheus ("the Forethinker") and Epimetheus ("the Afterthinker"). Prometheus was the wisest of beings. He taught mankind every art and science. Above all, he brought man the precious gift of fire, which he stole from Zeus the god of thunder, and brought safely to earth as a smoldering ember concealed in a giant fennel-stalk. Furious at the loss of his monopoly, the tyrant Zeus determined to punish mankind and to check its advance to civilization. He created from clay a woman of supreme beauty, called Pandora ("All-gifts"), and gave her a sealed treasure-jar—Pandora's Box. Prometheus warned his brother against Pandora, and urged him, above all, not to open the box. But Zeus had Prometheus seized and chained to a rock in the lonely mountains of the Caucasus. Then Zeus sent Pandora to Epimetheus, who was too frightened to resist. It was not long before they opened the box. Out flew all the evils that have plagued mankind ever since.

All myths contain elements of truth. In Prometheus, we see all that is most creative in man. In Zeus, we see all that is irrational and destructive. In Epimetheus, we see the inertia or momentum of human behavior in the mass. But also, the clay-woman Pandora is the unpredictable earth, and the thunder-god is the violence of the atmosphere. This legend is the story of man and nature: a story of bold creative discovery, and of evils let loose by action or inaction, sometimes thoughtless or mischievous, often simply misguided, from ignorance of the intricate ways of nature. But nature, in fact, is neither tyrannical nor deceitful. It is just incredibly complicated. For nature is only another word for the surroundings, or environment, in which human societies live.

## Three Views of Man and Environment

This book is about the story of man and nature. This is the subject of the science of human *ecology*. The word (like *economy*) comes from the Greek word *oikos*, meaning a household. It could mean a very big and complex household. The *oikos* of an ancient Pharaoh meant the land of Egypt. The earth is a big and complex household indeed. And, whether we run it well or badly, it has become the household of man.

Many people in many ages and many places have contributed to the study of human ecology, of man and his

In Greek mythology, fire was brought to mankind by Prometheus, who stole it from Zeus and carried it back to earth in a fennel-stalk. The illustration above is from a painting by the Flemish artist Rubens (1577–1640).

Right: An 18th-century engraving of a volcano erupting. A decisive moment in man's history was his discovery that he could make use of fire produced by nature—for instance, a burning piece of wood picked up after an eruption.

Three important figures in the study of man and nature. Top: Henry Buckle; center: George Marsh; bottom: Gordon Childe. Their ideas—which all stress that man's history is a story of increasing control of nature—form the basic themes of this book.

environment. But we can take two ideas from two books written about a century ago. The first, by the British historian Henry Thomas Buckle (1821–62), saw the history of man as one of increasing independence of nature, achieved by discovery and invention. Buckle showed that human societies were at first completely at the mercy of their surroundings. These dictated each society's history in relentless detail, giving opportunities to some and terrible handicaps to others. But as a society became more independent of nature, its history began to depend more and more on the social behavior of the human beings composing it, and on the social organization that developed.

The second book was written by the American diplomat George Perkins Marsh (1801–82). He showed that man's influence on his surroundings had steadily increased until he himself had finally become the most important single factor on earth. His influence could be used to increase his independence; but only if he learned how to run his household well. Civilizations of the past had succumbed not only to the pressures of uncontrolled nature, but also to the results of man's own uncontrolled actions upon it.

In the twentieth century, the Australian archeologist Gordon Childe developed a third theme. He showed that all the progress that so impressed Buckle had been achieved by means of a *surplus of food.* If each human could produce only enough food for himself, nobody would have time for discoveries or inventions. But if one man could produce more food than he himself required, others would be free to devote their time to different skills and, above all, to make and apply new discoveries. We shall see that every advance has in fact depended on a rising surplus. Food production, and especially agriculture, will be one of our main concerns in this book. Even our fantastic twentieth century civilization, with its computers and nuclear reactors, still rests on the shoulders of the farmer and the fisherman.

In order to achieve a food surplus, man had, literally, to change the face of the earth. Suppose three satellites with cameras had remained in fixed orbit over the earth for the last million years, so placed that together they could view almost the whole surface. And suppose also the composite film they took could be speeded up. We should then see huge, cyclical changes in the landscape throughout this period. These would all be natural changes. But in the last 10,000 years, the film would show changes of a cumulative kind, for man was beginning to take over the household. We might then begin to look further back in the film for smaller man-made changes. It is possible we should find these beginning as far back as a quarter of a million years ago.

Above: These harvest scenes from a tomb at Thebes, in ancient Egypt, symbolize the importance of a food surplus in the rise of a society. Such a surplus frees some men from producing their own food, allowing them to develop other skills.
Below: Model of ancient Egyptian grain storage vessels.

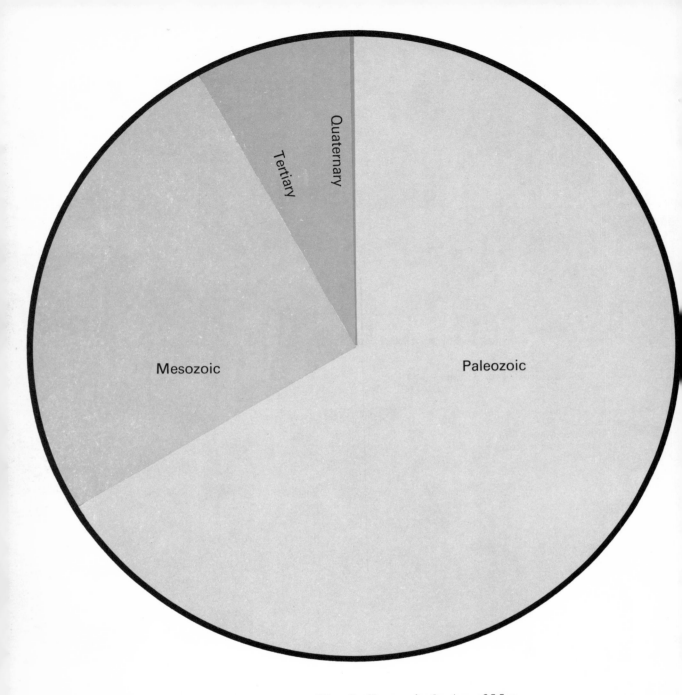

Quaternary

Tertiary

Mesozoic

Paleozoic

Clock diagram shows to scale the four great geological eras of life on earth. Throughout the total period, life is advanced enough to provide abundant fossilized traces. Man appeared at the start of the Quaternary, less than two million years ago.

## Climatic Changes in the Age of Man

The age of man coincides with what geologists call the Quaternary Period, the fourth great period of life on earth. So far it has lasted over a million years (see diagram, p. 14). In the third period, or Tertiary, the land filled with grasses, trees, mammals, and insects. Plants and animals familiar to us today began to dominate the scene. When the Tertiary began, the world landscape was rather dull and uniform. There had been little change for a long time. Now, a period of mountain building began, reaching

a climax in our own age. This had happened before, at fairly regular intervals, but in the Quaternary the world *climate* suddenly went mad. The complete new cover of higher plants, actively modifying the atmosphere, may have had something to do with it. But nobody really knows what made the Quaternary a time of such change and contrast. At any rate, for the first time in 200 million years great caps of ice covered the polar regions. The age of man is the age of ice.

However it came about, the freezing of the poles

During the Tertiary, the earth's climate was much warmer than it is now. There were no great icecaps over the poles, and temperate plants grew there. Photo shows a poplar leaf fossilized in a rock dug up from beneath the ice in Greenland.

produced violent contrasts in climate over the earth. Climate really means temperature and humidity near the land surface. In principle, temperature simply falls at higher altitudes and latitudes. It is colder as you go up a mountain or toward the poles. In practice, this simple principle is disturbed by movements of warm and cold currents around the oceans. These currents may have different effects on coastal and inland regions, on west and east coasts. The same latitude spans frosty Newfoundland, the Gobi desert, and England's mild "Riviera."

Humidity is more complicated than temperature. Water evaporates from the seas and is taken up by warm air. If the warm air comes into contact with a zone of cold air—say, around a mountain top—it is cooled, and the water condenses, falling as snow or rain and moistening the earth's surface. So everything depends on wind movements from sea to land. Winds in turn depend on two things. At the equator, the air goes around with the earth once in 24 hours, just as it does near the poles. But the air at the equator covers a much greater distance in that time, so it travels much faster. Also, the air at the equator is warm. It rises and flows north and south over the cool air in higher latitudes until it gets so cold that it sinks and returns. This process makes the great wind belts (see diagram). At the equator, the air stagnates in the doldrums. In the tropics, it blows from the east, and in temperate regions it blows from the west. When the winds reach a coast, they gradually give up their moisture, especially if they strike a mountain. So regions far inland, on the wrong coast, or on the wrong side of mountains, may suffer from drought. All this is complicated by ocean currents and other factors. But again the freezing of the poles, by intensifying the mixing of air from different latitudes, has moved the stormy west-wind belt nearer the equator, and changed the pattern of moisture for the whole world.

Thus there is contrast from region to region in space, but there is contrast in time, too. During the Quaternary, probably all around the world, the icecap has advanced four times to cover much of the great northern continents, and four times receded again, each time producing huge changes in the climate of all regions. Each such *glaciation* (as it is called) and the intervening period (the *interglacial*) shifted great masses of rock as the huge ice glaciers surged over the land. And as great quantities of water were locked up in the ice and then released the level of the oceans fell and rose, bridging or separating land masses. It was a time of incredible upheaval, with continually shifting climates, changing vegetations, and migrating animals and men. It still is. The great period of human progress, the rise of agriculture and civilization, falls in

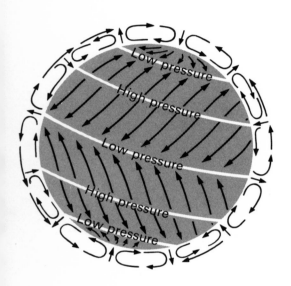

The world's major wind systems depend on two factors. (1) Air circulation. Hot air at the equator rises and moves toward the poles. At about latitude 30° (the high-pressure regions), some of this air has cooled enough to descend to earth, though some drifts on to the poles. At latitude 60°, low-pressure regions are formed by warm air rising as it meets cold air from the poles. (2) Winds near the equator move faster than at the poles. Together these factors produce a continual mixing of air traveling at different speeds, resulting in the great wind belts.

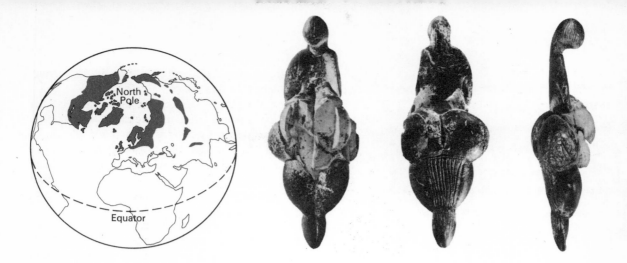

Top left: Black indicates land covered by ice during the four glaciations of the Quaternary. The photograph above shows the edge of the Greenland icecap. During the glaciations, such a scene would have been visible as far south as central England and northern United States.

Man's physical history begins with the Quaternary, but he began to shape his environment only at the end of the fourth glaciation. Among his early creations were carved human figures such as the "Venus of Welendorf" (above right; three views), which is about six inches high.

the fourth interglacial. And, for all we know, there may be a fifth glaciation in due course.

Within each glaciation there have also been smaller cycles of glacial advance and retreat. And within each interglacial there have been similar smaller cycles of climatic change. In Europe, the last interglacial began about 8000 B.C. with the Pre-Boreal period. The continent began to warm up, and in the Boreal phase (from about 7000 B.C.) it became warm and dry. Next came the warm, moist, Atlantic phase, from about 5000 to 2000 B.C.—a critical period for European man, as we shall see. In the succeeding Sub-Boreal, Europe became drier again. Finally, in the Sub-Atlantic period, from about 500 B.C., came an age both colder and wetter, and this is still with us. But even within this tiny 2500-year period there have been still smaller oscillations.

From A.D. 1000 to 1300, Europe enjoyed a warm spell, when the south of England grew excellent grapes. But from 1550 to 1850, Europe had a Little Ice Age, when oxen could often be roasted on the frozen Thames. The latest warm spell began in 1900 and, it is thought, was on the turn again by 1940. These little ripples, so trivial to a geologist, have not been trivial for plant and animal life, still less for human history. Vines in England may be paid for by drought in parts of Africa. Nor can we stop at the ripples. The North American drought from 1928 to 1937 was an historic event. Every farmer knows that climate fluctuates from year to year—we then begin to call it weather. All in all, we have been living, and are living still, in an exceptionally agitated world. Climatically speaking, there's never a dull moment.

**The Vegetation Responds**

All this contrast and change has been reflected in the vegetation that makes up the landscape of the earth. It would show up dramatically on our imaginary satellite film. To begin with, we shall stop the film at some recent point in time and see how climate affects vegetation in different parts of the world. On such a still, the world divides into climatic *zones* (see diagram). Around the poles, it is too cold and frosty nearly all the year round for most plants. Near the equator, it is warm and rainy all the time. In some regions (the great deserts) it is nearly always dry. In others, notably in North China, in parts of India, and in a great belt running from north to south across the middle of Canada and the U.S.A., there is a dry season that may limit vegetation if there is a climatic ripple. In most of Western Europe, it is rarely dry or frosty for long—a climate very friendly to plant life.

Few plants survive prolonged frost or drought. But, within limits, plant species vary enormously in their

Top: An 11th-century manuscript showing work in an English vineyard in February. The warm spell that affected Europe at this time was succeeded by a cold spell, beginning about 1550. Lower illustration is an engraving of a fair held on London's frozen Thames River in February 1814.

living requirements, and each is adapted for particular conditions. The three chief factors in the life of a plant are climate, soil, and the influence of *other* plants and animals. Soil in itself is a complicated household (which we shall examine in later chapters) and depends on the other two factors. Soils do vary from place to place, and this helps to determine the pattern of plant distribution. The pattern is complicated by the fact that plants and

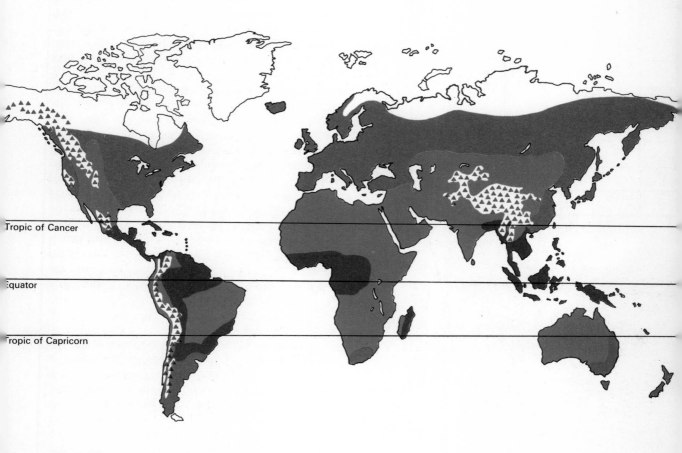

Tropic of Cancer

Equator

Tropic of Capricorn

desert, area liable to drought, savanna, woodland and desert

temperate, varied climate and vegetation

wet tropics, rain-forest

mountain ranges

polar, cold, sparse vegetation

The map above divides the world into the broad climate/vegetation regions that are used throughout this book.

Each combination of soil and climate favors a particular sort of vegetation. The flora of the tundra—like this Iceland poppy—are hardy, especially suited to the cold and windy conditions and to the brief summer.

animals themselves tend to change the conditions of soil and even of climate. Hence, when a piece of ground is colonized by plants, we observe a gradual *succession* of events.

Trees, for instance, differ in their tolerance (as young seedlings) of direct sunlight. Some like sunshine, others prefer shade. In certain conditions, trees may begin to grow in a field of grass. The first to get a foothold (in parts of North America) may be certain kinds of pine, birch, and poplar that can stand the sun. As they grow, such trees offer shade for tulip poplars or red oaks, which in these conditions can grow better than the original trees. These trees, thriving in moderate shade, eventually crowd out the pioneers that gave them their nursery. In time they grow so thick that their own seedlings die from lack of sunlight. In the dense shade, beech, sugar maple, and hemlock thrive, and finally these shade-loving trees take over the forest.

At the end of any such succession, we may come to a kind of vegetation (such as beech, sugar maple, and hemlock) that is equipped to make the most of the local soil and climate conditions. When this *climax* stage is reached, we have the richest possible vegetation for the region. Up the sides of a mountain, as soil and climate change, we see a series of such climaxes, belts of different trees, each equipped to exploit its own bit of the mountain. And, on a wider scale, the climatic zones of the world are reflected in zones of vegetation, each the climax for its own region. In less hospitable regions there are deserts or bogs, or the brief-flowering *tundra* vegetation of the frozen north. In more hospitable regions there are, on the whole, two chief kinds of natural vegetation. They are forests (of different kinds) and grasslands.

In general, forests are adapted to take advantage of long growing seasons and plentiful water. Deep rooted and continuously dropping their dead leaves, they make a kind of soil that stores water and releases it slowly. The dense foliage cuts down wind and sunlight, reducing the evaporation of water. Grasses, on the other hand, have evolved to take advantage of a short growing season, and to extract every ounce of water from transient rains. Their roots form a huge mat or sod near the surface of the soil, ready to drink greedily. But they must also have plenty of sunlight. In areas of seasonal drought, therefore, forests are liable to give way to grasslands. Given a few moist seasons, trees begin to edge into the prairie, shading and dominating the grasses. But a few seasons of drought, and the grass wins back its territory by drinking up the rain before it sinks to the deep tree roots. Over large areas, there may be various degrees of compromise: woodlands with clearings, savannas with scattered trees or copses,

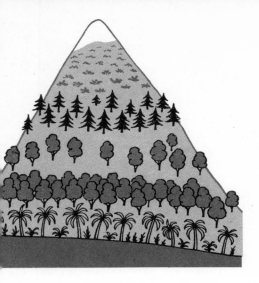

Above: Diagram shows the succession of vegetation up a mountainside. First come tropical forests, then hardwood forests, then cone-bearing forests. Above the treeline come shrubs and herbs, and finally—nearest the snowline—mosses and lichens.

prairies with an occasional tough shrub. When we remember that we stopped our film to see all this, we can see that, as climates fluctuate, the boundaries of forest and prairie must be continually changing as well.

Once a vegetation is established, it supports a great and complicated community of animals, some pruning the vegetation, others preying on the vegetarians. A delicate balance is reached, but the slightest disturbance may be enough to finish a forest. For instance, in the White River National Forest in Colorado, a heavy wind one year blew down a few spruce trees. Bark beetles attacked the fallen trees. Woodpeckers, which formerly kept the beetle numbers down, could not get at them on the branch-tangled undersides. The beetles multiplied until the woodpeckers could no longer control them, even when they emerged from shelter. The uncontrolled beetle swarms spread out and killed the forest. The forest soil was still there, and new trees could have grown, but now a new factor appeared. Over large areas of this forest, the dead trees dried out until they were like tinder. Came the lightning (or maybe, in this case, the careless smoker), and the dead trees went up in a blaze. The special forest soil was burned, and could no longer store water. Today these areas are covered with grassland.

Fire is, in a way, an extreme consequence of drought, for most vegetation will not burn unless it is very dry. Fires caused by lightning or volcanoes have been common enough for plants to evolve that are specially adapted to cope with them. Grasses can stand having their leaves burned off, even every year. Roots, suckers, and seeds underground enable them to survive. Indeed, in the shattering conditions of the Quaternary, annual grasses and other annual plants seem to have evolved in large numbers. A brief spell of leaf growth is enough for them to flower and store the food in tough seeds, and, provided they get these spells, it does not matter what happens above ground. These annuals were to be of vital importance to man, for from them came most of his crop plants. A few trees can also stand fire. They have a fireproof bark, or maintain much of their growth below ground, so they can sprout again when the fire has passed. Naturally they are prominent in areas where both grass and trees are to be found.

So much for our film still. If we start the film moving again, it will reveal a picture of continuous change in space and time. It is sometimes said that there is a balance of nature. In the Quaternary at least it is a hair-trigger balance. Yet over the earth as a whole, the ratio of forest to grassland might have hovered around a broad average. Such was the state of the earth when man arrived to change it.

Above: Engelman spruce trees encroaching on grassland in a park in Colorado.

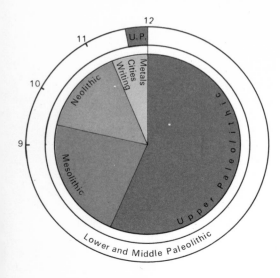

Diagram of archaeological eras, which are based on levels of cultural advance. The outer clock shows the Lower and Middle Paleolithic in relation to the Upper Paleolithic. The inner ring repeats the Upper Paleolithic (from 12 to about 7), then shows, to scale, the approximate "times" when more advanced stages first appeared somewhere on earth.

Dots in diagram below indicate first use of fire in four regions of the world. Also shown are the times of the glaciations in Europe (left column) and of the broad climatic changes in Africa (right column).

| | Europe | West Asia | Far East | Africa | Climate Africa |
|---|---|---|---|---|---|
| Glacial | | | 50,000 | | Wet |
| | | ● | 100,000 | ● | |
| | | | | | Dry |
| Glacial | | | | | Wet |
| | ● | | 250,000 | | |
| | | | | | Dry |
| Glacial | | | ● | | Wet |
| | | | 500,000 | ❓ | Dry |

## The Gift of Prometheus

Just as geologists have divided the age of life into eras, so archeologists have divided the age of man into phases (see diagram). But, whereas the geological eras are the same for the whole earth, the archeological phases are based on levels of cultural advance, and thus vary in different places. Even today, there are tribal peoples living in every phase back to the Mesolithic (or Middle Stone Age). But one thing emerges clearly: Over the whole earth, more than 90 per cent of man's existence has been spent at the very low cultural level of the Lower and Middle Paleolithic.

During the long reaches of the Lower and Middle Paleolithic, man was a food-gatherer. Modern experiments have shown that his crude stone tools, admirable for butchery, were poor missiles for bringing down big game. So he snapped up all available trifles—roots, berries, grubs, small game, carrion left by carnivores. Now and then, with a little bit of luck, he brought down or trapped a big-game animal. It has been estimated that his diet was 75 per cent vegetable matter.

Nevertheless, for a quarter of a million years the food-gatherer had one potent weapon that must at last have begun to make hunting profitable and to pave the way for later refinements—the gift of Prometheus.

In the eighteenth century, Benjamin Franklin, the Prometheus of Philadelphia, gave man a second and still more potent fire by flying a kite in a thunderstorm. He showed that lightning, and therefore electricity, could be controlled by man. It is probable that Franklin's predecessors, who gave man his first fire, stole it, like him, from the thunder-god. That is, they found a fire started by lightning and learned to control it.

To *start* a fire is a difficult operation. It can be done by striking stone containing silicon against stone containing sulphur, or stone against steel, as in the striker of a modern cigarette-lighter. Or it can be done by the friction of wood on wood—rubbing one piece along a groove in another (fire-plow), sawing one piece across a slot in another (fire-saw), or twirling one piece in a hole in another (fire-drill). Such methods are so laborious that modern tribes with primitive strikers always carry embers in some portable device that keeps them lit for long periods. This has been reported, for instance, in New Guinea, Patagonia, Australia, Chile, and almost all the tribes of western North America. Greek islanders still carry fire in the pith of a giant fennel-stalk, just as Prometheus did in the legend.

The oldest fire-striker known is a lump of iron pyrites with a groove in it (the result of repeated striking by a piece of flint). It was found in a cave in Belgium, and

Top: Crude stone tools of Paleolithic man, ranging from pebble tools (1 and 2) to a hand ax (3), a scraper (4), and other pointed tools (5 and 6).

Above: To these Australian aborigines, as to all primitive peoples, fire remains important as a source of heat and as a versatile hunting weapon.

Drawing of the oldest known piece of
fire-making apparatus—a lump of iron
pyrites with a groove in it, found in
the Trou de Chaleux cave in Belgium.
The sparks produced by striking the pyrites
with a piece of flint will easily ignite dry
tinder.

A representation by the 16th-century
Italian artist Nicoletto de Modena of
an ancient Roman vestal virgin, who
carried out the state worship of the
goddess Vesta. The ritual surrounding
the sacred flame, which was kept always
burning, was considered essential to the
survival of the state. Flames were
also kept continually alight in homes.

dates from the Upper Paleolithic. The method may have been discovered while working flints, and was probably the earliest known. It is still used in Greenland and Tierra del Fuego. The power to *start* fire was probably a very late development. As late as the 1950's, the Camayuras of the Amazon jungle did not have this art. But they knew all about *controlling* fire. They kept a fire continually burning in each village (probably started by "foreign technicians" from more advanced tribes further north). Anyone going on a journey took with him a smoldering torch of resinous wood, lit at the village fire before he started. The same thing is reported of the Andaman islanders. And we know that the power to keep the home fires burning goes back a quarter of a million years, to the caves of Choukoutien, the earliest known hearths of mankind. Before these fire-using men took them over, the caves were occupied by bears and hyenas. It has been suggested that man's first use of the precious fire was to drive off dangerous animals. The first reward was the occupation of caves, an unprecedented luxury. Other bonuses must have followed: cooking, heating, lighting, and the power to colonize the cooler lands of earth.

## Controlling the Environment

As soon as man could keep fire alight, he became a potent new factor in the perpetual struggle between forest and grassland. When fire was so difficult to start, and still more when it was necessary to wait for another natural fire if it went out, keeping fire alight was enormously more urgent than putting it out. This concern survived in the perpetual flame of the hearth-goddess Vesta in ancient Rome, and in the Olympic torch to this day. Tribesmen from all parts of the world (not to speak of civilized peoples) have been reported as leaving campfires burning—none have ever been reported as carefully putting them out. So when the vegetation was dry enough, man must often have been responsible for burning it, even without any special motives.

In fact there is every indication, from the behavior of modern tribes, that man had plenty of positive motives for changing forest to grassland as soon as he could do it. The first obvious advantage was to improve visibility and ease of movement, making it easier to see both game and dangerous animals. In Oregon and northern California, Klamath and Pomo Indians complained to the anthropologist Omer C. Stewart that modern forest conservation was ruining their hunting. "Now," said one of them, "I just hear the deer running through the brush at places we used to kill many deer. When the brush got as thick as it is now, we would burn it off." The next step, of course, was the deliberate fire drive—that is, setting fires to drive animals into an area where they can be hunted down. This method is used by hunters today in parts of America, Africa, Asia, and Australia, but it must have been even more valuable in the days when man's weapons were so poor.

These are all motives for getting rid of forest and opening up the countryside. A more sophisticated practice, adopted by hunting tribes in America, Asia, and Africa, is the deliberate maintenance and improvement of grassland by burning to attract—and also to allow to multiply—grazing game animals. This must have been a fairly late development, and we are here on the threshold of pastoral stockraising. In fact, when agriculture and stockraising eventually began, burning was, and remains to this day, a widely used method of improving pasture in many parts of the world. The most primitive form of agriculture is to clear forest by burning, cultivate for a while, and then move on. When this happens, grasses invade the plot, and later this new grassland is maintained as pasture by burning. This is, to a large extent, the story of agriculture in Africa.

It is clear that Paleolithic man, from Choukoutien times onward, had motive, means, and opportunity for creating grasslands. And we have circumstantial evidence that he actually did so. In the southeastern U.S.A., there is a large area of grassland mixed with longleaf pinewoods. Now the longleaf can survive having its leaves burned off several times. Lightning is rare here, and the first Europeans in the area told of vigorous fire-drives by the Indians. When they put a stop to this in the parklands of the Shenandoah Valley, back came the fire-vulnerable hardwood forests. Between 1829 and 1854, after burning had been stopped, trees and brush returned to 60 per cent of the Wisconsin prairie. Much of Illinois—prairie when the Europeans arrived—is now heavily forested where it is not farmed. Forest has made similar gains over prairie in Kentucky, Ohio, Michigan, Indiana, and Texas. All this suggests that the Indians were using fire to maintain grass in large areas where forest would normally prevail. On Long Island, the Hempstead Plains (250 square miles) were being burned by Indians as long ago as 1670, mainly for snaring migrant birds. When the burning stopped, tree cover took over.

We must remember that the Europeans did their best to stop fires caused by lightning as well as man-made ones. Primitive man was not the only cause of fires, and hence of grassland. Lightning set large Kansas ranges on fire in the summer of 1911. But in parts of Pennsylvania and northern California, where lightning is rare, scars of ancient trees betray repeated fires for the last 2000 years. And since we know that the Indians made fires in historical

Two photographs taken during the plot-burning experiments carried out from 1949 to 1960 in northern Ghana. The photo on this page shows an area of savanna grassland that was burned each year early in the dry season. The picture was taken at the height of the growing season and shows the relatively scattered trees, and tall and medium grasses.

Photo above shows an area protected from fire. The trees are densely distributed, and the grasses are tall and thick.

times, they may have been doing so ever since they reached the continent. Thus it seems likely that the grasslands of North America were greatly enlarged by man. There are similar reasons to believe that he did so in many other lands—India, Ceylon, Sumatra, the Philippines, New Zealand, Brazil, even, to some extent, the great steppe of southern Russia.

A good example is the Guinea savanna grassland zone of West Africa. A careful experiment was carried out from 1949 to 1960 by J. M. Ramsay and R. Rose Innes, near the Red Volta River in northern Ghana, on three 10-acre plots of land. Every year, one plot was burned late in the dry season, when the vegetation was like tinder. One plot was burned early in the dry season, when the vegetation was still green and more resistant to fire damage. And one plot was protected from fire altogether. The late-burned plot ended up as open grassland with scattered fire-trees, the early-burned plot as a fairly equal mixture of trees and grass, and the protected plot as a woodland

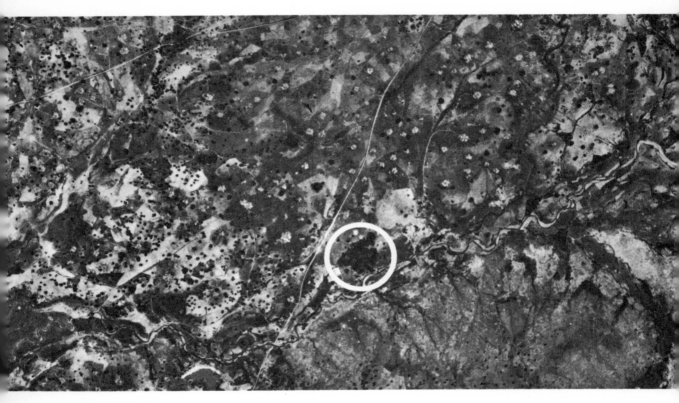

with some tall grasses. This all happened within a period of 11 years.

In the Guinea savanna zone, fierce fires rage in the dry season. Nearly all, according to Ramsay and Rose Innes, are started by man: "Hunters fire the grass to flush wild animals out of hiding; graziers burn off harsh stubble to promote the growth of fresh green herbage for their herds; others seem to start fires merely for the excitement of seeing a good blaze; but the commonest cause is undoubtedly due to allowing 'legitimate' fires (for clearing farms, cooking meals in the bush, etc.) to spread to surrounding land." This has been the story of the African grasslands for a long time. Sailing down the west coast of Africa in search of openings for trade in the fifth century B.C., Hanno the Carthaginian saw many fires blazing in

Top: A fetish grove near Mayoro, Ghana. Regarded as sacred, the grove has been protected from fire and remains a dense woodland while all around it (see aerial view above) there are only scattered trees in open grassland. Light colored patches are currently cultivated ground.

inhabited regions every night. Flying over central Africa on his way to a conference on prehistory in A.D. 1955, the British anthropologist Kenneth Oakley saw signs of fire almost all the way. Sometimes he could "count up to a dozen columns of smoke rising from the landscape spread out below."

But where land in this zone has not been burned by man, it remains as woodland. This can be seen, for example, in the Red Volta area, where "fetish groves" of up to five acres exist. These have been protected from fire as sacred cemeteries, and their vegetation is dense woodland. Sacred groves of this kind, densely wooded in the midst of grassland, have been found elsewhere in Africa, and also in Asia and Indonesia.

We must be careful not to suppose that all grasslands in the great continents are man-made. The mere fact that large numbers of grazing animals evolved in these places before man controlled fire is conclusive evidence that extensive grasslands were there anyway. Indeed, the animals may have contributed to their formation. The evidence does suggest, however, that Paleolithic man, once equipped with fire, greatly enlarged the grasslands and reduced the forests. So already, in these early sequences, our film shows evidence of human activity. One piece of evidence, small and local in itself, gives us a revealing glimpse of events in those early days, in a close-up shot that takes us right onto the scene.

In 1956 the British scientist Richard West reported the results of a study of layers of deposits in an ancient lake-bed at Hoxne in Suffolk, England. The site was already famous, for it was here, in 1797, that John Frere recognized the artificial nature of certain stones: crude tools of early Paleolithic man. West was studying layers of pollen. Now the skin of a grain of pollen is almost indestructible, and the pollen of every flowering plant species is different. Moreover pollen is light and therefore blows over wide areas. So, ever since the method was suggested by the Swede Lennart von Post in 1916, pollen has been an invaluable signpost for the archeologist. By noting the relative frequencies of different kinds of pollen in successive layers at a site, he can tell the proportions of different kinds of plants (the vegetation, in fact) over a wide area during successive periods. West was studying pollen sequences in part of the second interglacial, not far from the time of the Choukoutien hearths in faraway Asia. He found that, over this period, the pollen of a mixed oak forest became rarer, while grass pollen increased in frequency. There was no indication of a change in climate—but just at this point there appeared, for the first time, the rough stone tools of Paleolithic man.

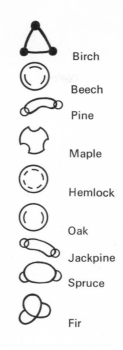

Birch

Beech

Pine

Maple

Hemlock

Oak

Jackpine

Spruce

Fir

Diagram below plots relative quantities of pollen grains of different plants found beneath a lake in Quebec. Borings were made of depths between about 28 and 40 feet; this represents one to two thousand years. Key to pollen grains is above. The type of climate indicated by the vegetation is listed on the right of the diagram.

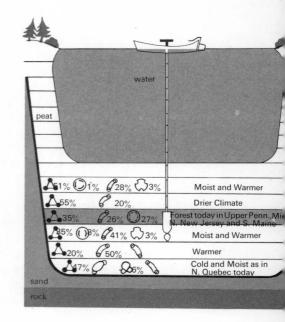

# 2 The Pioneers

Through the long reaches of the Lower and Middle Paleolithic, there were great shifts of vegetation, as ice sheets advanced and retreated in the temperate latitudes. Meanwhile the zones near the equator grew wetter or drier in their corresponding periods—known as the *pluvials* and *interpluvials*. Barely noticeable against these swings, and yet with increasing persistence, the grassland gradually increased at the expense of forest. During the long ages after the Choukoutien hearths, the advance of human culture was extremely slow. Small human groups spread over most parts of the Old World, retreating before glaciers or deserts, but always returning to spread a little more widely. Then, in the fourth glaciation, the scope and diversity of tool manufacture suddenly leapt forward, and man became a superlative hunter and fisherman. This jump was so striking that many people believe it was based on the greatest of all human advances—the appearance of language that allowed techniques and ideas to be passed on much more rapidly than by visible demonstration. Certainly, by the last few millennia of the fourth glaciation human hunters and fishermen were equipped with impressive sets of stone, bone, and probably leather tools.

We have seen that the great achievements of human societies are based on a food surplus. The only permanently reliable surplus (so far) has been provided by agriculture. But when game is especially plentiful, efficient hunters may enjoy a temporary surplus and use it to remarkable effect. Hunters of the last part of the glaciation in France and Spain enjoyed such a surplus. The result is seen on the walls of the caves at Lascaux and Altamira, in animal drawings and paintings of great beauty and astonishing accuracy. This extraordinary culture lasted only as long as the game that supported it remained in abundance. The societies of the Mesolithic that followed it in Europe continued to advance impressively in hunting technology and in the elaboration of tools. Meanwhile, two other things happened. During this glaciation, when the Bering Strait was partly bridged by the accompanying fall in sea level, some Columbus of the Paleolithic led his tribe to the discovery of the New World. Many other people followed. When the ice receded and the sea level rose, the Indians of America (as we now call them) were cut off from the mainstream of human advance. For some thousands of years these small parties of pioneers spent their energies in filling two vast new continents. But they

Drawings (right) show tools made during the fourth glaciation. Left to right: Bone fish-hook and bone harpoon head, both found at Star Carr in Yorkshire, and a wooden bow found in Denmark.

Top: Drawing of a herd of reindeer
engraved on a piece of bone, from
France. Above: A detail of a Lascaux
painting showing wild ponies and,
above them, a wild cow, painted later.

brought with them a technology on which some at least of man's later advances could be based.

Meanwhile, in certain parts of the Old World, man finally made his second breakthrough: He began to practice agriculture and stockbreeding. Up to now, his effect on the landscape had been merely to alter the balance between natural vegetations. From now on, he began to make the world his household.

In southwest Sikkim lies a region remote from the mainstream of the modern world—in some ways still medieval. Here rise the mighty foothills of the Himalayas. Under natural conditions, the slopes of each hill would be divided into belts of vegetation, each the climax for its altitude: For instance, near the snowline we would find alpine flowers and grasses. Then, going down the mountain, tough, scrubby mountain trees and rings of different kinds of forest would follow, one below the other. What do the hills of remote Sikkim look like today? In 1960, the Japanese botanist Hirō Kanai visited them, and this is what he saw. Above 13,000 feet there was still an alpine meadow, but the meadow grasses had been modified by centuries of summer yak-grazing. Below this level came cone-bearing forests, but they carried the scars of repeated fires, made to clear the fields for temporary cultivation. In places the undergrowth had been changed and was now filled with fire plants. In one large area, the forest had been completely burned down. But from 7500 down to 3000 feet, natural vegetation had virtually disappeared. On slopes shaped into neat terraces, nothing could be seen but cultivated food crops. Even in this remote spot, man had created an entirely new landscape, which had never existed before the last glaciation of the Quaternary Era. He had found a way to channel the riches of soil and climate into a totally new kind of vegetation, designed to amass and store energy, and to yield it every year in the form of unprecedented amounts of human food. Man had gained his permanent surplus, by changing the face of his world.

The change began as the fourth glaciation gave place to the last interglacial. Some people think the first true agriculture began with tuber crops, chickens, and pigs in Bengal, but clear evidence is still lacking. What is certain is the appearance in the Near and Middle East (Israel, the borders of Iraq and Iran, the southern shores of the Caspian) of recognizable agricultural societies as early as the eighth millennium B.C. By about 7000 B.C., the farmers of Jericho had built themselves a respectable and long-established town.

The surplus on which most human civilizations have been built is derived from energy-giving carbohydrate food in the grain or seed of a group of annual grasses that

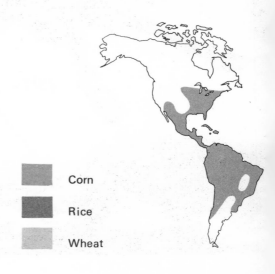

Corn

Rice

Wheat

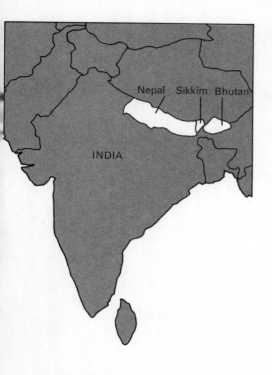

Above: Map locates the kingdom of Sikkim, northeast of India. Left: Harvesting barley in the lowlands of neighboring Nepal, once covered with forests, but now permanently under cultivation.

Map below shows the three great grain areas of the world in A.D. 1500, based on the cultivation of wheat, corn, and rice. The three areas had been independent up to that date.

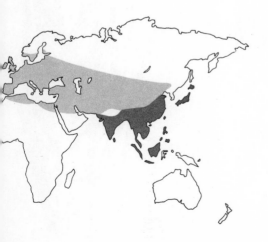

are called, in their cultivated form, the grains, or cereals. Some of these species, such as sorghum and millet, have rather small grains, but are still widely cultivated in parts of Africa and Asia, and here and there in other parts of the world. In the cool, damp north, oats and rye come into their own. But the kings of the grains are the large-grained temperate crops, wheat and barley; in warmer regions, rice; and, the most generous of all, maize, or corn. As late as A.D. 1500, wheat, rice, and corn divided the world into three huge regions. Corn, unlike the others, is a product of the New World, where agriculture began independently at least as early as the fourth millennium B.C., although probably long after the first farmers of Jericho.

Grains in use today are profoundly different from their wild ancestors. Their seeds do not fall when they are ripe —a suicidal arrangement for a wild plant, but extremely convenient for harvesting. In the more advanced kinds (of wheat and barley, for instance), the precious grains are easily separated from their protecting sheaths by threshing. The grains themselves are very much bigger. These changes were brought about by man in two ways, as Charles Darwin pointed out. One way was by methodical selection of seeds from plants with desired characteristics. The other was by unconscious selection, which Darwin defined as "the preservation by man of the most valued, and the destruction of the least valued individuals, without any conscious intention on his part of altering the breed."

It is difficult now to know how great a part each of these two processes played in the early development of agriculture. It is the same with all other human innovations, as far back as fire control. Paleolithic hunters are unlikely to have been as sophisticated as twentieth-century Oregon Indians. They may actually have burned land to get a better view of the game. More probably they went on doing it because hunting went better after the burning. Such is the crude slow process known to modern scientists as *conditioning*, that is, the repetition of activities—often useless and irrelevant—even before something good happens to prove them worthwhile. This is transmitted to later generations as unquestioned tradition. The rapid creative process, whereby an individual sees the advantage of doing something, and convinces others, can hardly have been important before the last glaciation. Both the slow and the rapid processes have been going on ever since, and in early periods we cannot disentangle them.

Methodically or unconsciously, in the eighth millennium B.C. man certainly changed the wild wheat and barley that grew in the Near and Middle East. We can actually see the transition in remains or traces of wheat and barley

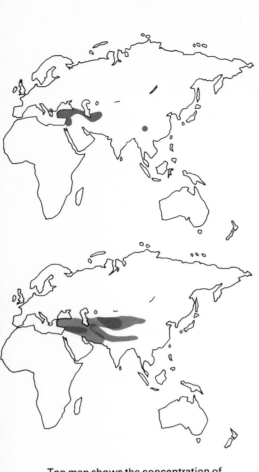

Top map shows the concentration of grains (barley and wild wheat) in the near Middle East. Lower map shows the distribution of wild goats (blue) and wild sheep (red), which were the next animals to be domesticated after dogs.

Above: Six carbonized grains of wheat (of both varieties) found at Jarmo, Iraq. They date from about 6000 B.C. Above right: Carbonized grain of the flower part of a wild barley, also from Jarmo.

Right: Drawings show (from the left) one variety of wild barley and two varieties of wild wheat.

from the ancient sites. About the same time in the same places, man began to change animals too. He began both to graze and to breed them under his own control. First came goats and sheep, native to these or nearby regions; later came cattle and asses. And so we find mixed farming: humans eating the grains of cultivated grasses, or letting farm animals eat grass, and using the animals for horn, hide, meat, and (probably later) milk.

The new way of life at once brought a rising population —which in itself would vastly increase man's impact on the landscape. The higher numbers and new opportunities could be, and were, used in two ways. First, certain peoples were able to build the first cities and the first civilizations because of the new food surplus. This naturally happened in three favored regions near the pioneering farming areas—the three rich, fertile river valleys of the Nile (Egypt), the Tigris and Euphrates (Iraq), and the Indus (Pakistan). It happened with astonishing speed. In the fourth millennium B.C., there were already elaborate cities, highly organized societies, many specialized crafts and trades, and, above all, the art of writing. Meanwhile, elsewhere in the well-endowed Near and Middle East region of this period, others had begun smelting metals. Thus along with civilization came the Bronze Age.

The second process was the spread of the new techniques of agriculture, and, in due time, of the arts of civilization. These passed into Europe, Asia, and Africa from the Near and Middle East, so neatly situated at the intersection of the three Old World continents.

## Clearing and Populating the Continents

In the 1837 edition of his *Guide for Emigrants to the West*, a Baptist missionary called John Mason Peck described the process he had watched in Indiana, Illinois, Missouri, and Michigan for nearly 20 years. His account will apply in broad outline to the great movements that cleared all the continents of the earth. "Three classes, like the waves of the ocean, have rolled one after the other. First comes the pioneer, who depends chiefly upon the natural growth of vegetation . . . and the proceeds of hunting. His implements of agriculture are rude, chiefly of his own make, and his efforts directed mainly to a crop of corn and a 'truck patch' . . . a rude garden. . . . The next class . . . purchase the lands, add field to field, clear out the roads, throw rough bridges over the streams, put up hewn log houses . . . occasionally plant orchards, build mills, school houses, court houses, etc., and exhibit the pictures and forms of plain, frugal, civilized lives. Another wave rolls on. The men of capital and enterprise come. . . . The small village rises to a spacious town or city. . . . All the refinements, luxuries, elegancies, and fashions are in

Gilgamesh, hero of an epic poem of ancient Iraq, holding a lion he has captured. At one stage in the poem, Gilgamesh journeys into a large, mysterious cedar forest to fight a terrifying monster. Stripped of its legendary trimmings, the journey probably commemorates the first expeditions of the ancient Iraqi peoples to find wood for their cities.

vogue. . . ." Here, in miniature, is the history of agricultural man.

Even the first waves of men must clear land for crops. The second, and even more so the third, begin to need wood, for building, furniture, and—notably where metals are smelted and industries are arising—fuel. One of the earliest recorded stories tells of Gilgamesh, king of Uruk (in Iraq) in the third millennium B.C., and of his expedition to a cedar forest in Syria or Iran to get timber for his city. In the folklore of most countries, as indeed in the epic of Gilgamesh itself, the forest is a place of mystery and challenge, where knights hunt monsters and where younger sons seek their fortunes. Let us briefly see what man has done to it, beginning with Europe, where the change has been most complete.

Long before the first literate civilization arose in Iraq, the new technique of agriculture began to spread from the Near East. Pioneers were on the move by the end of the sixth millennium B.C. One wave, partly sea-borne, poured westward from the eastern shore of the Mediterranean to found farming settlements along the other coasts and islands of the Mediterranean. Another passed through Asia Minor (modern Turkey) into the Balkans. From there one pioneer group went up the Danube valley. These Danubians, as we call them, spread across Europe as far as Belgium. They colonized only one kind of soil, which forms a corridor across the continent. This soil is known as *loess*—fine powdery stuff, ground long before by the glaciers and spread by winds. Loess is naturally well-drained and easy to till with simple hoes, and was, at that time, covered by a woodland less dense than the surrounding forest. The Danubians, who had few animals except pigs, cleared a piece of ground and grew wheat and barley until the soil was exhausted (in about 10–25 years). They then moved on, to return when the soil had recovered. They cut plenty of timber, building wooden houses 90 feet long. As their numbers rose, the surplus population (perhaps younger sons, as in the folk tales) pressed ever farther west into the forest. By 4220 B.C., they had reached Magdeburg, Germany. In the wake of the pioneers, towns sprang up. A trading network developed, reaching right back to the Mediterranean—even a piece of African ivory found its way to Worms in Germany.

About the time the Danubian advance came to a halt, before 3000 B.C., two other movements occupied the lighter soils and thinner woodlands of northern and western Europe. One separate group, also coming from the southeast, pushed into Denmark. Meanwhile, from the now well-populated Mediterranean, seafaring pioneers ventured up the coasts to penetrate Spain, France, Switzerland, and the British Isles. These people were

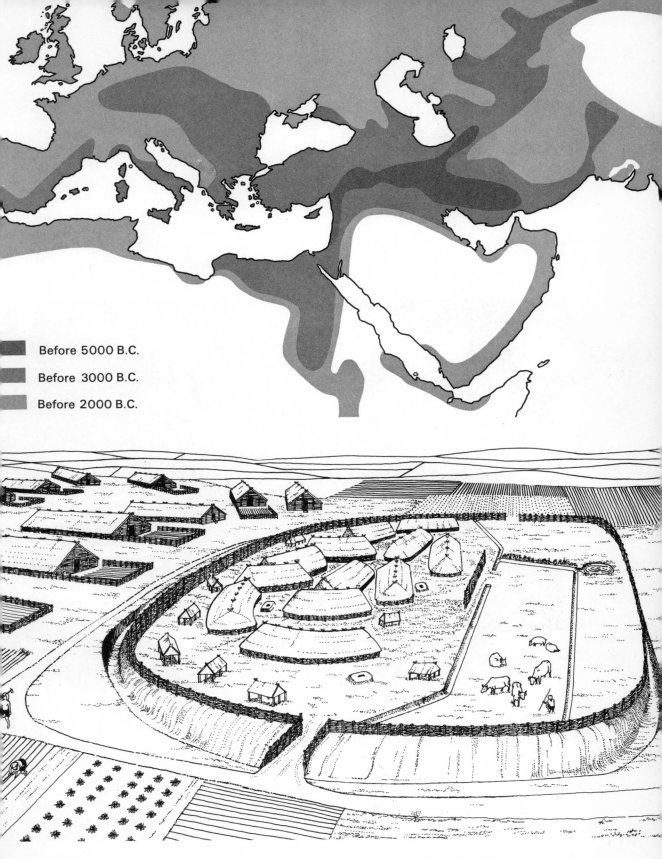

Before 5000 B.C.

Before 3000 B.C.

Before 2000 B.C.

Top: Map plots the spread of agriculture
from its origins in the Near and
Middle East, until it eventually
covered most of Europe by about
2500 B.C.

Above: Neolithic village of the
Danubian people, near Cologne, Germany.
The defensive ditch was probably dug
when site was occupied for the
second time, and land was running short.

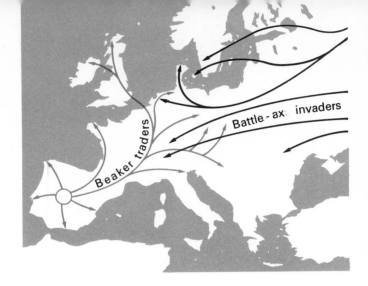

Map shows routes taken by the Beaker traders from Spain around 2000 B.C. and the routes of the Battle-ax invaders from central and southern Russia. Note their convergence in central Europe.

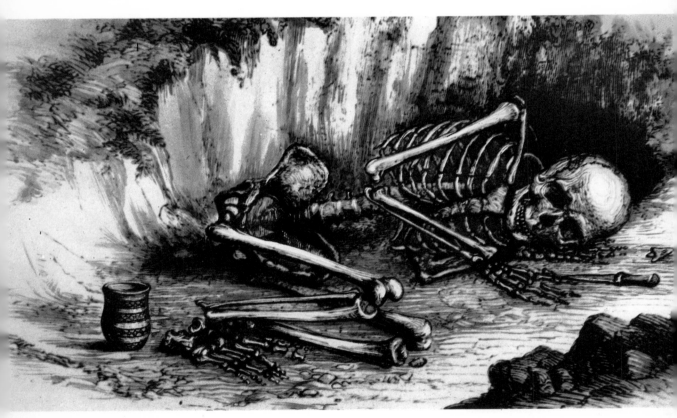

Drawing of a Beaker burial in England, uncovered by building excavations. Beaker burials were often marked by circular mounds, or barrows. These are still recognizable features in parts of the English countryside.

mixed farmers, with cattle and sheep as well as crops. Some of these western pioneers brought a cult of great stone grave monuments that still dot the coastal areas of western Europe.

By the time the Bronze Age began to reach Europe, around 2000 B.C., the lighter soils were covered with farms and prosperous settlements. About this time, two new waves broke upon Europe. Up the Atlantic coasts sailed a

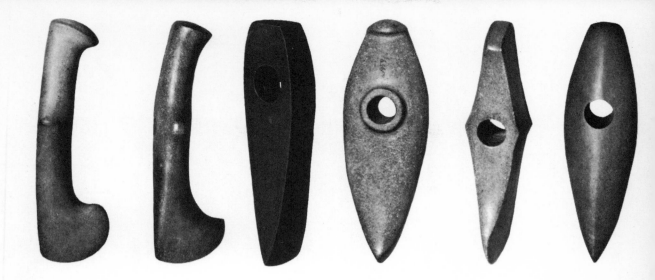

The elegant, finely worked battle-axes of polished stone that gave the Battle-ax people of southern Russia their name.

Below: Beaker with a corded design from near Leipzig, Germany. It is 5½ inches high.

trading people known from their drinking vessels as the Beaker folk. In southern Russia another group of mixed farmers appeared with an emphasis on livestock (especially sheep). Known from their finely shaped stone weapons, they were called the Battle-ax people. These may well have been the first people of Indo-European culture, from which derive the languages and dominant cultures of India, Iran, and all Europe. The Battle-ax people spread rapidly over Europe, favoring sandy soils less fertile than loess, and bringing quantities of sheep. Apparently they established themselves as joint leaders, with the Beaker merchants, of complex new societies. With the spread of the Celts, Germans, and Slavs in the Iron Age of the first millennium B.C., the peopling of Europe was almost complete. Two last incursions from Asia, in the first millennium A.D., planted the Bulgars in Bulgaria and the Magyars in Hungary, and closed the chapter. Other newcomers were sooner or later driven out.

We know these peoples from the tools and other articles they left behind. What kind of Europe did they live in? From various evidence, notably from pollen sequences (p. 29) preserved in Danish and Irish bogs, we can trace the changing vegetation of Europe in the fourth interglacial. At first, tundra sprang up with the retreat of the ice sheets. In the Boreal period, as the temperature rose, forests appeared. First came the softwoods such as pine and birch, then pine and hazel, and finally a forest of oak, elm, and other hardwood trees. As the Atlantic period began, about 5000 B.C., Europe was completely covered with a forest of oaks and their companions, thinning a little on loess or chalk downs, but dense elsewhere. This provided a happy deer-hunting ground for scattered groups of Mesolithic "natives." This forest might have survived in full (or nearly—the hunters were burning it in places) until about 500 B.C. By then the colder Sub-Atlantic period (still with us) would have turned

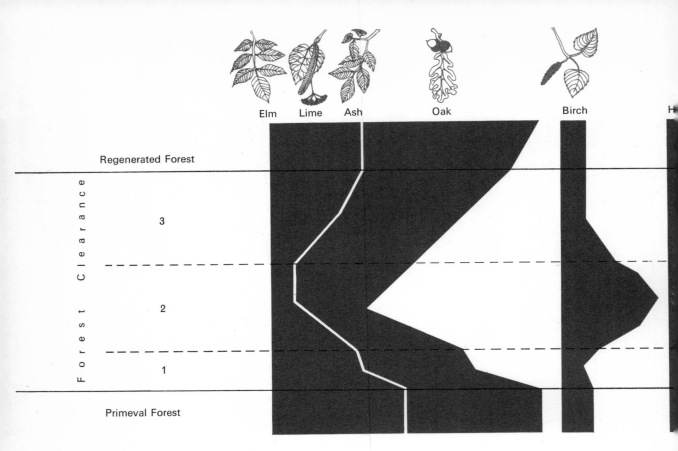

Elm  Lime  Ash  Oak  Birch  H

Regenerated Forest

Forest Clearance

3

2

1

Primeval Forest

much of it gradually back to pinewoods. But from about 5000 B.C. it had to contend with agricultural man. And by the end of the Atlantic period, in about 2000 B.C., he was there to stay.

The pollen in the bogs tells two stories. First, we can see what happened when early settlers (like the Danubians) cleared land, used it, and left, to return later. As such a sequence starts, the oak forest reigns. Then comes a layer of charcoal—the settlers have burned a clearing. The oak and its companion trees shrink. The light-loving birch appears, grasses spread, and suddenly the cultivated cereals spring up along with their fellow-travelers, the weeds (notably plantains). After a while, the trend is reversed. Crops and weeds vanish, grasses retreat, the forest returns—the settlers have moved on. In due course, the whole sequence is repeated several times on the same spot.

The second pollen story tells of the doings of people with more grazing animals (like the Battle-ax people on their sandy soils). It begins as before. This time, however, the forest never returns, for its tentative seedlings are trampled by cattle or browsed by sheep. Grasses and clovers take over—the materials for pastures and hay meadows. In this way arose the broad grassland heaths of northern and western Europe, and probably even the great grassy

Penwith Region  Graig Lwyd

Tievebulliagh  Langdale

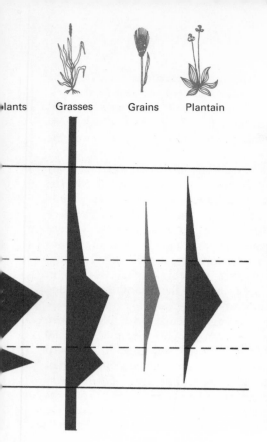

| lants | Grasses | Grains | Plantain |

Diagram above, based on pollen samples from bogs in Denmark, shows the agricultural effects of forest clearance about 2500 B.C. Width of shading represents percentage of various pollens. As forest was cleared (primeval forest to stage 1—read from bottom up) big trees declined and herbaceous plants increased. The great increase of birch pollen during stage 2 suggests that clearings were burned, because birch seeds need light for germination, which would be afforded by the clearings. At this time grains and weeds appeared. As the farmers moved to new areas, large trees reappeared and the regenerated forest was eventually very much like the primeval forest. Above right: Photo taken during the Danish experiment in which three men using Neolithic stone axes cleared 600 square yards of forest in four hours.

Left: Four of the main Neolithic stone ax factories in Britain, and (smaller symbols) sites where axes from these factories have been found.

plain of Hungary and much of the south Russian steppe. Even in the surviving forests, elm trees declined. Their shoots and leaves were used for cattle fodder.

In the great pioneer movement that cleared the forest from so much of Europe, fire was one tool. The other, no less indispensable, was the ax-head of polished flint or hard stone. These axes were indeed superb tools. In a recent experiment in Denmark, a genuine Neolithic ax-head was fitted into an accurate modern copy in ashwood of an original Neolithic haft. With this instrument, three men cleared 600 square yards of silver-birch forest in four hours. More than 100 trees were felled with one ax-head that had not been sharpened for about 4000 years.

The huge demand for these axes was met by an elaborate industry and trade. On chalk downs, flint-miners drove shafts 40 feet deep, and cut horizontal galleries. By the light of lamps in niches, they levered out the flint with antler picks and shoveled it up with the shoulder-blades of cattle. At Grime's Graves in Norfolk, England, 34 acres were mined, with hundreds of shafts, each sunk by shifting up to 5000 cubic feet of chalk. Meanwhile, in other areas, expert prospectors tracked down outcrops of suitable hard stone. They found one (of a rock called *porcellanite*) at Tierebulliagh, County Antrim, Ireland, so small that it was missed by the Geolo-

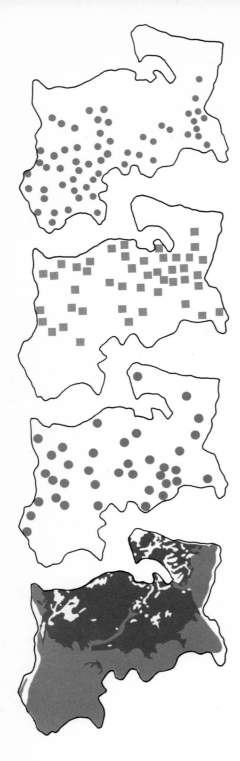

Evidence of forest clearance from place-names in Middlesex County, England. Top map marks place-names, mostly Saxon, which do not indicate woodland. Here the Saxons settled on land previously cleared. Second map locates later place-names indicating wood. Here they cleared for the first time. In the bottom map, light green indicates gravelly soils. Dark green indicates clay soil, scene of the later clearances. Third map shows woodland according to Norman records of 1086, and suggests that there were still heavily wooded tracts.

gical Survey of Ireland until archeologists traced the Neolithic trade route. Near such sites, or near flint-mines, regular ax-factories were set up, from which manufactured ax-heads were carried far and wide by traveling salesmen: the ax-heads of Tierebulliagh were exported as far as the London area.

By the end of the Neolithic, an agricultural economy reigned over Europe, and, except in the far north, the way of life of the Mesolithic deer-slayers was plainly out-of-date. How could they find a place in the new economy? In the British Isles, at least, there is evidence that the problem was brilliantly solved. Since the Mesolithic hunters knew the country, were used to long-distance travel, and were superbly skilled workers in stone, they played a key part in the clearance by taking over the industry and trade in ax-heads.

Throughout the Bronze and early Iron Ages (when metal was still expensive for peasants), from about 2000 B.C. to A.D. 500, little clearing was done in northern and western Europe. On the areas already won, settlement became fixed and more intensive. Towns grew into cities, and civilization began to spread from the south. But vast tracts of dense woods still covered the heavy clay soils. Caesar tells of men traveling through the German forest for two months without finding an end to it. In the last centuries of this period, and most spectacularly in the sixth century A.D., there was a human *retreat* all over continental Europe, from the Mediterranean to Sweden (see Chapters 10 and 11).

By the eighth century A.D., however, the advance began again. The emperor Charlemagne was telling his officials "whenever they found capable men, to give them wood to clear." This time, with iron tools, the peasants began to clear the dense forests and to till the clay soils and the difficult uplands. The story has been pieced together from the useful evidence of place-names and from a mass of documents (for we are now in the age of written history and legal record). The Anglo-Saxons, for instance, began by cultivating the easy soils already tilled in Roman Britain. Later, these indomitable farmers began to tackle the heavy clay (frequently stumbling, to judge from the characteristically fractured limbs of their skeletons). By the Norman Conquest, there was still plenty of forest left. On the continent of Europe, up to about this time, there were human obstacles. Many lords were brutally struggling to preserve the woods for hunting. When the Count of Vendôme in France found unauthorized clearings in his woods, he pulled down the houses and pulled up the crops. But from the eleventh to the thirteenth centuries A.D., the tide of settlers surged forward in the greatest forest clearance yet.

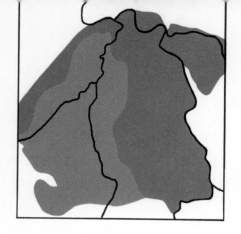

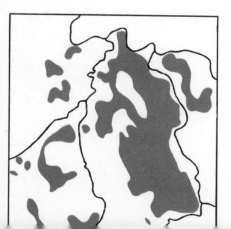

Above: Clearing of woodland in Europe, from an 11th-century manuscript.
Left: Maps of an area of about 350 square miles around Hofgeismar, Germany, showing extent of forest. Top map, about A.D. 500, distinguishes between light and dense forest. By 1290 (second map) much forest clearance had been done and map marks forest of varying density. By 1430 (third map) forest had crept back in many places. Situation in 1950 (bottom) shows more forest than 700 years ago.

The advance was led by monks, at first the Benedictines, later the Cistercians, who had 500 abbeys by the end of the twelfth century, each a focus of forest clearance and up-to-date agriculture. The Order of Hospitalers alone settled 40 villages near Murat, France, on the river Garonne, between 1100 and 1110. And by now many lords, eager to extend their jurisdiction, began looking for settlers to carve more lands from the forest. They had to offer inducements, in the form of greater freedom than peasants enjoyed elsewhere. Thus the lords who colonized the Grisons in Switzerland from upper Valais offered their settlers, the "free Valaisians," the right to elect their local administrator. In northern France, agents toured the markets, reading out charters full of tempting liberties to attract settlers to the hard work of clearing some new slice of forest. So, just as happened centuries later in the United States, it was the more independent folk who struck out as pioneers. The most adventurous of all, attracted by the best terms, went east where the Germans were forging into the forests of Prussia and Austria in a tremendous drive eastward through the lands of the Slavs. "Locators" scouted likely bits of forest, recruited settlers, and reaped their reward in fat land grants and trading rights. But the Slavs themselves were clearing too. Place-

Recent forest clearance in Europe. Below: A scene in England in 1853, showing trees being cut down and a drainage system being installed in the clay soil. Right: Maps of central Europe compare areas covered by forest in about A.D. 900 and in A.D. 1900. Scale of the maps is about 100 miles to the inch.

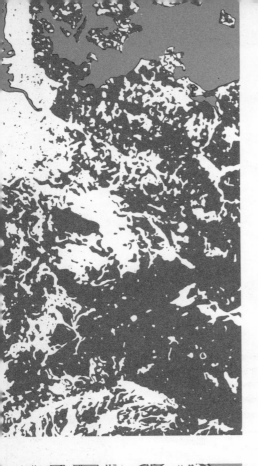

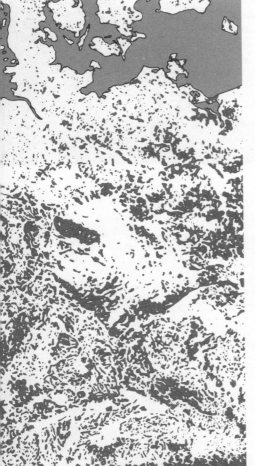

names in French, German, and Czech all tell the same story of new settlements in the woods. Everywhere new villages and towns arose. More than 100 towns were founded in England alone between 1100 and 1300. It was not long before the "men of capital and enterprise" moved in, to form great new trading cities, notably in northern Germany. It was an age of tremendous excitement and enthusiasm. In 1222, Caesarius of Prüm summed up the work of the past century: "many forests were felled, villages founded, mills erected, taxes ordained, vines planted, and an infinite amount of land reduced to agriculture."

Then, in the thirteenth century, there was another staggering human retreat, for reasons we shall see later. It has been estimated that one quarter of the cultivated land in Germany was abandoned, and back came the forests. But again the advance was soon resumed. From the sixteenth century onward, the lost ground was steadily regained. In the course of the nineteenth century, Sweden alone quadrupled her cropland at the expense of her forests. And over much of the period, the demand for wood boomed as never before. Indeed, in this period, forests were increasingly *planted* to meet the demand. But there is no doubt about the general outcome—a prodigious shrinkage of the forests. What all the pauses and retreats and

Land clearance by women in England during World War II. Home-produced food becomes important during wartime and all available land is utilized.

renewed advances means, we shall see in later chapters. But nobody could doubt that the pattern of European vegetation since 5000 B.C. is predominantly the handiwork of man.

The clearing of Asia and Africa seems to have lagged behind the clearing of Europe (the continent most easily reached from the Near East source). Through Iran, the techniques of agriculture spread into the Indus valley (Pakistan) in the fourth millennium B.C., to form the basis of the third great early civilization (after Iraq and Egypt). From there, farther advance into the Indian subcontinent seems to have been slow. But the Indians made important innovations. In the northwest, they bred zebu cattle. Farther south, they began to breed rice, the rich indigenous cereal of the Old World tropics, and they spread this technique to southeast Asia and Indonesia. Meanwhile, probably via the oases of Turkestan, agriculture reached northern China from the Near East in the third millennium B.C. At first millet was grown, later wheat. From India, rice cultivation may have reached more southern Chinese regions in the second millennium B.C. The Chinese, like the Europeans, began their clearance in the broad loess lands of their northwest, and later spread into the fertile lower valley of the Yellow River; it was not until the first millennium B.C. that they opened up the lands of the Yangtze. And it was not until the first millennium A.D. that the Chinese penetrated the forests to the south of it, where even today large tracts of wild country remain.

While agriculture was being carried westward by the Danubians, it was also spreading into southern Russia, where impressive signs of wealth were evident long before western Europe grew rich. In Greek and Roman times, the great steppe still carried much forest, but much had already been cleared for crops. The black earth north of the Black Sea supported flourishing principalities, grown rich from the export of grain. Much of the political history of classical Athens (fifth century B.C.) turned on her need to control the Black Sea trade routes, for access to the granary that fed her. But, after a promising start, the history of Russia was repeatedly distorted by unremitting movements of peoples westward from Asia through the steppe. After a long period of chaos, Russia advanced again in the early Middle Ages, basing a prosperous league of princedoms and city-states on the great river systems between the Black Sea and the Baltic. In this age, when the Russians were in close touch with the rest of medieval Europe, they pressed on into the enormous forests, their princes recruiting settlers just as in the west. But the Mongol invasion of the thirteenth century A.D.

Dark red on this map of China indicates loess areas. Light red indicates areas having a soil of similar properties.

Plan of the Russian city of Novgorod in the 15th century. The city had great importance as a European trade center in the early Middle Ages.

Opposite, top: Pot found at Baluchistan, to the northwest of India, featuring the Zebu cattle. Bottom: Excavated ruins of Mohenjo-Daro, city on the Indus that flourished about 2500 B.C..

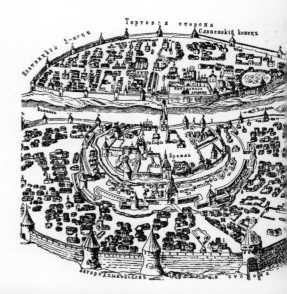

devastated much of Russia and cut off the rest from Europe, dominating it for centuries and grievously slowing agricultural advance. It was not until the late eighteenth and nineteenth centuries that Russia made her own mighty expansion, clearing forests, pioneering the vast lands of central Asia, driving steel plows into the great grassland steppe. Eventually, in the twentieth century, the Russians pushed cultivation into the deserts beyond.

In Africa, meanwhile, the spread of agriculture seems to have taken two steps. In the third or second millennium B.C., agriculture spread south from Egypt to Sudan, and west along the great savanna belt that spans the continent between the Sahara desert and the tropical rainforest. Unlike the Egyptians, who grew wheat and barley —typical Near East crops—the Sudanese grew sorghum and millet, characteristic small-grained native cereals of Africa that could stand the continuous heat. They also became herdsmen. Agriculture soon stretched from end to end of the belt, but it did not yet penetrate the particularly stubborn tropical rain-forest to the south.

Iron technology, discovered in Asia Minor in the second millennium B.C., probably became established in eastern Sudan in the fourth century B.C. This was during the reign of King Harsiotef of Kush—the great Sudanese kingdom that had conquered and briefly ruled Egypt a few centuries earlier. By the first century B.C., Meroë, capital of Kush, was an industrial city surrounded by huge slag-heaps. By this time, too, iron technology had reached the Nok people in northern Nigeria. In the first half of the first millennium A.D., western Sudan developed its earliest

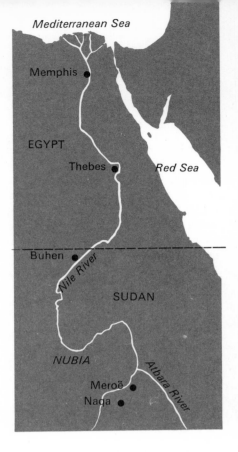

Map locates Meroë in Sudan, near the junction of the Atbara River and the Nile. Below: Some of the slag-heaps of Meroë, evidence of the extensive iron-smelting industry there about the 1st century B.C.

great empires. During this period a Sudanese group in Nigeria, whom we call the Bantu, must have begun to cultivate the yam, a tuber plant that yields more than twice as much food energy per acre as the small-grained cereals, and is suited for cultivation in the rain-forest. With yams and iron tools, the Bantu proceeded to populate half a continent. Just as Indo-European languages came to dominate from Ireland to India, so Bantu languages are spoken through almost the whole of central and southern Africa. Those who colonized the easier plains or highlands beyond the rain-forest often turned or returned to other crops. But some of these tribes even today devote special rituals to the yam. By the European Middle Ages, the Bantu had built great empires in Rhodesia, where later they raised the colossal palace walls of Great Zimbabwe. Although the story here lacks the rich documentation of Europe, the Bantu in their spread undoubtedly cleared great areas of forest.

From the sixteenth century onward, the great stream of European emigration began, rising to a flood in the nineteenth century with the industrial era. The emigrants' numbers were greater and their equipment better than that of any earlier pioneers, and so the nineteenth century saw the most spectacularly rapid clearances of all. In New Zealand (where the Maoris had already burned a good deal of forest into grassland) and Australia, settlers concentrated almost entirely on making, improving, or remaking grasslands for pasture. But the clearance of vast lands for crops has a final and stirring chapter—the colonization of the United States of America.

Gray area on map shows where Bantu languages are spoken in Africa today.

Below: Iron hoe-blades made by the Jo Luo people of southern Sudan. The Jo Luo process iron in six-foot-high clay furnaces, probably very similar to those used in Meroë 2000 years ago. These blades were sometimes used as money.

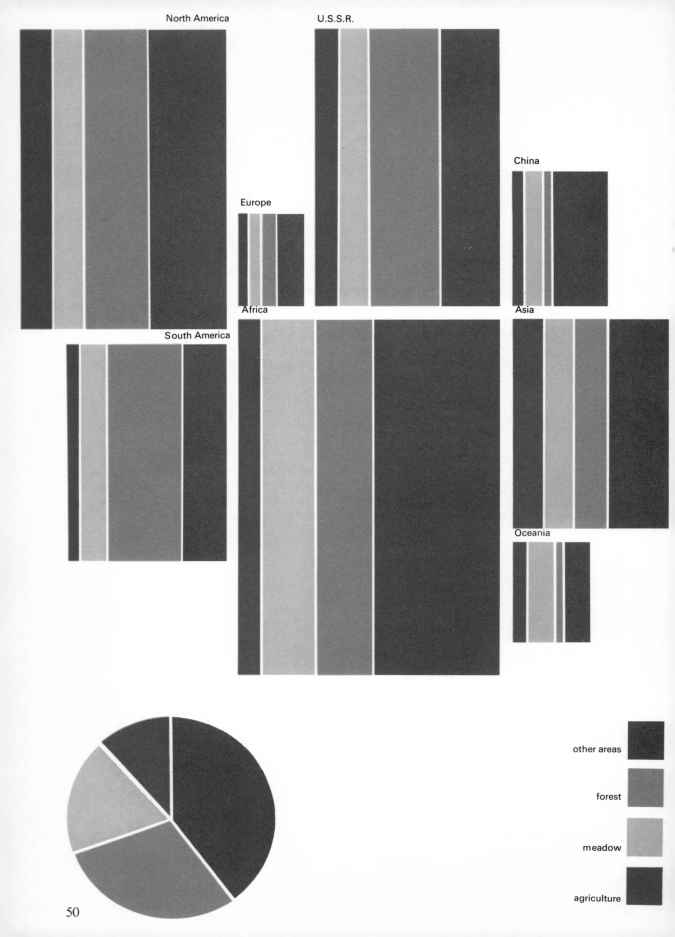

North America

U.S.S.R.

China

Europe

Africa

Asia

South America

Oceania

other areas

forest

meadow

agriculture

50

In the eighteenth century, the American colonists were largely confined to the East Coast states. As the nineteenth century opened, the great move west began. One drive in the South carried tobacco and cotton crops, grown by slaves on huge plantations. A second drive in the North was made by independent pioneer small farmers. The two drives converged at their western edge (in Kansas, for instance), where disputes between farmers and slave-owners over new lands formed a starting point of the great North-South conflict that finally broke out into the Civil War. By then, the two movements had between them cleared a huge area of forest.

In the South, the advance of the huge plantations swept the forest away in great swaths. In the North, the small farmers cleared more gradually but no less surely. What happened to the forest can be illustrated by its history in Cadiz Township, Green County, Wisconsin, carefully surveyed five times between 1831 and 1950. Changes that took millennia on the map of Europe were completed in Green County in 120 years, as illustrated on this page. In Europe, land was cleared in order of its fertility, giving an irregular pattern of clearings. In Wisconsin, the earlier land-holdings were arbitrarily allotted in square blocks, so that even the few stands of trees left in 1950 tended to have geometrically straight edges—man's handiwork is thus plainer than ever. The few surviving wood-lots actually became denser and better established, thanks to fire protection. This is the pattern over the whole forest belt and the mixed savanna on its fringe.

Like the first European clearance, this drive through the forest was made possible only by the production of thousands of axes, this time of steel. We do not know the names of the inventors and "men of enterprise" who created the stone-ax industry of Neolithic Europe. In the American clearance, we are better informed.

In the early nineteenth century, the newly independent Americans were desperately short of skilled labor. To bypass the shortage, a handful of American technologists took a great new step, and gave the world the technique of mass production. An early field of application was in

Opposite page: World land utilization. Size of rectangles is in proportion to the land area they represent. Divisions within them are similarly in proportion to the amount of land covered by (left to right in each case) permanent cropland, permanent pasture or meadow, forest, and other landscape. The circle shows the world picture. Such features as the high proportion of cropland in Europe and the particularly small area of forest in China at once stand out.

Right: Changes in wooded area in Cadiz Township, Wisconsin, during settlement. Shading in top diagram shows forest in the area (of about 35 square miles) in 1831. Second diagram shows wooded areas in 1882—less than one third of the forest of 1831. (Geometrical patterns arose because of arbitrary allotting of land.) By 1902 (third diagram) the wooded area, now only one tenth that of 1831, began to reflect the topography of the area. Current forest areas (fourth diagram) are mostly confined to rocky outcrops and thin-soil hilltops.

Portrait of Elisha King Root, pioneer of mass production in ax-making. He later applied his new techniques to other industries.

the provision of large numbers of steel axes of uniform shape and temper. In 1826 Samuel and David Collins of Connecticut assembled a few expert blacksmiths at South Canton, Ohio, and installed a few machines (such as triphammers) to lighten their labors. In 1832 they engaged a new foreman, Elisha King Root. Root analyzed all the stages of ax-making, divided them among specialist operators, and introduced at South Canton every possible device for standardizing each job. For instance, a batch of 100 ax-heads was hung on a drum revolving in a furnace, so that each would receive identical heat treatment in tempering the steel. Methods such as this resulted in a mass production of uniform axes stamped with the Collins trademark. Without them, the pioneers would have had a difficult time in clearing the forests. Root's solution of the problem of producing the axes helped to advance the American method of mass production, now so basic to our way of life.

In the mid-nineteenth century, the pioneers emerged from the forests into the great grassland belt that ran across North America from south to north, ending in the prairie provinces of Canada. Much of this grassland was itself ready-made by the Indians. Now, oddly enough, once the trees have been cut and burnt, forest soils are relatively easy to cultivate, some by iron, some even by stone tools. The tough sod of the grasslands is another matter. A single plant of the grass family (actually a cultivated grass, rye) was once grown for four months in a box with less than 2 cubic feet of earth. It grew 20 inches high, while underground, the root system had developed 378 *miles* of roots! The tangled sod of old grassland, bound together by miles of grass roots, can be cut only by steel plows, developed during the second quarter of the nineteenth century.

And so, despite all its millennia of forest clearance, Europe had never before been able to tackle the grasslands of Hungary and southern Russia, which were actually cleared for crops about the same time as American pioneers cleared theirs. They drove rapidly into the grass belt, continuing to grow corn at first and then turning to wheat in the drier land farther west. But once the sod could be plowed, the flat or gently rolling prairie was more thoroughly cleared than the more rugged forest land. Over huge areas, all trace of the original vegetation was totally destroyed. Over millions of acres in the Middle West, we know the original vegetation only in the way we know it in some of the African and Asian savannas, by a modern equivalent of fetish groves—the strip of grass fenced in between the railway tracks.

With this last sudden spread of cropland into the grass, we come to the end of our clearance story. Some

advance of cropland continues, notably in Africa, and it may be possible to plow farther into some deserts. But there is reason to believe that man is already cultivating almost the whole area of land best suited for agricultural crops. Indeed, he is now actively protecting or even enlarging the remnants of forest. The upshot of man's activity is clearly seen in a report published in 1962 by the United Nations. (The report was used to prepare the diagram on p. 50.) More than 10 per cent of the entire land surface of the earth is seen to be under crops. Most of this would certainly be forest, and the rest grassland, if man had not come to clear it. As for the remaining grassland and forest, we must assume a considerable gain by grass over trees as another of man's doings. Here is the massive and visible evidence of mankind's impact on nature.

The gift of Prometheus was the first great breakthrough in man's relations with nature. As we have seen, he began

The man-made landscape of the central part of the United States—mile upon mile of cultivated fields laid out in neat rectangles.

The earliest known form of Chinese writing, incised on a piece of bone. It probably dates from the 12th century B.C.

at once to make his mark on the land surface. With the new increase of security and leisure so gained, he first spread over the world. And then, in the fourth glaciation, he began suddenly to make rapid progress in handling his surroundings. Very likely, this was the result of a new development of human language, which facilitated the rapid spread of innovations made by creative individuals. By the dawn of the fourth glaciation, this had led to the second great breakthrough—agriculture. From then on, advances in communication, and hence in the growth and spread of knowledge, came thicker and faster than ever.

These new advances in communication began with writing, which evolved in the fourth millennium B.C. At first it was essentially what we call ideographic, each symbol representing some object or activity or idea. For such writing, which the Chinese still practice today, an enormous number of symbols (more than 50,000 in Chinese) are needed, all of which must be learned to become a really literate person. In the second millennium B.C., alphabetic writing was invented in the Near East. By means of a couple of dozen symbols, put together in endless ways, any number of objects or activities or ideas could be expressed. Alphabetic reading and writing is easily and quickly learned. Early in the last century, a gifted Cherokee Indian called Sequoya realized the advantages of the writing activities of Europeans. Knowing only that it was possible, he set out to present his tribe with the art of writing. At first he thought there would have to be a written symbol for each word. Then he realized (it can only be called genius) that letters should represent sounds, combined in any number of ways. In 1821, he submitted to the tribal council an alphabet of 85 letters for the Cherokee language. The council accepted the idea and within seven years were producing two newspapers in Cherokee. Sequoya was made an honorary chief by his own people, and received a financial grant from Congress. The Austrian botanist and language-student Stephan Endlicher named the giant redwood trees of California *sequoias* in honor of this wise Indian. The striking fact is that Cherokee children could now learn to read and write their language *in a few days*. When the ancient forerunners of Sequoya made their discovery in the second millennium B.C., reading and writing ceased to be the monopoly of a few professionals, and could be used to exchange knowledge between many people.

The actual process of writing was still laborious, and for a long time this limited the number and cheapness of copies of written works. Then in the sixth century A.D., the Chinese invented block-printing. The earliest known printed work is a notice "Beware of the Dog," dating from A.D. 594. Like ideographic writing, block-printing

Portrait made in 1838 of the Cherokee Indian, Sequoya. He points to the alphabet he devised for his people.

The Chinese invented movable type
printing. But it was almost as cumbersome
as block-printing because of the large
number of symbols in the Chinese script.
Compare part of a Chinese typesetter's
case, above, with that of a typesetter
working in an alphabetic script (top).

was a limited gain. Every page of a book had to be made
into a block as a completely new undertaking.

But just as the alphabet made writing easy and flexible,
so the invention of movable type made printing infinitely
easier, for now a printer had only to make type for a few
letters, and set it up in any required combination. It was
in about A.D. 1050 that a Chinese laborer called Pi Sheng
invented movable type. But in China, where the language
was ideographic anyway, the gain was not obvious.
Printing reached Europe, where the languages were
alphabetic, in the twelfth century. But since it was only

Afcenfianū.

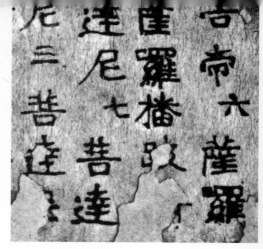

Above: The earliest surviving example of block-printing. It composes Buddhist charms printed between A.D. 762 and 769 from wooden blocks .Left: Engraving of a printing press from the title page of a book printed by Jacobus Badius Ascensius in Paris in 1507.

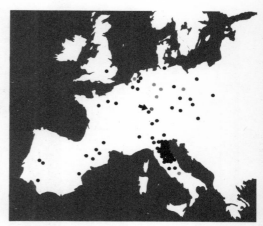

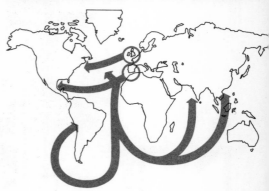

Upper map: Arrow marks Europe's first printing press, set up by Johann Gutenberg in Mainz in about 1450. By 1465 printing had started in Holland, Italy, and France (green dots). Fifteen years later there were presses all over Europe (black dots). Lower map shows the spread of presses to Spanish, Portuguese, Dutch, French, and English overseas territories by 1638.

For centuries, man's only real sources of power had been the muscles of men and animals, and wind and water (right). Then came the great technological breakthrough and new sources of power were discovered. Coal was the first. Coal can boil water to produce steam, and many steam engines were developed, able to do tasks formerly impossible or which had required many men. Below: James Watt's steam engine of 1788, used for pumping water.

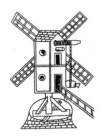

quoniam ipfe cognou

block-printing, book production was still laborious. By the end of the fourteenth century, however, Pi Sheng's discovery (improved by the Koreans) reached Limoges, France, and with the combination of the alphabet and movable type, an astonishing new advance began. After fire and agriculture, this was the third great step in human progress—the forerunner of the technological breakthrough.

To gain control over nature, man needs physical energy. Agriculture, by providing a surplus, freed some human beings to expend energy in new ways, as well as to think. But until the end of the Middle Ages, the only sources of energy or power were human and animal muscles and some locally available natural forces such as gravity, water, and wind (used in such devices as mills and sailing ships). From the technological breakthrough arose new sources of power—coal, oil, atomic energy—driving machines that could do the work of many men or animals. Meanwhile, mass production, and its successor automation, began freeing human beings from even the routine of controlling their machines. With the growth of really systematic science and technology, man acquired a new confidence and capacity to understand and control the complex workings of nature. In this way he came to influence his surroundings as never before, thus creating the conditions of modern life.

A key factor in the Industrial Revolution was the substitution of machines to do work normally done by man. In a poor country like India many tasks are still done by hand, including projects like dam building (above). By contrast, in technological societies whole engineering processes can be controlled by machines (below) in the charge of just a few men.

# 3 The Forest Farmers

Everyone knows that the technological breakthrough began in Europe a few centuries ago. Why did it happen there? We can dismiss any notion that the Europeans are inherently wiser or more creative than other peoples. Nearly all the early discoveries on which the European achievement was based were made by other peoples outside Europe. Agriculture itself came from the Near and Middle East, partly because of the concentration there of useful plants and animals. Writing came from Iraq, and the alphabet from the Phoenician trading cities on the coast of Lebanon and from neighboring peoples. Iron was first worked in the mountains of the Near East. Modern mathematics depends on the system of numbers worked out in classical India and further improved by Arabs and Persians. Block and type-printing, cheap paper,

Map shows how the vast Sahara, a desert for the last 5000 years, largely cut off the rest of Africa from outside influence, although some civilizations, such as Zimbabwe, did arise. Map also marks possible routes of the Americas' first colonizers. They probably came from somewhere in Asia and may well have crossed overland from Siberia to Alaska during the last glaciation when there was a much lower sea-level.
When the ice retreated, America was cut off from the Old World.

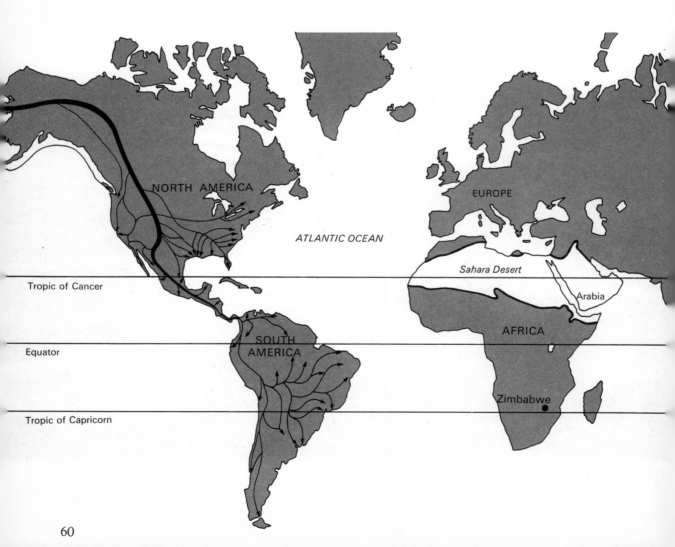

the compass and gunpowder came from China, which in the fifteenth century A.D. was technically far in advance of Europe. Horses were probably tamed by peoples of Central Asia. The civilizations of India and the Middle East leaned heavily on the skill and enterprise of metal miners in the heart of Africa. Clearly enterprise and inventiveness are not European monopolies. Nor have the Europeans been specially constructive and peaceful. Their history reeks of blood.

This list, a small selection, shows the importance of the spread of discoveries (and materials) made by anciently established peoples. From this, however, America could not benefit. Soon after it was first colonized by Paleolithic man, the retreat of the ice and the rising sea-level completely cut off America from the rest of mankind. A few Bronze Age or Celtic adventurers may have landed in the New World, and Vikings certainly did. But none of these adventures came to anything. Until certain advances in navigation and shipbuilding were made (chiefly by the Chinese, although finally exploited by Europeans), America evolved in total isolation.

Most of Africa, too, was somewhat isolated, although not by an ocean. The ice ages, bringing cold to the temperate zones, brought also the pluvial ages to the tropical regions, and heavy rainfall spread far north and south of the equator. The last interglacial thus meant the drying-up of once well watered regions. When it began, the Sahara was covered with fertile stretches occupied by peoples skilled in engraving drawings on rocks. As late as the third millennium B.C., large herds of cattle grazed in lower Nubia, where, according to the British archeologist A. J. Arkell, ". . . desert conditions are so severe today that the owner of an ox-driven water-wheel has difficulty in keeping one or two beasts alive throughout the year." From about the fourth millennium B.C., the Sahara began to turn into a vast desert, which merchants died trying to cross.

The Americans and the Africans were thus thrown back not only on their own unaided inventiveness, but also on their own natural resources. Africa was desperately short of *native* useful plants. America, richly endowed with useful plants (such as corn and potatoes), was

Corn, or maize, is a plant of American origin. It was an important factor in the development of early American civilizations. Above: The first European drawing of the plant, from Leonhard Fuchs's *De Historia Stirpium*, 1542.

Right: Plan of the area known as The Temple at Zimbabwe (see map opposite), a city that rose and fell within the last thousand years. It controlled the production of superbly wrought iron that cities on the coast exported across the Indian Ocean. The Temple itself was nearly 300 feet across at its widest part. Key to numbers on diagram: (1) parallel passage; (2) conical tower; (3) platform; (4) enclosures with remains of huts.

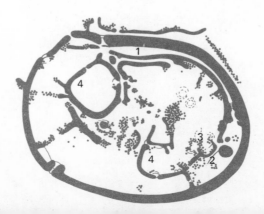

desperately short of useful animals. The horse, for instance, although it originally evolved on the plains of North America, had been completely wiped out there, possibly by a great epidemic, about the time man arrived. The wonder is that both the Americans and the Africans were able to build great civilizations at all.

Europe's easy access to other parts of the Old World was one reason for her success. But much has also depended on the forms of agriculture adopted by human societies, and hence on their relations with nature. These forms are immensely diverse in detail. But, on the whole, after the pioneer clearance, human societies have followed three different agricultural pathways. These three pathways can be traced in three great climatic divisions of the world. Very roughly, we can think of these as the wet regions, the dry regions, and the temperate regions. We begin with the wet regions, the hot damp rain-forests of the tropics.

### The Forest Fallow

The belt called the tropics lies on either side of the equator, is more than 3200 miles wide, and contains about 40 per cent of the earth's surface (including waters, which make up about three quarters of the area). It receives more than half the world's total rainfall, and is extremely hot. Much of it is covered by dense rain-forest.

Now we saw that the Danubians, the first pioneers of Europe, practiced what has been called shifting cultivation

Below: Two sketches made in 1883 of farming in Finland. Left picture shows a felled woodland being fired. Right picture shows the fired land being plowed. The ancient Finnish epic *Kalevala* speaks of "the hoe among the pine roots." Later the plow could be used here, for the tree-stumps are far enough apart.

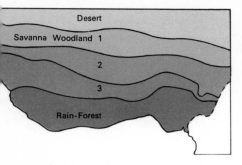

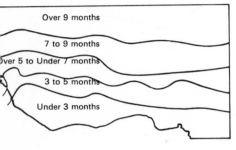

Maps of tropical West Africa show how vegetation is linked to climate. Upper map shows the transition from desert, through three stages of savanna with progressively less grass and more trees, to dense rain-forest near the equator. Lower map shows the number of months in the year with less than one inch of rain (dry season).

—that is, they cleared a plot, burned it, grew crops there for awhile among the stumps and roots, and moved on, leaving it to revert back to forest. And in fact, as John Mason Peck (see page 35) was later to notice in North America, this has always tended to be the first stage of clearance. In regions outside the wet tropics, a wave of more permanent settlement normally followed, with the use of other kinds of agriculture. This has been true all over Europe, except in the damp spruce and pine forests of the far north. Here shifting cultivation was still going on in Russia in the late nineteenth century, and in Sweden till 1918. In Finland it has continued to this day. By the eighteenth century shifting cultivation had evolved into a systematic method: The farmers grew crops (oats and rye) on a plot for 4 to 6 years, let the land grow back into forest, and then returned 20 or 30 years later to use it again. But the amount of food yielded by this practice was always small. The trees became more and more valuable as timber for the peoples farther south (as their own forests disappeared), and thus shifting cultivation in the far north is dying out.

But in the tropical rain-forest all over the world, this "freezing" of agriculture at its first pioneering stage happened on a grand scale, resulting in a great agricultural system. In 1957, it was estimated by the Belgian agriculturalist P. De Schlippé that shifting cultivation was being practiced on over 13 million square miles of land, by 200 million people—nearly one person in ten of the

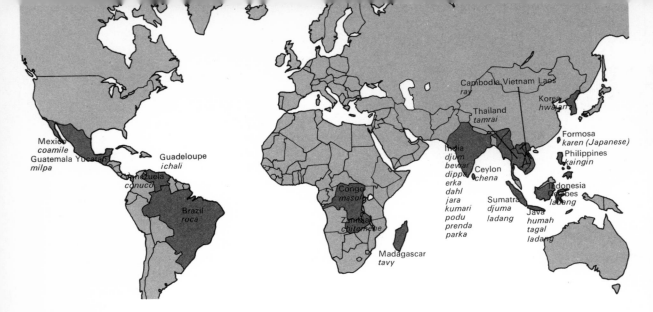

then population of the world. The practice ranges from haphazard use of one clearing after another to agricultural systems of extraordinary subtlety and complexity, like those of the Zande people in the Sudan or the Hanunóo people of Mindoro Island in the Philippines. But more often that not, it is a systematic alternation (*rotation*), in which a given plot of land is cleared, burned, used for crops, left unused (*fallow*) to turn back into forest (*bush*), used again, left again, and so on. This is called *bush fallow rotation*, or slash-and-burn farming. It has arisen again and again, often independently in different places, all over the tropics. Everywhere it is basic to the whole way of life of the people who work it. They have given it a series of names, usually referring both to the system and to a plot of land so used (see map). English-speaking scientists, seeking to impose order on the diversity of names, have begun to call the typical plots in these places *swiddens* (from an old English country word for burned clearings), and the system *swidden farming*.

## The Way of the Tropics

It is fair to use one word, for everywhere in the tropics the sequence of work on a swidden is the same. First, an area of forest is chosen (sometimes very carefully). Then it is cleared. Small saplings, creepers, and underbrush are slashed cleanly away, some big trees are trimmed of their branches, others felled (a dangerous moment in these giant forests), leaving sizeable stumps. The work may be divided up, as among the Hanunóo. Men do the heavy felling, women the lighter slashing, and small boys climb to the tops of trees to trim them. All debris is cut up and spread evenly over the swidden. The whole operation is timed so that debris can dry out for burning during the short dry season. The more careful farmers clear strips around the swidden as firebreaks. Harold C.

Map above gives the local name for swidden farming (bush fallow rotation) in a number of places throughout the world. It indicates how widespread the system is in the wet tropics.

Above right: Map locating the position of Mindoro Island in the Philippines, and, far right, the territory in the southeast part of the island that is occupied by the Hanunóo. The small area marked Yagaw is where the swidden-farming techniques of the Hanunóo were studied in detail.

Right: A slashed area of swidden in Yagaw, prior to burning. The swidden is in an area where clearings have been made previously. In the background, part of a primary forest is visible.

65

Left: A Hanunóo man felling a large tree with an ax. He is standing on a wooden scaffolding especially constructed for the purpose. Only men participate in the tree-felling, which can sometimes be a dangerous task. Opposite page, top: A woman planting taro in a cut, but unburned, swidden. She makes a hole with the planting stick, then drops in a young taro plant from her basket. Such root crops as these can survive later burning of the area. Most crops are planted after burning.

Below: Firing a swidden with a bamboo torch. During the few days before firing, the Hanunóo clear a fire-path around the swidden to minimize the risk of fire spreading to the surrounding forest. Opposite page: Indians from near the Essequibo River, in South America, firing a field cut about a month previously. Here, the dried branches have to be constantly lighted with a torch.

Conklin, the American anthropologist, lived for several years with the Hanunóo. In 1953–55, during the burning of more than 150 swiddens, less than one acre of neighboring bush was burned by accident. When he remarked on this, they simply said, "All our swiddens have firebreaks." Not all peoples are as meticulous as these masters of the art of swidden farming. At all events, when the debris is tinder dry, the swidden is set ablaze from several places, and in an hour or so it has burned out, leaving a thick layer of ash.

Now begins the sowing and planting of crops. The ground is prepared for seeds by simple tools, hoes or digging-sticks. The people of temperate lands are used to seeing fields laid out with a single crop—wheat, barley, potatoes, etc. But tropical swidden farming is quite different. A large number of different crops are grown all together, sown or planted and harvested in turn in a continuous sequence through the long wet season. There is always something to be done and something to be eaten. Just as the hunters of Lascaux were practical zoologists, so some of the swidden farmers are observant botanists. The Hanunóo recognize not only different plant species, but different types or varieties within many of them. Western scientists distinguish about 1200 plant species in the Hanunóo lands of Mindoro Island. The Hanunóo people themselves can recognize 1600 different kinds of plant, and treat them all differently. More than 400 are bred, by sowing seeds or planting parts that can reproduce new plants. Others are destroyed as useless weeds. Some, although reproducing themselves, are more or less cultivated. They are protected from fire when the swidden is burned by being wrapped with green plant materials. Among such experts, a swidden is a regular botanical garden.

Usually, however, there is one main food plant that gets special attention and is the object of elaborate rituals. Often this is a cereal—corn in America, millets or a local kind of rice in parts of Africa, and rice in the East. Sometimes it is a starchy root crop, like the yam in much of Africa; this is always so on the Pacific islands, for the peoples there seem to have left their original homes in Asia before the coming of rice. Besides the main crops, each society may grow other cereals and root crops in the swidden. Usually too there are leguminous plants rich in protein—we shall come across legumes again later on. A variety of small plants provide spicy tastes or medical remedies. And finally, there may be fruit trees that, as they grow, provide shade for the new sprouts of the returning forest.

Map shows Yagaw area of Mindoro between 1953 and 1955. Dark blue shows 1953 swiddens; mid-blue, 1954 swiddens; and light blue, 1955 swiddens. Primary forest is shown in a dark gray, regrown forest is white, and grassland is light gray. Capital letters are settlement sites.

After a time, the swidden is gradually abandoned, and the forest grows back. Only when the land has been forest again for some time (bush fallow) will the swidden farmers return to clear it afresh. Meanwhile, they clear and use other swiddens elsewhere in the forest. Timing varies in different places, but when swidden farming is working efficiently the bush fallow period is always considerably longer than the period when the land is cleared and used for crops. Among the Hanunóo, the intensive cropping period averages 2–4 years, and the bush fallow 8–10 years. In Sierra Leone, the cycle is 2 years cropping, 12–15 years fallow; in Ceylon, 1–3 years cropping, 8–20 years fallow; in New Guinea, 1 year cropping, 15–20 years fallow. Everywhere the older traditional systems follow this pattern of a long bush fallow period.

In some places we find special versions of the bush fallow rotation. A famous one is the *chitemene* system, most advanced in Zambia. This is basically a bush fallow rotation, usually with finger millet as the main crop. But besides clearing the swidden itself, the farmers cut off branches from trees in the forest for some distance around, bring them to the swidden, and burn them with the rest of the debris. We shall see that this refinement probably has real value. The chitemene system is found in fact all over East and Central Africa as far north as Sudan and northern Nigeria. The first European to describe it (in 1866) was the great missionary-explorer David Livingstone, who saw it on the Rovuma River in Malawi. The Indian systems called *parka* and *dippa* are similar, too. In Sudan, several tribes have found another trick. Instead of burning the debris on a swidden, they leave it to the termites. In four months these formidable little animals reduce it to a powder. The Dinka people enrich the debris with branches from the forest around (as in the chitemene system) and let termites pulverize the lot.

Swidden farmers of the tropics have two kinds of neighbors. In the flood plains of rivers, settled agriculture has developed, using the same land for crops year after year. This becomes possible due to certain properties of the soils, to irrigation (a subject of Chapter 5), and (except on steep slopes or where farms are only tiny plots) to the use of the plow, drawn by oxen or buffaloes. The stumps of tropical rain-forests grow too close together to admit cattle and plowing, so swidden farmers still use the hoe and digging-stick. In the East, where settled farming is common, swidden farmers have largely been driven up into the hills. In Africa, where river flood plains are less favorable for settled farming, they spread wider.

The other neighbors of the swidden farmers live on the edge of the rain-forest, where the dry seasons lengthen and the country turns gradually into grassland. They are nomadic (wandering) herdsmen, driving their flocks in search of pasture and water. A few swidden farmers (like the Hanunóo) keep small grasslands on which they raise a few cattle. But, in general, domestic animals form no part of swidden farming, and swidden farmers and stock-raising nomads live quite apart. We shall see that this splitting of the two original foundations of agriculture (crops and herds) has always been unfortunate. Since in the tropics both groups are very busy and continually on the move, especially the nomads, they have not been able to integrate into one system of farming or society. In the East, farmers and nomads are rather strictly divided by the boundary of rain-forest and grassland. In Africa, vast areas of open woodland and savanna are dominated by "the rulers of Africa"—the terrible bloodsucking tsetse flies that carry a number of deadly diseases to both man and his animals. The human diseases so spread are being brought under control by drugs, but the cattle diseases are still an unsolved problem, and wherever the tsetse rules, herds must leave or die. In the absence of herdsmen, swidden farmers can often spread for hundreds of miles outside the rain-forest. Africa is, above all, the continent of bush fallow rotation.

*Chitemene* cultivation in Zambia, Africa, a variation of bush fallow rotation. Branches are cut from trees over a wide area, collected in piles, and burned on the area to be cultivated. This provides more fertilizing ash.

Tsetse flies are still found in a large area of Africa (marked blue on map above) and the diseases they transmit to animals are one reason why herdsmen occupy relatively little of that continent.

# 4 The Tropical Dead End

In the nineteenth and early twentieth centuries, European agriculturalists assumed control of farming in the tropics—for instance, the British and Belgians in Africa, and the Dutch in Indonesia. The Europeans were shocked by the apparent inefficiency of the traditional farming systems they found there. Accustomed to the economic and highly productive agriculture developed (as we shall see) in Europe, but not realizing how this had happened, they observed that bush fallow rotation used a great deal of land and labor to produce very little food. They assumed that swidden farming was a crude and primitive system, used only because local peasants knew no better. And so, in many parts of the wet tropics, often with good intentions, Europeans set about clearing the forest, plowing the land, sowing one or two crops in each field, and growing them repeatedly year after year. But in man's interplay with nature, the road to famine is often paved with the best intentions. At first the harvests were splendid, but after a few years they fell and fell, and eventually the land became unusable. This happened, for instance, in Malaya, Sierra Leone, Uganda, and the Congo. The Europeans began to realize that there were reasons for swidden farming, after all.

They might have inferred this from the fact that the system of bush fallow rotation had arisen and persisted (often independently) in so many different places in the wet tropics. Even local differences in detail are closely related to local conditions of topography, climate, and natural vegetation. In all the islands of Melanesia (in the Pacific), for instance, six different forms of swidden farming have been found, with different crops, used in six different settings (lowlands, foothills, highlands, and so on). In each island, the people of each region have evolved the same way of exploiting it. Swidden farming and its various forms may have come about by slow unconscious experience of crop and land success or failure. In some places at least, observant individuals may have played a more creative part—legends of gifted ancestors are common enough. Even today, farming systems are often largely, and always to some extent, kept up by unthinking traditions and rituals. But there is sometimes method even in the rituals, and people like the Hanunóo can often give practical reasons for the things they do. At all events, in the 1930's, scientists began to study the special conditions of farming in the wet tropics, and they discovered that

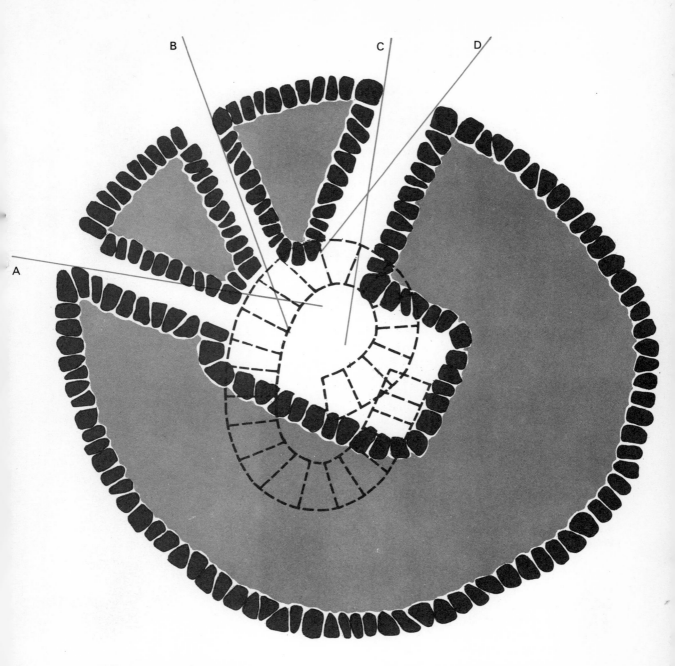

The Mayan civilization of Middle America arose between the 3rd and 8th centuries A.D. Based on swidden farming, it achieved great skill in numbers and astronomy. Its sudden collapse is the story of the inevitable tropical dead-end, told in this chapter. Left: Two views of the observatory in the Mayan city of Chichen Itza. Above: Plan showing astronomical sight-lines (A, south; B, setting of moon, March 21; C, west, and sunset at equinoxes; D, sunset at summer solstice).

bush fallow rotation, properly conducted, has its point. With all the wealth of modern scientific knowledge and technical equipment, the problem of farming these lands more productively is still a formidably difficult one, far from solved. The wonder is that local pioneers and peasants, lacking all this, produced a system so well suited to their surroundings. To understand how it works and what it does, we shall first have to take a quick look at the problem of soil fertility.

## The Living Soil

Soil looks like simple stuff, but it is one of the most complicated things in the world. It is made up, near the surface, of three components: minerals, organic matter (made from the chemical remains of dead plants and animals), and millions of small living organisms ranging in size from the microscopic viruses and bacteria to the relatively mighty earthworms. The mineral part, also present lower down, is made from the rocks of the earth's surface, ground into small particles (sand), smaller ones (silt), and very small ones (clay), and moved from place to place by wind, water, or glaciers. The organic matter, starting as dead organisms, becomes a sort of paste, called *humus*, between the mineral particles, coating each of them. The amounts of different-sized mineral particles and humus, among other things, determine the structure of the soil. It may form visible "crumbs" (much bigger than the mineral particles), between which air and water can enter and move freely. Or it may become a sticky mass. When air and water are present in the right balance, soil supports unimaginable numbers of live organisms. In an acre of soil, there may be up to half a million earthworms; in a square yard, up to 20 million tiny threadworms; and in a saltspoonful, up to 4000 million bacteria. Many other kinds of organisms are present too. The busy organisms, as they feed and excrete and die, make the soil a scene of ceaseless chemical change. Some of them make organic matter and break it down again. All of this is true for soils everywhere.

The green plants, on which we and our livestock depend, get materials for energy and growth from air and soil. From the air, they get oxygen and some water. Also, by means of the green chlorophyll in their leaves, they can use the energy of sunlight to take carbon dioxide from

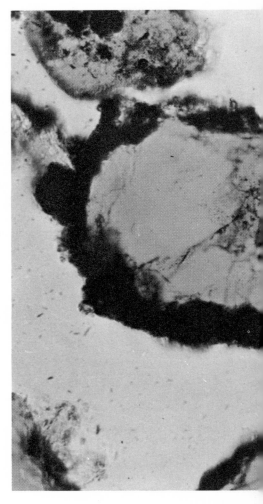

Left: Section through a cacao-root system in a well-drained upland soil in Ghana. Note how the root exploits the soil layers by forming a mat of roots near the surface, penetrating deep, and dividing into fibrous ends on reaching the gritty clay.

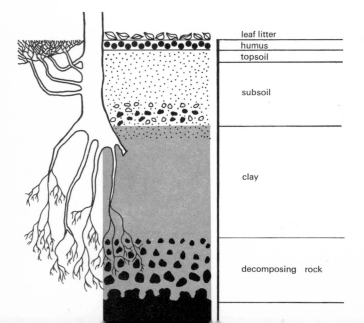

leaf litter
humus
topsoil

subsoil

clay

decomposing rock

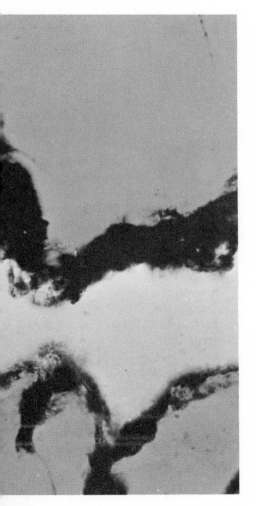

the air. Plants then discard the oxygen (so surrounding the earth with a breathable atmosphere for themselves and all other life) and use the carbon to build up energy-storing carbohydrate compounds—sugars, starch, and others. From the soil, through their roots, plants get most of their water, and supplies of a number of vital mineral elements —nitrogen (for making protein, the main material of living bodies), phosphorus (for making nucleic acids, the "blueprints" for all other processes), potassium, calcium, magnesium, sulfur, and other elements needed in smaller amounts. Most of these elements got into the soil originally from the "parent" rocks. The soil mineral particles are the powdered remains. Nitrogen, however, is another matter.

There is plenty of nitrogen in the air, but plants cannot use free nitrogen. They can only take it from certain compounds containing it—ammonia and nitrates. But air enters the soil through the spaces between crumbs, and here the nitrogen is extracted and turned into elaborate compounds by three groups of bacteria. Two of these (*Clostridium* and *Azotobacter*) live free in the soil. The third group (*Rhizobium*) begins its life in the soil, waiting for the roots of plants of the family Leguminosae (legumes), or a few other plants about which little is known. These roots release a substance that stimulates rhizobia to swim up to the roots and go inside. Once within the root, they multiply, and the legume makes them at home in a little bulge (a root nodule), where they live in a mutually profitable partnership. The legume provides sugars and the rhizobia bacteria assist in making nitrogen compounds. When the legume dies, the compounds are left in the soil.

Many mineral elements in the soil, such as potassium and calcium, are stored on the surface of the smallest mineral particles (clay). Others, especially nitrogen, are

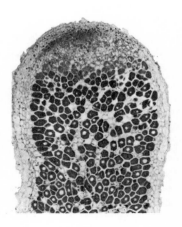

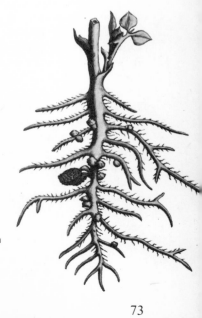

The skeleton of soil is formed of particles of highly resistant, inert rock. Top photo shows clay particles, each less than two-thousandths of a millimeter across. The particles are coated with organic matter humus, seen clearly in the lower photograph.

Right: Drawing by 17th-century Italian anatomist Marcello Malpighi shows nodules on root of bean plant. Photo above shows root nodule and the concentration of boron (dark), an element essential for the development of nodules on leguminous plants.

73

stored in the organic matter. For, once the soil is occupied by plants, it becomes a going concern. All the plant food elements (including carbon from the air, which most soil organisms could not otherwise use) are continually being returned to the soil in the dead bodies of plants and animals. Some microbes, or microscopic organisms, build nitrogen from these sources into *organic matter*, in which form the nitrogen is unusable by plants but safely stored. Other microbes break down the organic matter into nitrates, which plant roots can use. Others are liable to grab the nitrates and turn them back to free nitrogen, which returns to the air. Thus arises an elaborate and continuous exchange called the *nitrogen cycle*.

The trouble with nitrates is that they are easily washed out of the surface soil into lower depths where most plant roots cannot reach them, or from where they are drained away to the nearest stream. To achieve the right activity-balance of all the various microbes for successful agriculture is quite a trick. For instance, crops are sometimes grown especially as "green manures" for other crops. Their dead leaves and stems work into the soil, where they add to the organic matter. Sometimes this actually does more harm than good, for if soil microbes are given too much carbon from such plant remains, they use their surplus energy on the organic matter originally present. They thus make so much nitrate that much is washed away or broken down by other microbes before the main crop can get the benefit of it. On the other hand, if the microbes are too idle, the nitrogen is safely stored in organic matter and inaccessible for the plants. Ideally, a balance between these extremes is to be achieved.

### The Uses of the Forest Fallow

In the wet tropics, two special conditions are present. First, the heat makes all microbes very active, so the nitrogen cycle revs up. Second, the very heavy rainfall in the long wet season is especially liable to wash nitrates into the lower depths—a process known as leaching. Other necessary minerals are also washed away, particularly where there is too much sand and not enough clay to hold them. Such soils, which tend to become rather acid, are called leached soils. They occur in damp sandy places even in Europe, under heaths and pinewoods, but are especially widespread in the wet tropics. In the flood plains of rivers, however, water does not easily drain away, and here less leaching occurs. If, as in Africa, the great rivers bring down soil from other tropical regions that have been leached themselves, this does not help much. But if, as elsewhere, the great rivers come from richer soils outside the tropics, their flood plains are highly fertile. As we have seen, settled agriculture appeared in the flood plains of the

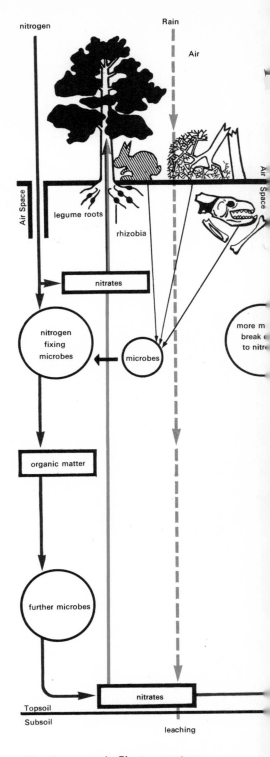

The nitrogen cycle. Plants cannot use free nitrogen. They have to obtain it from nitrogen compounds (nitrates), which are manufactured by bacteria in the soil. Right: In tropical rain-forests, although nitrates and useful mineral elements are liable to be washed into the lower soil depths, the deep tree roots recover them. This makes possible a lush growth, as in this forest in the Congo.

East. So bush fallow rotation was clearly evolved for leached tropical soils.

The rain-forest has several ways of dealing with the problem presented by these soils. To begin with, the trees continually and rapidly return large quantities of dead matter to the soil—some of it woody material, that holds plant food elements firmly. The microbes go at it very fast, and leaves and other debris are broken down so rapidly that there is little litter on the rain-forest floor (such as you find piled up in temperate forests), and little humus in the soil. But the rapid turnover makes the rich forest vegetation possible. Forest trees can flourish even on a ledge thinly covered with soil, where less lavish plants would soon fail through not returning enough dead matter to the soil. The Hanunóo never make a swidden on such ledges, even when they see vigorous forest growth there, because they know it would not work. Where soil is deep but leached, the trees have another advantage. They throw down very deep roots (down to eight feet in some species) to bring up leached elements from the lower soil layers. Finally, the rain-forest is full of leguminous trees (which make up 50 per cent of all plant species in forests of Ghana and Central America), and the rhizobia in their roots counteract the loss of nitrogen by leaching. Legumes and their rhizobia evolved in the later Mesozoic period, when there were no polar icecaps, and when the wet tropics and their leached soils spread much farther than they do today. They only later made good in temperate regions. They are one of the largest families of seed plants, with 13,000 species, ranging from little clovers to giants of the forest. Many are useful food crops, and, owing to their special power of winning nitrogen, they are rich in protein. Some legumes are used as swidden crops. The Hanunóo, for instance, grow pigeon-peas, mung beans, lima beans, groundnuts, and several other legumes.

When man clears the trees and the land is occupied by smaller plants with surface root systems (grass or crops), the turnover of plant matter is reduced or stopped. Not enough dead matter returns to the soil, and elements leached downward cannot be recovered—hence the eventual crop failures. The *first* crop on a swidden does fine, because it has the benefit of the long bush fallow. The elements drawn up the deep tree roots are lavished on the

An expedition led by the British explorer Sir Henry Stanley threads between the towering trees of an African forest. In such forests, there is a rapid turnover of vegetation, and the dead matter—even the large tree-trunks—soon decays, so aiding further tree growth.

*Koompassia excelsa*, a leguminous tree in South America. As many as half the plants in a tropical rain-forest are nitrogen-providing legumes, and help to make up for nitrogen lost by leaching.

surface soil of the clearing when the tree debris is burned. Farmers who practice chitemene (see Chapter 3) are even making use of supplies from elsewhere in the forest around. Experiments in Zambia have shown that chitemene ashes enrich the soil with phosphorus, potassium, and calcium, and make it less acid.

Early European experts had been horrified by the practice of burning debris on the swidden. They pointed out that during the fire large amounts of nitrogen must be vaporized and returned to the air, and claimed that the fire must destroy much of the organic matter of the forest soil. But, as long ago as 1932, the British agriculturalist G. Milne took up the defense of swidden farming, and listed a number of advantages of burning. Later work has fully vindicated him. In 1948, for instance, an experiment in growing rice on forest clearings near Njala in Sierra Leone showed that, when all the debris was removed, the first year's yield of rice was very low. If the debris was removed, and burned somewhere else, and the ash brought back and spread over the clearing, the yield was higher. But it was more than twice as high again if the debris was burned on the spot. So not only the ash but the actual burning is valuable. Similar results have been obtained with finger millet in Malawi in 1935–37, and in a long series of experiments in Zambia from 1932 to 1950. In 1959, G. Baldanzi was in Brazil comparing the benefits of burning vegetation or plowing it into the soil. He surveyed the whole history of burning as an agricultural method, right back to the comment of the poet Virgil in the first century B.C.: "It has often paid to set fire to sterile fields." Baldanzi concluded that the burn affects only the topmost layer of the soil, and destroys little organic matter; that it improves soil structure; and that it kills or encourages exactly the right microbes to get the best possible balance of nitrogen cycle in the soil. Once again, it seems, the swidden farmers were, without knowing the mechanism of the process, on the right track.

After a few years (three in Vietnam, four in Sudan, for instance), crop yields from a clearing fall to negligible amounts, and only another long bush fallow will restore the leached elements and repair the nitrogen cycle again. So the normal timing of bush fallow rotation is vindicated. The only exception so far recorded in a swidden region is in a rather dry (and therefore less leached) area in Ceylon. There, in experiments in 1948, it was found that a long bush fallow was unnecessary, and crops could be grown on a clearing for a longer time. Yet here, too, the swidden farmers practiced their rotation (1–3 years cropping, 8–20 years fallow).

The reason is interesting, and suggests that swidden farmers, elsewhere may have got the benefit of restoring

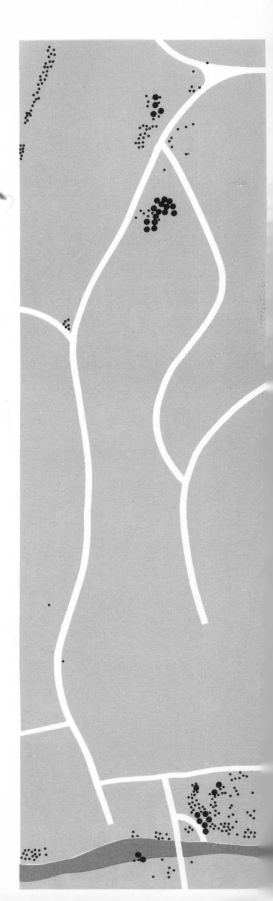

soil fertility by doing their rotation from a quite different motive. After a year or two, a swidden is so completely overgrown by weeds (which compete with and crowd out food crops) that the labor of weeding it becomes too much. As a result, farmers have had to abandon the clearing some time before soil exhaustion would have brought about crop failure. When the trees grow back, bringing deep shade, the weeds die out. By the time the swidden is cleared again, weeds will take a year or two to get a new foothold. The appearance of weeds in the first place was a direct result of cutting down the trees and opening the clearing to the sunlight.

We think of weeds as useless *wild* plants, but this is only a half-truth. Many weeds of temperate lands, where only one or two crops are grown on otherwise bare soil, are almost as man-made as the crops themselves. We call them "weeds of cultivation." Before agriculture, a few of them eked out a precarious existence on the few spots (such as riverbanks) where nature left the soil bare, as these species need it to be. Man provided unprecedented amounts of bare soil. He opened Pandora's Box, and out came the weeds and flourished exceedingly. In the pollen sequences of Europe, a weedlike plantain is as sure a sign of the presence of agricultural man as is wheat. And man also spread weeds over wide areas, when their seeds got mixed up with those of his crops. Excavations at Caerleon in Wales in 1964, for instance, showed that the Romans had brought certain weeds to Britain in grain consignments.

Many weeds, however, are simply grasses that were already common before man arrived. Unlike some other things from Pandora's Box, they have not been an unmixed curse. Oats and rye, for instance, appeared as weeds in the first European wheat and barley fields. (Wild rye grows today as a weed in the wheatfields of Afghanistan.) They became better and better fitted for cultivated life, without any conscious human intention. Thus when the pioneers reached the cold north, where the oats and rye did better than wheat and barley, man began to sow them deliberately as crops.

In tropical swiddens, weeds are essentially the plants of the grasslands, especially grasses themselves. They flourish in clearings because man, by removing shade and

Two maps of an area in America show (near right) geographical features and land use, and (far left) occurrence of pokeweed (dots). Like most weeds, the plant thrives on open soil, and is therefore native only along the flooded soil of riverbanks. Note how it has been spread by man to his garden sites and cultivated land, where it is classed as a weed.

reducing soil fertility, tips the balance in their favor. The forest trees, so lush once their cycle is established, cannot get started if the soil has become too poor. Short cropping periods and long bush fallows ensure that the forest can always return. Experts like the Hanunóo deliberately take care by protecting certain trees from the burn and by planting new ones, to maintain enough shade to keep grasses at bay till the forest recovers properly. But for even the least knowledgeable swidden farmers, the time to stop cropping is obvious. It is the time when grasses and other weeds are getting out of hand. Stopping at this point ensures the recovery of the forest, and by so doing it guarantees the restoration of soil fertility.

It also ensures the continued *existence* of the soil. For, when the Europeans made their bare plowed fields in the wet tropics and kept them under cultivation, fertility declined. Often, too, the soil was actually lost by excessive erosion. Natural soil erosion is the gradual removal of the surface of the soil by wind, water, or glaciers, which carry it to streams and so either to their lower reaches and mouths (forming rich flood plains and deltas) or on into the ocean. This natural erosion is going on all the time at an appreciable rate. Natural soil erosion is the normal process whereby soil is distributed over the land, and it makes the river valleys lush with soil from the rocks of the mountains. On a world estimate made by the earth scientist Jean Corbel in 1964, something like 10 billion cubic yards are eroded every year. This soil loss is naturally balanced by the equally gradual wearing away of the rocks beneath to form new soil. The two processes together maintain a roughly constant thickness of soil on the

Above right: A meadow grass showing root system. Grasses have an advantage over trees in dry country because they have a far larger root system in proportion to leaf area and their roots are nearer the surface. The roots thus take all available moisture from brief rainstorms so that none reaches the tree roots deeper down.

Upland rice-growing on land in Sumatra that had been used the previous year for tobacco. Note the carefully preserved bushes and trees. These prevent erosion, and allow the forest to reestablish itself quickly before grasses can get a foothold. After about eight years of forest, another tobacco crop is grown.

This area in San Rafael de Mucuchies in the Venezuelan Andes has suffered severe erosion following continual cultivation. Although wheat is still planted in some parts, most of the slope is quite useless for crop-growing.

lands of the world, and the persistence of plants continually renews the fertility of surface soil. But whereas the provision of new soil cannot be hastened by man, the erosion of old soil *can*, as when he exposes bare earth to the unbridled action of wind and water. When this happens the soil may simply be lost, and we cannot wait millennia for new soil to form—we have to eat tomorrow.

Destructive soil erosion becomes a real menace on level plains swept by fierce winds, or in places, especially with steep and irregular slopes, where rain is heavy. On the central plains of North America, owing to the pattern of air movement around the two ends of the coastal mountain chain and up from the Caribbean, furious winds and tornadoes are common. Here the whole soil surface may be whipped up as a dustcloud, leaving only lifeless subsoil or even bare rock. All over the wet tropics (where, as we have seen, swidden farming is commonest on the steep and irregular slopes of the hills), raindrops come down like volleys of bullets. As they hit the soil in exposed areas, bits of it splash into the air, while the rest is beaten into a compact, waterpoof state. Instead of sinking into the soil, rainwater tends to run off down the nearest slope, carrying bits of soil with it. The whole top layer may be washed away by this "runoff" (sheet erosion). Or, the escaping water may dig gullies that deepen and widen as bigger and bigger soil fragments, or even rocks, are torn away and batter the floor and sides of each gulley. By such vicious spirals, the living soil of an open field may be washed away, and carried to streams, to rivers, to the sea itself, silting up harbors and making treacherous bars across river mouths.

There are several ways of protecting soil from destructive erosion, even in the wet tropics. One method is to spread on the soil surface a layer of material (such as dead plant matter) to take the first force of the rain (or wind). For this, English-speaking farmers have the expressive word *mulch*. Better still, however, is a cover of living vegetation. A forest cover is best of all. It intercepts heavy raindrops, letting them fall gently on to a soil that can absorb all this moisture and release water in a trickle, deep down, to flow out as springs. But any continuous plant cover is a great help against erosion. And so it is that lowered soil fertility—which means that a continuous plant cover cannot be maintained—itself brings soil erosion in its train.

The Hanunóo people of the Philippines know something of all this from tribal experience. They take enormous care when choosing a new swidden site, and may discuss it for months, up to three years in advance of clearing. They use only firm soils on regular slopes, not too steep, and classify soils into many categories, rated in order of fertility. Their ratings have been found to agree well with the results of scientific analysis of these soils. As a final check, they drive a bamboo stick into the ground. If the soil does not come up the hollow interior of the bamboo, the site is abandoned. They regard this as purely a ritual activity, but obviously the outcome of the test depends on soil structure, and therefore must have practical importance.

While the swidden is being cultivated, the great variety of crops grown together, some upright, some creeping, ensures that every foot of soil is covered with vegetation. The period when a swidden is first cleared and exposed to the winds is critical. But, as we have seen, when they slash down the plant cover, the farmers take care to spread debris evenly over the soil surface as a mulch. Teen-agers, who find this spreading job less fun than slashing, are supervised by older Hanunóo, who give them their first "lectures" on soil erosion and how to prevent it.

Left: Heavy tropical rain strikes
unprotected soil, throwing the fine soil
particles into the air. These particles
fall back to earth, filling the spaces
between the larger particles. This
prevents water sinking into the soil.
Instead it runs off in a flood,
eroding the soil as it goes.

Hill on the island of Mindoro, the
Philippines, shows, in the background,
climax rain-forest where clearance is
traditionally prohibited by the Hanunóo.
If clearance took place, the steep slopes
might well erode. Such patches of forest
provide a source of seeds for regrowth on
cleared areas.

Map of Southeast Asia shows population density on blue color scale in four categories: over 200 persons per square mile (darkest blue); 50–200 (next); 10–50 (next); and under 10 (lightest blue). Swidden farming is practiced in the lower density areas.

Hanunóo family eating rice and bananas. Swidden farming produces only enough food for present needs, and thus works only if population density remains very low.

## The Dilemma

When all has been said of the real merits of swidden farming the fact remains that in some respects early European visitors were right about some things. It does use a great deal of land and labor to produce a very low yield of food. Even the food yields of the Hanunóo from cropped swiddens, which are about 1,300 pounds per acre, are not high by the standards of permanently settled agriculture. The yield of swidden rice in Sierra Leone, in 1964, probably typical for this way of farming, was about 775 pounds per acre of cropped land. All advanced rice-growing settled farmers manage to produce several thousand pounds, and one prize-winning Japanese farmer has raised 11,879 pounds per acre! But of course, apart from the low yield on the swidden itself, most of the land at any given time is unproductive bush fallow. A given area of land will support relatively few swidden farmers. There are about 50 Hanunóo per square mile, but this is an unusually high density. On an estimate made in 1957, the average number among all swidden farmers is 15 per square mile. This means that swidden farmers take up only a little less room than hunters, who in very good conditions may reach a population density of 2–3 persons per square mile.

When Europeans brought modern medicine to the wet tropics, and often peace from local feuds as well, the populations of swidden farmers began to rise. The results showed all too clearly that swidden farming will work *only* if the population stays very low. In 1940, J. A. van Beukering of the Java Department of Economic Affairs estimated that swidden farming could support, at the very most, 125 people per square mile. This figure has been generally accepted. Whenever populations became denser than this, things started going wrong. To feed the extra mouths, peasants had to have more land under crops and less under bush fallow. On any given plot, the cropping period became longer and/or the fallow period shorter. By 1964 the bush fallow period in parts of Sierra Leone had shortened from 12–15 years to 3–4 years. The reduced periods were often too short to enable the forest to recover and restore soil fertility. Hence, with populations rising all over the wet tropics, land became less and less fertile.

Over vast areas, especially where the dry season was fairly long and swiddens were repeatedly burned after the original clearing, grass won the battle against trees. The forest failed and swiddens were covered with tall grasses, especially *Imperata* (cogon) in the East and *Hyparrhenia* in Africa. These new grasslands, or *cogonals*, cover 18 per cent of the whole land surface of the Philippines, spread far and wide in Vietnam, and are common all over the tropics. Modern agriculturalists are only just

If swiddens are repeatedly burned, the forest may never return and grass may move in. Once such grasslands get a foothold, the land becomes useless to the swidden farmer because the matted root system below the surface defies his simple tools and continually shoots up grass. Photo below shows cogon grass established in Mindanao, in the Philippines.

beginning to find ways of using them. For swidden farmers (except in parts of Africa, where a grass fallow rotation gives modest returns with much burning) they are a complete loss. Grasses from an established sod of roots and suckers are merciless weeds. Elsewhere—notably on the hills of Africa, India, and Burma—soil erosion took its toll, removing large areas (especially in India) from any kind of productive use.

In the annual reports of the Department of Agriculture of Northern Rhodesia (now Zambia) from 1933 onward, we can follow the progress of an heroic attempt to conserve the land by controlling the length of chitemene fallow. In the end, this attempt disappears from the reports, and one supposes that population pressure was too much for the agriculturalists. In the Congo, where another controlled

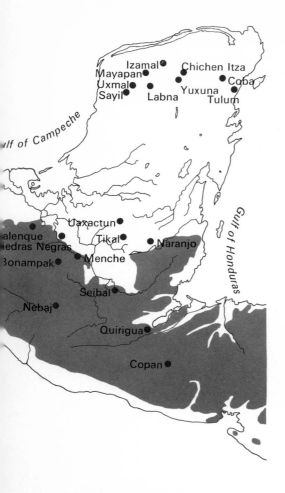

On the above map of southern Mexico and Guatemala are marked the early Mayan sites on the uplands (gray) and also the later Mayan sites in the Yucatan peninsula in the north. Below: Bas-relief from an altar at Copan, showing astronomer-priests at the great congress in A.D. 503.

system was introduced, interest also seems to have shifted to other kinds of farming. All over the wet tropics, scientists are trying new methods. Often they use legumes for cover and soil fertility conservation, and sometimes they plant particular trees to make artificial bush fallows. With all the resources of modern science, they may eventually solve the problem of productive tropical farming, at least when farm animals, with their manure, can be integrated with it. What emerges clearly from the whole story is the fact that swidden farming in past ages could never support population increase without incurring the nemesis of lost fertility, invading grassland, and soil erosion.

We can now finally understand why the agricultural system of the wet tropics could not produce the sustained advance of cities and civilization that led to the technological breakthrough. With all its merits, it is still to a great extent a passive submission or adjustment to natural conditions. To begin with, only some swidden farmers have settled homes—like the Hanunóo, who live in small groups and make swiddens within a radius of about 500 yards from their houses. Many, perhaps most, move their homes as well as their plots. Both ways of life are found side by side in Malaysia. Even when settled, swidden farmers must work continuously as a small, self-contained group, and such groups are difficult to integrate into societies larger than tribes. But the critical factor is the low food yield per unit of land area. Even the Hanunóo can spare only about 10 per cent of their hard-won food to trade for beads and salt with the people of the coast. To support the fulltime specialists needed for cities and civilization, a large surplus is indispensable. In the lands of swidden farming this surplus could be won, for a time, only by putting more land under crops. This led to shortening fallows and, in turn, to all the consequences we have seen.

Some enterprising peoples have tried to escape from this dilemma. Two ancient civilizations in Asia (the Khmers of Cambodia and the people of Anuradapura in Ceylon) are thought to have been based at least partly on swidden farming, and to have succumbed to the invasion of cogonals. Both civilizations certainly used some irrigation as well, and may have met other disasters we shall consider later. But one great civilization is known to have been based entirely on swidden farming. We may illustrate the insoluble dilemma of this way of life with the story of the tragic fall of the early Mayas in Middle America.

The great cities of the Early Empire of the Mayas were built in the relatively healthy uplands of Guatemala, Honduras, San Salvador, and southernmost Mexico, from the third to the eighth century A.D. Chief among them were

Drawing of a stone pillar at Copan.
This city was the great astronomical
capital of the Old Mayan Empire and
the site of the great congress.

Uaxactun, Tikal, Yaxchilan, Palenque, and above all Copan, scene of a great congress of Mayan astronomers (as their own records tell) convened on September 2, in the year 503, to reform the calendar. The need for accurate timing in farm operations has made astronomy the earliest civilized science. The early Mayas (who had ideographic writing—see p. 54) were remarkable in this respect. They appear to have invented the modern number system independently of the Indians and Arabs, and they could compute astronomical events to an accuracy of one day in 33 years. Moreover, they seem to have been at least relatively free from the obsession with human sacrifice that infected many other American civilizations, and reached appalling proportions in Mexico. The early Mayas were, indeed, the hope of America.

But in the eighth and ninth centuries, the cities of the Early Empire were abandoned one by one. The Mayas retreated to build new ones in the fever-ridden jungles of Yucatan, where (according to a peasant proverb) it rains 13 months in the year. The later Mayas were constantly on the move. Under Mexican influence their societies were riddled with human sacrifice and their once promising civilization gradually decayed.

Three reasons have been suggested for the abandonment of the cities of the Early Empire, and all turn on the fatal dilemma of swidden farming—or slash-and-burn farming, as it is often called when discussing the Mayas. Some scholars think they succumbed to soil erosion. A study of soil fertility on a Guatemalan hillside (where swidden farming, here *milpa*, is still going on) led one agriculturalist, in 1960, to predict erosion here if the population rose to any extent. We know that the Mayas moved from steep hillsides to flatter lowlands. Others think the Mayas' fields were invaded by cogonals, both around the early cities and later in Yucatan. In the course of centuries the forest climax finally triumphed again over the grass in man's absence, so that eventually the fantastic Mayan cities became overgrown with vegetation. Yet others have emphasized the social effects of soil exhaustion. Some peasants seem to have remained when the city folk left.

Perhaps the peasants, seeing their lands exhausted by the hungry mouths of the cities, revolted and drove out these city people who ruled but did not mix with them.

On any of these views, the Mayan tragedy shows the ultimate dilemma of the wet tropics. Man here had reached a dead-end, from which he could never emerge until others elsewhere had brought civilization to the final breakthrough. We may wonder why, all over the wet tropics, bush fallow rotation continued to work for so long. The answer is that the system worked because populations remained small. And if we ask why this was so, the answer is simple and grim. In the wet tropics, for reasons we shall see, people died young.

Copan sculpture of a youthful Mayan god, patron of the precarious cultivation of corn, on which the cities depended for food. Their demands probably exhausted the capacity of swidden farming and the civilization collapsed. The Mayan cities were overgrown by forests when they were discovered in the 19th century (right).

# 5   The Dry Belt

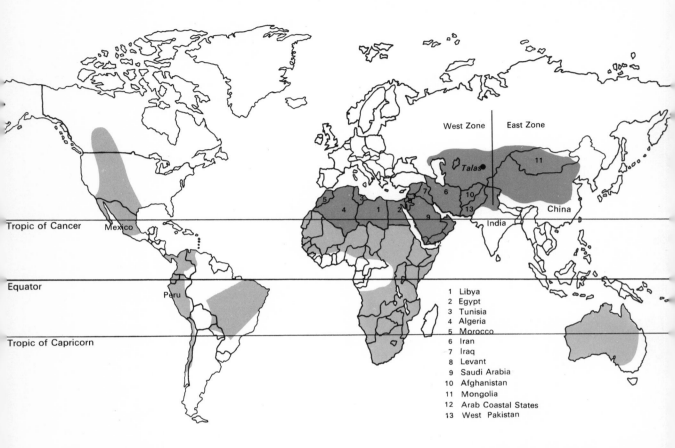

West Zone   East Zone

Talas

11

7   6   10
3       13
5   4   1 2       China
8   9       India

Tropic of Cancer   Mexico

Equator

Peru

Tropic of Capricorn

1   Libya
2   Egypt
3   Tunisia
4   Algeria
5   Morocco
6   Iran
7   Iraq
8   Levant
9   Saudi Arabia
10   Afghanistan
11   Mongolia
12   Arab Coastal States
13   West Pakistan

From the wet tropics, with their poor, leached soils and cruelly handicapped agriculture, we now turn to a very different group of regions—those of the great dry belt. Here the soils are generally rich and the promise of success appears much greater. In fact, splendid civilizations have flourished there at times when most of Europe was barbarous and illiterate. Yet, in the long run, the progress of mankind was thwarted here, too, by nature, although in a much more complicated way.

The first of this group of regions is a continuous belt right across the Old World, running from the north coast of Africa through the Near and Middle East, bending north around the Himalayas through the vast lands of Central Asia, to end on the plains of northern China. In the course of history, it has tended to divide into two zones. The eastern zone was dominated by the influence of Chinese civilization, and shaped by thinkers like Confucius. The western Zone, stretching from Morocco to Central Asia,

The dark red areas on this map indicate the lands of the dry belt we are primarily concerned with in this chapter. Light red areas mark other arid regions. The Talas River in Central Asia roughly divides the eastern area of Chinese influence from the western Islamic zone.

Two great figures of the dry belt. Above right: The prophet Mohammed, 7th century A.D., from a 15th-century Turkish manuscript. Right: Confucius (figure on right) c. 551–497 B.C. Illustration is from a 19th-century painting.

was eventually united by the culture of Islam, the way of life founded by the Arab prophet Mohammed in the seventh century A.D. The boundary between the two can roughly be set in Turkestan, where the Arabs defeated the Chinese at the battle of the Talas River in A.D. 751. The Arabs, however, were unable to invade China. The close cultural connection between the two zones is evident from the fact that in 1939 there were reported to be 48,104,240 Muslims (Mohammedans) in China, or about one Chinese in ten. Nevertheless, the two zones had rather different histories, as we shall see.

The great subcontinent of India lies partly in the dry belt, and its past history has been disastrously influenced by that of the belt as a whole. The grasslands and savannas of Africa echo the main story at a distance. Other dry regions cover large areas of North and South America, and almost the whole of Australia. Hindus, Chinese, and Muslims in turn fell short of reaching Australia, and so that far continent played no part in history until the coming of Europeans in the seventeenth century A.D. But the American civilizations of Mexico and Peru had much in common with their counterparts in the Old World dry belt.

Rainfall over all these regions is not prolonged enough to leach plant food out of the surface of the soils, which are often richly fertile, unlike those of the tropical forests. The problem here is just the reverse. The critical factor for plant life is *lack* of water. The total amount of rainfall per year varies widely even between places close together. For instance, there are $20\frac{1}{2}$ inches of rain per annum at Jerusalem but only $1\frac{3}{4}$ inches at Máan in the desert of Jordan, less than 120 miles away. Rainfall generally increases with height above sea level, and it also tends to fall with distance from the coast. But throughout the entire belt, rainfall is liable to be irregular, and above all it is restricted to one part of the year. In Jerusalem, for instance, all but two-fifths of an inch of the rain falls between November and May. The long dry season presents a formidable obstacle to the growing of even one crop in each year. Over favored parts of the belt, there are permanently flowing streams, notably the great rivers Nile, Euphrates, Tigris, Indus, and the Yellow River. But over vast tracts, like the Sahara and the Rub al Khali desert of Arabia, there are only *wadis*—beds that carry raging torrents (swift to erode soils) during the brief rains, but are dry for the rest of the year.

In the pluvial period corresponding to the fourth glaciation, the Sahara desert was full of life. Freshwater shells from that age bear witness to permanent rivers in the heart of the Rub al Khali. It is generally agreed that the dry belt became dry early in the fourth interglacial. A more difficult question is that of the changes in humidity and rainfall over the dry belt during the five millennia or so of recorded human history. It used to be thought that the course of human civilization here was shaped in a simple way by alternating periods of wetter and drier climate. It now seems unlikely that such regular and drastic oscillations really occurred. Certainly the fortunes of dry-belt man are not simply related to climatic change.

The level of water in the ground is good evidence of the total amount of annual rainfall. In several places in Jordan, the construction of Roman wells shows that the level of water in them (and hence in the ground) was the same in Roman times as it is in the present century. The same thing has been observed in Byzantine wells in the Negev desert of Israel. So rainfall must have been the same when the Romans and Byzantines ruled these regions (first century B.C. to seventh century A.D.) as it is today. Yet, as we shall see, at that period Jordan and Israel were at the height of their prosperity, and covered with productive farms, while by the early twentieth century A.D. they were a scene of utter desolation. So their societies clearly did not go up and down because of climatic cycles. True, small fluctuations in rainfall are constantly observed in modern times. We may well suppose that a run of bad drought years may often have secondarily intensified the action of other factors. But other factors were of importance as we shall soon see when we study the tragic upheavals of human civilization in the dry belt.

## Water Works for Man

Throughout all recorded history, over most of these dry regions, agriculture was either impossible or dangerously unreliable for farmers depending only on rainfall to water their crops. Nevertheless, it was precisely here that human civilizations first appeared. The agriculture on which these civilizations rested was achieved by controlling the distribution of water in such a way as to supply it to crops in the dry season—in other words, to irrigate them. The water used for irrigation might be rain naturally stored in the ground and tapped by artificial wells or natural springs, like the spring that made possible the early success of irrigated agriculture in the oasis of Jericho. Or rainwater could be caught and channeled as it ran off the surface of the land downhill toward the sea.

The greatest opportunities for irrigation were presented in the great river valleys. Here the control of water meant

Above: Map of Arabian peninsula shows the distribution of its many wadis. After winter rainstorms these river beds become raging torrents that erode away soil in the hills where they originate. This silt, deposited on the plains, blocks up many wadis before they reach the sea. In summer (below), with no rain to water them, wadis are as dry as the barren landscape around them.

not only getting it to the crops, but also getting it away from them when necessary (drainage), and preventing destructive floods. Once launched on the technology of water control, man could go further, sending water over long distances by aqueducts or digging great canals to link up rivers for boat and barge transport of food and other goods. Thus, from scratching crude channels in the earth to lead water from some brook to his plot, man in the dry belt graduated to such feats of engineering as the Grand Canal linking the Yangtze and the Yellow River, completed by the seventh century A.D.

From the river valleys of the dry belt, the technique of irrigation spread in due course up into the hills and deep into the deserts. It also spread into regions outside the belt, in or near the tropics, where soils were fertile enough

The ancient civilizations controlling the Near East opened up large areas of desert by means of long-distance aqueducts, like this Roman one near Caesarea in Israel. Plentiful water supplies made this city a prosperous commercial and artistic center for a thousand years.

to grow warmth-loving rice, vastly productive when flooded with water during part of its growing period. In some of these regions, such as Thailand and southern China, irrigation made possible the growth of two rice crops every year, thus doubling the productivity of the land. Water-controlling, or "hydraulic", societies (as the historian Karl A. Wittfogel has called them) developed in southern China, southeastern India, southeast Asia, and Indonesia, as well as in the lands of the dry belt. From records compiled by the Food and Agriculture Organization (FAO) of land areas irrigated in 1962, it appears that the dry belt and the tropics are still the principal homes of irrigation. The one great irrigating country outside both regions is Japan, just warm enough for rice. Here, as we shall see, conditions have been unusual.

The agricultural system based on water-control was extremely efficient and productive. To begin with, soil erosion by runoff water was automatically controlled. In the valley plains, uncontrolled eroding floods were prevented, and the water was gently led from field to field, so that it sank into the soil. At the same time, it deposited on the surface just the right amount of fertile silt brought down from the hills—an annual supply of mineral food for the crops. On the steep slopes of the hills, rainwater was likewise trapped and controlled as it ran downward, by the

Below: Rice terraces in Indonesia. Over many parts of the world, man learned to terrace steep slopes. He thus prevented soil erosion and was able to irrigate hill land. The picture shows how the water drains from level to level flooding the rice in each plot.

The invention of the plow meant efficient soil preparation and, especially, weed control on settled land. Below: Model of an Egyptian plow, *c.* 2000 B.C., with one man to drive it and another to guide the oxen. The Kassite plow from Iraq (above), from a clay tablet, 14th century B.C., was more sophisticated. The seed was sown through a hopper attachment.

construction of walled steps or terraces. The steps of these terraces were straight and regular. The horizontal lines followed irregular natural contours, making man's control of nature visible in a beautifully composed landscape. By the first millennium B.C., such terraces covered many areas —for example, the slopes of the Lebanon Mountains, of southern Arabia, and of such remote spots as the island of Luzon in the Philippines. Later, similar terraces appeared in Peru, in East Africa from Sudan to Rhodesia, and in many other regions.

The water-controllers no longer had to shift their ground like swidden farmers. A field once cleared was potentially cleared forever, annually refertilized by the silt, but protected from the danger of erosion. The ground was not encumbered by tree roots or stumps, and the crop was sown or planted in neat rows for easy access of small water-channels. The farmer could work meticulously over the soil to prepare it for seeds and keep it free of weeds. By the third millennium B.C., the ox-drawn plow had appeared in both Egypt and Iraq, to make furrows. In Iraq it was sometimes equipped with a hopper (funnel) through which seeds were dropped behind the share (blade). In this millennium too, the Iraquis in their written records distinguished different varieties of the same crop (for instance, late-ripening barley and early-ripening

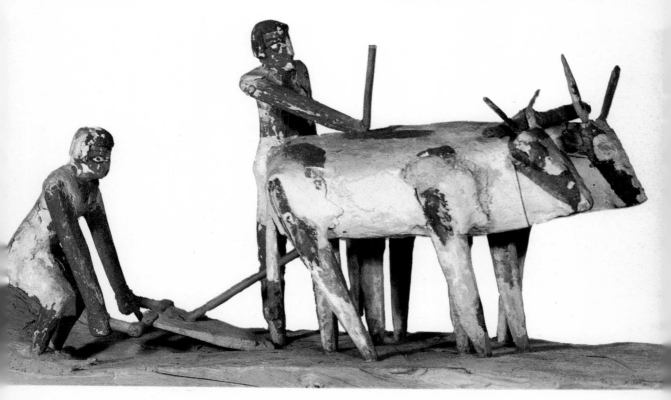

Detail from *The Harvesters* by Peter Breughel the Elder (1520–69). With plentiful regular rainfall, European farmers have always found life easier than hydraulic peasants. Harvesting leaves time to enjoy a hearty meal among the rain-fed crops.

barley), which they must have selected for sowing in different places.

An agricultural manual already widely known in 1700 B.C. describes the elaborate sequence of operations on a farm on the lower Euphrates. To begin with, the farmer had to irrigate the field, making sure the water did not rise too high. Then the water was drained off, and oxen driven over the field to trample the weeds. Afterwards the surface was carefully leveled by men with mattocks, and worked over with a harrow. After thorough plowing, harrowing, raking, and breaking the clods with hammers, barley was sown, using a plow with a seed-hopper. The seeds had to be dropped into the hopper at a uniform rate. Some more clod-breaking, and the barley was left to grow. The next job was to scare off the birds. The growing crop had to be irrigated three times, at stages defined by the exact height of the plants. Then the farmer had to watch out for a disease that would turn the barley red. But if all was well, he could give a fourth irrigation, which might increase the final grain yield by ten per cent.

Such intensive and productive farming was not seen anywhere outside the hydraulic societies until the final technological breakthrough in Europe. Even in the early nineteenth century A.D., Justus von Liebig, the founder of agricultural chemistry, asserted that Europe was in its agricultural infancy by comparison. With high yields on land all permanently in use, hydraulic agriculture supported a very dense population. In the first century B.C., for instance, the wheat and barley fields of Egypt probably maintained about 725 people per square mile. In the early twentieth century A.D. (before industrialization had really started there), the average for the whole province of Shansi in northern China, growing wheat and millet, was 183 people per square mile. For the whole rice-growing province of Chekiang in southern China, it was 554 people per square mile. By contrast, in the sixteenth century A.D., the province of Holland in the Netherlands was unusually densely peopled for Europe—at 95 people per square mile!

The irrigated land produced a huge food surplus that supported cities of hundreds of thousands of people. Ur and Babylon in Iraq already had populations of this order in the second millennium B.C. So did Cuzco (in Peru) and Mexico City before the coming of Cortez. And in the later history of the Old World dry belt, cities as big as Babylon were common. Except for ancient Rome (importing food from the dry belt), no cities in Europe reached this scale until the technological breakthrough. With such a surplus and such cities, it is no wonder the hydraulic societies of the dry belt were the ones that launched civilization, and carried it to great heights of technical and cultural achievement.

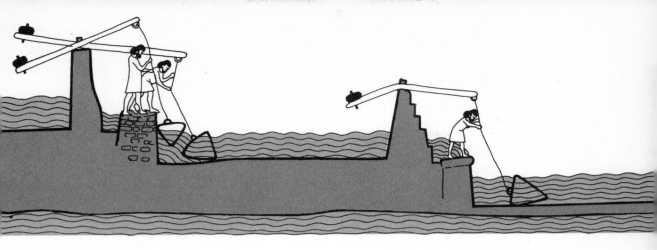

But these achievements were made at a price. Hydraulic agriculture is obviously far more economical of land than swidden farming, but it is even more demanding of labor. The early manual summarized above shows how much attention the farmers of ancient Iraq had to give to water control—a whole set of chores that could be omitted in lands (such as those of Europe) where a farmer could generally depend on rainfall throughout the year. In the early twentieth century A.D., wheat-farmers in the Chinese province of Hopeh spent 58 per cent of their working time on operations with water. Similar calculations made in other parts of China and in Pakistan showed that work done by the dry-belt farmer on water control alone took up more time than *all* the work done (on his own farm) by a rainfall farmer in medieval Europe. And on top of this,

Above: Assyrian peasants operating a *shaduf* to raise water from canal to irrigation channels (in picture redrawn from a relief in the palace of Sennacherib, 7th century B.C.). This simple mechanism —a bucket on a pole, counterbalanced by a weight—demanded constant labor from the operator who lowered the bucket into the canal. It typifies the amount of labor involved in water control in the dry belt.

Below: Drawing by a traveler in 18th-century China, where men and women were sometimes harnessed to the plow with animals in the continual struggle to feed the huge labor force.

Chinese Husbandmen, from Nieuhof

the hydraulic farmer generally did a good deal more work on actual cultivation (plowing, weeding, and so forth). This alone meant a life of unremitting toil for the peasants of the dry belt.

But watering and cultivating their fields by no means exhausted the duties of farmers of the hydraulic civilizations. The great engineering works for irrigation, drainage, and flood control, the canals and the aqueducts, all depended on the part-time labor of the peasants, whenever they could be spared from the farms, and the full-time labor of any of them who could be spared for long periods. These waterworks had to be built in the first place, the banks or dikes had to be continually maintained and

Egyptians not employed in maintaining irrigation works were used in time-consuming projects like the one below—building and moving the 22-foot-high alabaster statue of Prince Thuti-hotep. Overseer (on knee of statue) directs, and a scribe (center) records the process. Symbolically, statues of great rulers always towered, with godlike proportions, over their subjects.

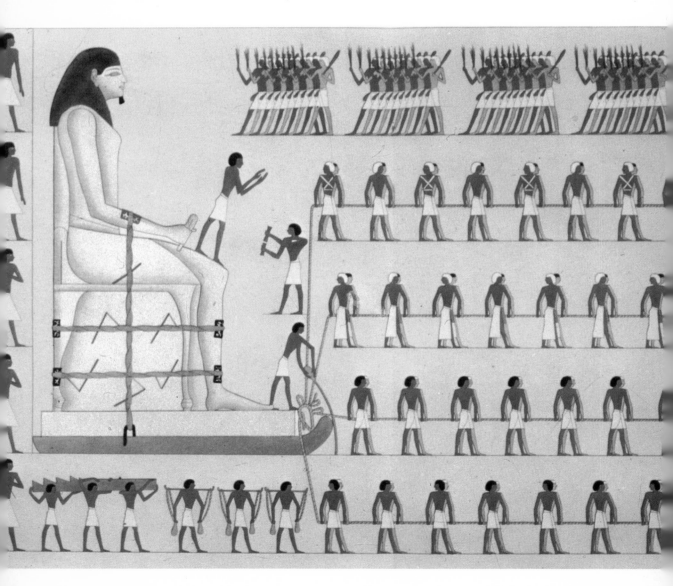

repaired, and then the channels had to be continually cleared of silt, which every year threatened to clog them and obstruct the flow of water. The mass labor of thousands, or even millions, of people governed the whole character of the hydraulic society.

This mass labor was enlisted by the state, as and when required, by compulsory drafts. What this meant for the individual is made vivid for us by a little bit of pottery found at Sbeita (modern Shivtah) in the Negev. On it, in A.D. 600, a Byzantine official had inscribed a dated receipt, which reads: "To Flavius Gormos, son of Zacharias: you have completed one compulsory work for the reservoir." How many shifts Gormos served, and how many such receipts he once treasured, we do not know. But we do know that receipts like this featured in the lives of fantastic numbers of human beings. In principle, the entire population was subject to these drafts.

A book written under the Sui Dynasty (about A.D. 600) describes the labor force used to build part of the Grand Canal of China. It is summarized thus by Joseph Needham, the British biologist and scholar of Chinese: "Some 5,500,000 workers, including all commoners in certain areas between the ages of fifteen and fifty, assembled, and worked under the guard of 50,000 police. Every fifth family was required to contribute one person to participate in the supply and preparation of food. Those who could not or would not fulfill the demands made on them were 'punished by flogging and neck-weights'; some had to sell their children. Over two million men were said to have been 'lost'."

Those impressive figures of population density now appear in another light. To control these swarming, overcrowded masses, to assemble them for forced labor operations and organize their work, to handle the vast stores of surplus grain that began to be gathered in state granaries for feeding the labor gangs, a special kind of state evolved. At the head of it was a dictator, the king or emperor, with absolute rights over the lives of all his subjects. He often towers over them, larger than life, in his portraits.

An example from ancient Persia gives us some idea of the exalted position occupied by the ruler. In 470 B.C., the Athenian statesman Themistocles, exiled by the Athenian people, took refuge in the domains of the Great King of Persia. Eventually he sought an interview with the Great King. He made his approach through a Persian officer called Artabanus. This officer was prepared to help, but wanted to make sure the Greek would commit no terrible breach of court etiquette, as this would get his sponsor into trouble. He asked for a promise that Themistocles would prostrate himself in the Great King's presence. For, as he

Absolute rulers were vitally necessary to control the massive populations of hydraulic societies. Typical of such rulers were Naram-Sin (above), 23rd century B.C., leading his Iraqi soldiers into battle, and (below) the Chinese Emperor Wu-Ti (late 6th century A.D.) of the Northern Chou dynasty.

Above: Account tablet of 3rd dynasty of Ur, listing the quantities of barley produced by various farmers in the reign of Shulgi. Invention of writing grew out of the need for records of food supplies and work in progress, but long remained a skill confined to a bureaucratic elite.

Below: 19th-century line drawing of the legendary emperor Shun consulting oracles with his ministers. Among them is Yü the Great, later emperor, revered as the founder of hydraulic civilization in China.

is said to have explained, "it is the habit of the Greeks, we are told, to honor, above all things, liberty and equality. But among our many excellent laws, we account this the most excellent, to honor the king and to worship him."

In hydraulic societies, would-be liberal reformers occasionally appeared at the top (where there was leisure to think of such things). For example, there were King Urukagina of Lagash in Iraq (twenty-fifth century B.C.) and the Caliph Al Mamun of Baghdad (ninth century A.D.), but their efforts were doomed to frustration. In all their millennia of history, the hydraulic societies never even dreamed of democracy, with laws made and changed by popular consent and binding all governments, with personal freedom from arbitrary arrest, confiscation, torture, and execution by state officials. No individual, however highly placed, wealthy, or useful to society, was safe from ruin or death at the whim of a ruler. All were servants of their supreme rulers. Until modern times, the numerous revolutions of the dry belt were fought deliberately to change masters.

However absolute his power, no one man can actually run the lives of millions of people. The ruler worked through enormous bureaucracies of state officials, supported by the surplus extracted from the peasants. This executive class, particularly in the earlier periods, made contributions of vital importance to human progress. The greatest achievement of the hydraulic societies was the invention of writing in Iraq. This was needed for keeping the copious inventories and records of food supplies and rations, equipment issues, labor gangs, projects, schedules, targets, and work progress. Once writing was available, it could serve for the exchange and recording of technical discoveries, and also for great literature, of which the first known example is the story of Gilgamesh from Iraq. But writing long remained ideographic, hard to learn, and restricted to the bureaucrat class. The mass of the people was illiterate, and expected to remain so.

Enormous strides were taken in sciences with obvious immediate practical applications, such as applied mathematics (for computing supplies, land survey, and engineering), astronomy (for predicting seasons, notably the annual Nile flood), and, of course, hydraulic engineering, in which the Chinese are outstanding experts even today. But pure fundamental scientific research, of no obvious immediate practical advantage to the state, had to wait for the emergence elsewhere of societies where at least some individuals enjoyed personal freedom. And once the bureaucracy had settled in, its officials more and more lost interest in anything but red tape, a little literary scholarship, and keeping everything exactly as it was, so that they could go on running it forever.

The ultimate justification of the whole system lay in water control, and the state came to be identified with this. This can be illustrated all over the dry belt. The founder of the first dynasty of the area that later expanded into the Chinese Empire was called Yü. We know of him only from legends, but some other early legends of China have been found to be based on fact. Yü was revered as the creator of great works for water control. Another example comes from Egypt. Every year, the Pharaoh himself performed the ceremony of cutting the dikes to admit the flood water to the crops. The Pharaoh Khasekhamui is shown doing so in a relief carved on the head of a mace. Again, the archives of the kingdom of Mari on the upper Euphrates (late third to early second millennium B.C.) include a letter from a high bureaucratic official, apologizing to the king for delay in obeying a summons to the court. He explains that his services were urgently needed to supervise irrigation works. As he pointed out (and it must have been a platitude even then), "if the waters are interrupted, the land of my lord will starve."

Once established, the system developed a momentum of its own. The status of rulers and bureaucrats depended on the control of mass labor and the disposal of large stocks of food. Therefore, they sought more and more labor and food, and they came to feel that this was the indispensable basis of civilization. Peasants were encouraged to breed like flies and to depend absolutely on the government surplus stocks, raised by taxing the peasants themselves. Populations rose dangerously, until any disturbance to the agricultural foundations of the system

Above: Carved mace-head showing Pharaoh Khasekhamui cutting a dike to release Nile flood water into irrigation channels c. 3000 B.C., an annual event of great importance. Failure of the water supplies, water shortage, and the ensuing bad harvest would reduce thousands of peasants to starvation level like those (below) on a carving in the temple of King Unis at Sakkara, about 2350 B.C.

(such as collapse of an important waterwork) emptied the granaries and caused frightful famines. Any attempt to invent and apply labor-saving machinery was discouraged as superfluous and subversive. This was a factor of great importance in blocking a further breakthrough. In a famous phrase of the British scientific writer Ritchie Calder, the traditional way of doing a large-scale job was to use "a million men with teaspoons." When no immediate large-scale waterworks were in prospect, the vast armies of workers were employed on impressive but unproductive projects such as the Pyramids of Egypt and the Great Wall of China.

At first the hydraulic societies were fairly small states. But if you tap a river in one place, you may deprive somebody lower down its course. Disputed water rights provoked wars. And then the increasing demand for more and more food-stocks and manpower led logically to the expansion of victorious hydraulic states into huge empires, linking larger and larger areas by ever more ambitious hydraulic schemes. These empires, built at the cost of frightful wars between rival states, became especially well-developed in the valleys of great rivers,

Below: The fertile strips of land along the banks of the Nile where hydraulic society developed very early, relying on the annual floods. The photo above of part of this strip shows how peasants still utilize every inch of the rich alluvial soil. Their animals graze on small patches of land among the crops.

whose waters could best be controlled in a coordinated manner all along their course. The earliest empire was that of Egypt, founded at the end of the fourth millennium B.C. to control the compact strip of irrigated land in the valley of the Nile. The hydraulic empire of China finally embraced great river valleys and much more. But by the time these empires were widespread, another consequence of the mass labor system had brought into being the hydraulic society's most deadly enemies, and given a final stamp to the history of the dry belt.

## Cain and Abel

We have already met one pair of legendary brothers, Prometheus and Epimetheus. In the Book of Genesis, we are told of another pair of brothers, Cain and Abel. Their story is the story of the dry belt. Of these two, "Abel was a keeper of sheep, but Cain was a tiller of the ground." In its beginning in the Neolithic Near East, agriculture was mixed farming, based on the combined use of crops and herds. But the growth of specialized, irrigated, crop agriculture in the hydraulic societies gradually divided people into two groups: farmers and herders. And it tended to drive the herders out into the wilderness. In this sense, Cain, the farmer, is accurately made the aggressor.

We have seen how intensively the peasant had to work during the whole growing period of his crops. The passage of the seasons, however, would in theory have left him free to vary his work and diversify his farming by keeping sheep or cattle on his farm. But, for every hour of his time that was not urgently required for growing the food surplus, the state needed him on the mass labor projects. It could not permit him any other occupations. He did indeed maintain a few beasts, oxen or buffaloes, to draw his plow and his carts. But maintenance of a sizeable herd of cattle or sheep, for meat, milk, hides, or wool, was out of the question. Moreover, livestock need plenty of room to graze, and as the population rose and farms huddled closer together and shrank to smaller plots, there was simply no room for stock.

One immediate penalty was the loss of animal manure that provided valuable organic matter for the soil and food for the plant crop. The few draft animals did not produce sufficient manure to fertilize the croplands. One answer to the problem was the fertile silt from irrigating waters. Another was the use of green manure, that is, a plant crop grown especially to be plowed back into the soil as food for the main crop. This technique, fully worked out, is described in Chinese documents from 1134 B.C. onward. In general, the hydraulic farmer could secure enough nourishment for his crops and organic matter for his soil without the manure from a large herd.

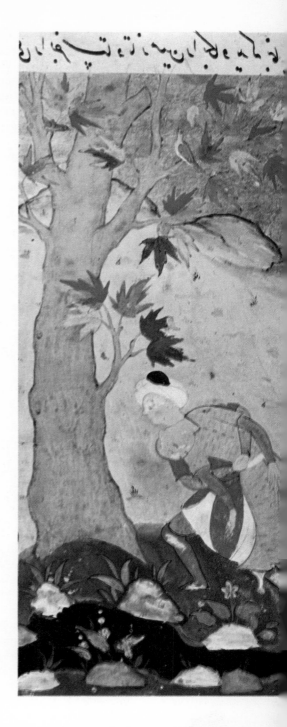

Cain the farmer, disposing of the corpse of Abel, the shepherd. This picture is from a Persian manuscript.

103

Another disadvantage of total specialization on crop farming was the disappearance of meat from the peasant diet. Human energy is supplied mainly by the carbohydrates in food. We have seen that the coming of agriculture meant unprecedented supplies of carbohydrate food from the grain crops or, in some regions, from starchy tuber crops. But man also needs protein for growing and maintaining the structure of his body. For this purpose, various kinds of protein, having different combinations of component substances called *amino acids*, are required in correct balance. Animal food is a good protein source, and the efficient Mesolithic hunters were adequately supplied. The new large populations based on Neolithic agriculture obtained their protein partly from their small herds of farm animals and partly from crops. Protein makes up only 6-14 per cent of grains, and an exclusively grain diet is liable to cause protein deficiency.

A solution to this problem came about through growing legumes. Legumes (such as various peas and beans, groundnuts, and other crops) have a protein content of 17-25 per cent (38 per cent in the useful soybean of the Far East). This high protein content is probably related to their special capacity for obtaining nitrogen (the crucial element in protein), which, as we have seen (p. 73), is so useful for conserving soil fertility, and makes them invaluable as green manures. Moreover, grain proteins are short of some amino acids (such as lysine) but well supplied with others (such as methionine), while legume proteins are rich in the former and poor in the latter. When corn (grain) and cowpeas (legumes) in different ratios are fed to young rats, it is found that a 50-50 combination gives the best protein balance. For man, too, the grain-legume combination provides a balanced protein diet without meat.

When grain-crop agriculture began, it was accompanied in every continent by the growing of legumes. Lentil beans were grown at Halicar in Turkey in the sixth millennium B.C. They were especially common in ancient Egypt, where lentil soup preparation is the subject of a fresco from the reign of Rameses III (late second millennium B.C.). The scale of lentil production in Egypt under the Romans was impressive. When an already ancient Egyptian granite obelisk was shipped to Rome as a souvenir for the Emperor Caligula (early first century A.D.), tons of lentils were used as packing. Remains of peas have been found in a Swiss Neolithic village of the fifth millennium B.C., and broad beans in another Swiss site of the second millennium B.C. Remains of kidney beans dating from 4000 B.C. or earlier occur in caves in Mexico, and kidney beans, lima beans, and a jar of groundnuts have been found in Peruvian tombs. Manuals on how to grow soybeans were among the earliest Chinese books (second millennium B.C.).

With little space for grazing animals and little time to tend herds, the hydraulic farmer depended almost entirely on crops for food. He thus turned to legume grains with a high protein content from plants such as the soybean *Glycine hispida* (left), groundnut *Arachis hypogaea* (top), and pea *Pisum sativum* (above). These could provide him with an adequately balanced diet when combined with grain crops.

Eventually, all these crops were spread far and wide, and lentils, broad beans, and kidney beans are now almost world-wide.

Men seem to have realized very early that legumes were a food substitute for meat. The first recorded nutritional experiment is described, with admirable scientific precision, in the Book of Daniel. At the end of the seventh century B.C., Nebuchadnezzar, the Chaldean king of Iraq, sacked Jerusalem and carried off most of the Hebrew upper classes to Babylon. The most promising children he decided, should be brought up in his palace, to be trained to become competent Babylonian bureaucrats. He instructed his chief eunuch, Ashpenaz, to feed them for three years from the royal table, after which he intended to inspect their health and educational progress. Among these young students was the prophet Daniel. He realized that the planned diet would include meat that was not kosher—that is, not permitted by the laws of Moses, because not prepared in the Hebrew way. He asked Ashpenaz, who liked him, if the Hebrew children could be excused. The official objected that if they did not eat the fine nutritious meats they would be less healthy-looking than the other palace children by the time of the

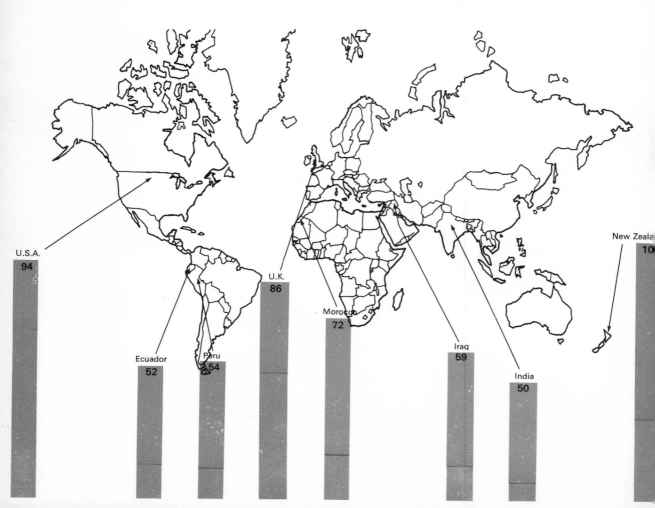

Below: Map compiled by the FAO in 1964 showing total intake of protein per head per day in various parts of the world. Blue sections indicate animal protein, red shows other (plant) protein. Diet of rich countries such as Britain and U.S.A. contains much more protein than that of dry-belt Asia and Africa, and a large proportion of it is animal protein. Now, as in the past, inhabitants of dry belt depend mainly on plants for protein.

U.S.A.
94

U.K.
86

Morocco
72

Ecuador
52

Peru
54

Iraq
59

India
50

New Zeala
10

king's inspection: "Then shall ye make me endanger my head to the king." The intelligent young Hebrew persuaded Melzar, a subordinate in charge of catering, to let the Hebrew children live on beans and water for ten days, and observe the result. "And at the end of ten days, their countenances appeared fairer and fatter in flesh than all the children which did eat the portion of the king's meat." So Daniel and his friends were allowed to stick to their leguminous diet.

The royal table of Babylon was certainly supplied with plenty of meat. Because of its scarcity, what meat there was in the hydraulic societies found its way to the larders of the king and the top officials of the bureaucracy. Meat became, and has remained, one of the most universal status symbols in human civilization. In later history influenced by Europe, meat became associated with wealth in money. The Greeks (in the fifth century B.C.) described a newly rich self-made man thus: "now he doesn't like lentils any more." An FAO survey made in A.D. 1964 shows that meat goes with higher incomes today, not only as between individuals but also as between the more and less developed nations (see map). The average New Zealander gets 2½ ounces of actual animal protein per day, the average Indian ⅓ ounce. In the U.S.A., animal protein makes up 70 per cent of all the protein in the nation's diet while in India it makes up only 12 per cent. Peasants of the dry belt, today as for so many millennia in the past, must make up most or all of their protein from grain and legume crops.

Being condemned to live on grains and beans was thus unpleasant but not altogether a disaster for the peasants of the hydraulic societies. In the long run, a different consequence of the absence of herds was to prove a far heavier drawback for the hydraulic societies as a whole.

In some at least of the hydraulic societies, the state did maintain some livestock, and a few of the peasants were split off from the rest to keep them. At Ur, around 2000 B.C., the state was able to profit from a considerable textile industry, based on the wool of sheep. But as the two forms of *food* production drew further and further apart, separate herding societies of outcasts or adventurers began to form beyond the borders of the hydraulic states. The peasants had taken first pick of the river valleys, and the herders had to be content with grasslands on the outskirts of the desert. These "pastures of the wilderness," as the prophet Joel called them, are pastures in the wet season only. When the dry season comes, the grass is withered by heat and drought, and there is no water for the animals to drink. So the way of life of the herders, like that of the peasants, was forced into a special pattern by the seasonal shortage of water. They evolved a system called *transhumance*. In the wet season, they grazed their herds on the

Above: Transhumant herdsman traveling across the barren land of the Near East with his small flock of goats in search of fresh grazing land.

107

Ashurbanipal, king of Assyria
(660–*c*. 630 B.C.), on a lion hunt. Kings
originating from herding communities
conquered and ruled hydraulic societies
but continued to hunt and eat meat, a
peaceful pastime that prepared them for
war. Below: Arab nomads, at war with
Ashurbanipal, fleeing on fast camels
(from a carving in a palace of Kuyunjik).

"pastures of the wilderness." In the dry season, they moved into the wetter hills or the river valleys where grass still grew. The herders of Syria to this day move their flocks in summer to the Antilebanon mountains or to the upper valleys of the Euphrates or the Orontes. This yearly pattern of transhumance meant that the herders could not settle in permanent homes. Their way of life diverged more and more from that of the settled peasant. But their dry-season need for the hills and river valleys drove them into a head-on collision with the expanding hydraulic societies, which needed just these regions all year round. The borders of the hydraulic states became the scene of repeated conflict.

The restless herders could never develop the elaborate paraphernalia of hydraulic civilization. But their way of life, which often included some hunting and gathering to supplement their food supplies, taught them mobility, resourcefulness, knowledge of large tracts of country, and efficient, flexible combined action. These qualities made them formidable in war. They became robbers and raiders. Sometimes, a herder chief and his henchmen actually conquered a hydraulic state. Their descendants were absorbed by the more complex society they now governed, and became typical kings and nobles of hydraulic societies. In this curious interaction, the ruling dynasties of the great kingdoms and empires were repeatedly supplied from the

outcast groups beyond their borders. In the second and first millennia B.C., lower Iraq (for instance) was successively ruled by Amorite, Kassite, and Chaldean dynasties, all typical kings of civilized states, but all originating from herding communities outside the valley. Throughout history, the kings and nobles of civilization have betrayed their ultimate pastoral origin in two ways. They practiced hunting as a sport, monopolizing extensive game preserves. And, as we have seen, they ate quantities of meat.

Some herders moved in on civilized societies and became meat-eating rulers otherwise utterly remote from their ancestors. Others began to develop a new kind of society in the open steppe or desert. Transhumance had prepared them for a wandering life, and eventually they took the next logical step. They became true nomads, migrating over much greater distances in search of water and grass. Instead of just commuting between summer and winter pastures, they now roamed over whole continents. Cut off from any close contact with civilization, other than a mixture of trading and raiding, these wild nomads of the steppe evolved a mode of life different in many ways from that of the hydraulic societies.

The transition to full nomadism was made possible by taming and harnessing fast riding animals, the horse and the camel. Between 1000 and 900 B.C., horse-riding nomads

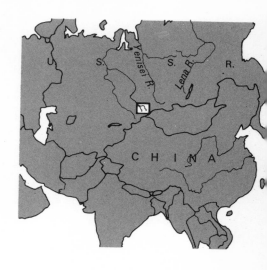

By 1000 B.C. man rode the horse as well as the camel. Square on the map (above) marks the area where the Scythians, the first great horse-riding people, originated. They built their nomadic civilization on the speed and mobility of the horses that carried them across the steppes of Asia. Below: Scythian horsemen, c. 500 B.C., on a cloth found in a burial chamber in the same area.

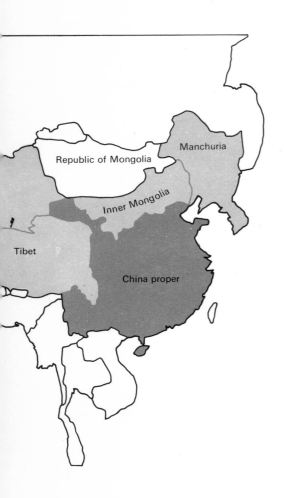

China proper (dark blue) was originally composed of hydraulic societies within the Great Wall. It has always been much more densely populated than the surrounding states of China (light blue) and the Republic of Mongolia, both inhabited by nomadic tribes. In time, the 18 central provinces have absorbed the surrounding states to form modern China.

began to appear on the steppes of Central Asia. It is thought that the earliest were the people called Scythians, between the rivers Volga and Irtysh. Horses had already been used for centuries (by the Hittites, for instance) to draw chariots, but the great new step was to saddle and train them for fast riding. This new technique, and the nomadic way of life, spread all over Central Asia in the course of the first millennium B.C. Meanwhile, in the deserts of Arabia, other herders had learned to ride camels. In about 1100 B.C., as we read in the Book of Judges, the hosts of Midian descended on Israel, camel-mounted. And early in the first millennium A.D. camel nomadism began to spread into North Africa.

The most striking difference between nomad and hydraulic societies was in numbers. The area of China within the Great Wall has been calculated as 1,532,795 square miles. The combined area of Outer Mongolia (now an independent state) and Inner Mongolia (now part of China), dominated until recently by the pastoral way of life, has been calculated as 914,100 square miles, or about three fifths the area of China. Yet the population of the two Mongolias in the 1930's—not counting recent farmer migrants from China—has been estimated as roughly 2,000,000, while that of China itself was estimated at the same time as roughly 450,000,000. So the number of Chinese per square mile was about 150 times the number of Mongols. The difference had persisted throughout history.

The life of the nomads was based entirely on their herds, which provided meat, milk produce, and hides and fleeces for clothing, harness, and even the tents that served them as their homes. To support the large herds, they grazed them for a time on one area, and then moved to another. Just as the forest farmers were always moving on to fresh woods, steppe nomads were always in search of new pastures. They needed even more land than the forest farmers, although their populations were less dense. On the steppe, as in the forest, numbers had to be kept low for the system to work.

A moderate amount of grazing is often good for the grasses and clovers that are most nutritious and palatable for stock. Periodic removal of their leaves stimulates them to grow again, more vigorously than before. Grazing animals have preferred them for millennia, so they are now best fitted to respond to the stimulus. Under moderate grazing, they often spread at the expense of less nutritious plants. If the number of stock on a given area is just right, the good grass on any given part of it is stimulated and also periodically rested. But if this stock-rate rises too high, the whole area will be continuously grazed, and good grasses will have no chance to rest and grow lush. They will begin to die out, and be replaced by the less nutritious plants

The effect of overgrazing on good pasture land is clearly shown by these four photos of the same area of land in Oregon. They were taken over a period of years. At first (left), with moderate grazing, there is a preponderance of perennial grasses, providing excellent range conditions for livestock.

Intensive grazing reduces the quantity of perennial grasses, and the proportion of scrub increases. Grazing conditions can still be termed "good."

Continued utilization by livestock soon reduces the pasture to "fair" as perennial grasses become scarce and weeds and sagebrush increase.

Finally, only poor vegetation—shrubs, weeds, and annual grasses—covers the land. Patches of bare ground invite soil erosion from wind or rain.

Above: Nomads breaking camp in order to move on across the steppes of Central Asia. Their tents are made of animal skins stretched over poles, easily folded away and transported. Drawing from Ashley's *Voyages and Travels*, (1745).

they formerly crowded out. The land will be overgrazed.

The effects of overgrazing have been observed in recent years in many countries of the dry belt (such as Iraq, Israel, and the Yemen). But they have been most thoroughly studied in the dry western states of the U.S.A., where much overgrazing went on in the nineteenth and early twentieth centuries A.D. The sequence of events can be illustrated by studies of ranges in southern Idaho. If grassland is grazed at a moderate rate, it is plentifully covered with nutritious perennial grasses that go on growing year after year. With heavier grazing, the perennials are killed off, and replaced by tougher but less nutritious annual grasses that die every year and grow again from seeds. If the grazing pressure increases further, the annuals are killed before they can set seed. They are replaced by unpalatable shrubs, notably the sage-brushes called *Artemisia*, growing in scattered clumps over otherwise bare, dry, easily eroded desert.

As less-nutritious plants take over, the animals need a larger area to get the same amount of nourishment. In Idaho, when perennials cover 50 per cent of a site, one cow can be supported on $3\frac{1}{2}$ acres; when they cover 25 per cent, she needs 5 acres; when they cover only 5 per cent, she needs 15 acres. When the land turns to desert, no cattle can be raised there at all. So overgrazing is a vicious cycle. Too many animals overgraze the land until it supports fewer than it did to begin with, so the overgrazing gets worse. As more land turns to desert, the rest is grazed more heavily than ever.

As long as nomads and their herds were few enough over a given area, they could graze each part of it just the right amount before going on to the next. But the balance was more precarious for them than for forest farmers because of the effects of drought. Drought has effects rather like those of overgrazing. A few good years, and herds began to increase. A few bad years, and the effects of overgrazing were added to drought. The combination was deadly.

The distribution of springs for watering the animals was another critical factor. On the Moghan steppe in northwestern Iran, where transhumant herders today bring their flocks down from the hills in winter, areas around springs and streams are always overgrazed. As long as there was plenty of room, the nomads could solve their problems by migrating long distances at times of crisis. But the nomads became so specialized for moving over long distances that they lost many opportunities for insurance against bad years. The migratory way of life discouraged staying in one spot long enough to raise a food crop for themselves or to grow a fodder crop like hay that could be stored for difficult periods, or even to dig a well. They became more

The rich fertile land of the valleys
in the Altai Mountains of Central Asia
draws the herdsman with his flocks from
great distances when land on the hills
and plains becomes barren and parched.
Above: Nomadic herdsmen make use of
this good pasture land today.

The plight of the Karamoja people in Uganda today spotlights problems arising when the numbers of livestock suddenly rise. Overgrazing leads to wars between tribes looking for new grazing land.

The Karamoja fortify their villages (above), building a compound to protect the cattle. They also develop warrior skills. Below: Karamoja boys learning to throw spears.

and more dependent on natural supplies of water and grass. The hair-trigger balance was too easily tipped. Stock was the only wealth of the nomads. (It is the main status symbol in many dry parts of Africa today.) So there was a constant temptation to increase the numbers of stock beyond safe limits. We have seen what happened to the forest farmers when they increased their numbers or tried to produce a large surplus. When the numbers of the nomads or their herds rose too far, the result could be more dramatic. Events on the steppe always moved fast.

A survey in 1962 of the Karamoja district of Uganda in Africa casts some light on what must have happened when stock became too numerous. Because of modern veterinary control of cattle diseases in Karamoja, the population of cattle in this district had risen steeply during the last few years. According to the report: "As pasture deteriorates from overgrazing, tribes begin to jostle. . . . With population growth, intersectional conflict has increased because groups, deprived of their traditional grazings, move

elsewhere to survive." As a result, there had been serious deterioration of law and order.

Karamoja is a limited district, where a civilized modern government frowns on range wars. In the vast open steppe, with no such restriction, disputes over pasture and water took a different course. Tribes, jostled by neighbors, jostled others in turn, in a chain reaction spreading across continents. If other conditions favored it (especially conditions on the borders of the hydraulic states), the result could be a forcible gathering of tribes into great empires, exactly as happened between hydraulic states disputing water rights. But the empires of the steppe formed a great deal faster. The conquered did not have to be reorganized and integrated into an alien bureaucracy. They just joined the horde. So a small group could grow by combining all its neighbors into one great army, through a snowball process in which each conquered group swelled the conquerors' numbers.

The rulers of these hordes allotted pastures, migration routes, and watering rights to their subjects. But they also had to be expert generals. The horde needed unified command, and nomad emperors were even more absolute than the hydraulic kings. Those kings found themselves equipped with mass labor, which they turned to any use they could. Likewise the steppe emperors found themselves at the head of formidable armies, spoiling for action and eager to invade the lands of the farmers, and convert as much as possible to pasture. They descended on the hydraulic societies like locusts, with equally destructive results. There was nothing stable about the restless hordes, and they could build nothing permanent. They subsided again into fragments when the force of their explosion was spent. But the explosion itself happened again and again. Outside the great inert hydraulic empires, the nomads were always poised like a timebomb, waiting to go off next time they fused into a horde. This fusion reaction supplied the final ingredient of human history in the dry belt.

Despite their far smaller total population, the nomads attacked the teeming millions of civilization with devastating effect. They used the principle of the American Civil War general, Bedford Forrest, who explained his victories with the words: "I git thar fustest with the mostest men." Their terrific mobility enabled them to concentrate hundreds of thousands of men at a single point, where they suddenly appeared in overwhelming force. To terrified peasants and city folk, they seemed innumerable swarms, like the Midianites in the Bible who "came up with their cattle and their tents, and they came as grasshoppers for multitude; for both they and their camels were without number: and they entered into the land to destroy it."

Above: Tunisian horsemen at a festival. Fast mounted hordes of this kind have played a decisive part in the history of the dry belt.

# 6　The World of Cain

In the dry regions of America, the absence of horses and camels meant the absence of nomad hordes, and so the hydraulic societies at first had the field to themselves. But they also had all the drawbacks of isolation from resources, ideas, and events in the rest of the world. In the Valley of Mexico, the farmers evolved a unique form of water control. On the marshy borders of a lake, they gathered mud to make an island, held it together with walls of reeds, and planted trees whose roots slowly bound it into a solid mass—the *chinampa*, or "floating garden." The lake itself provided irrigating water, and every year fresh mud was piled onto the surface by the farmers (like the fertilizing silt brought down by rivers in more usual irrigation systems). A grid of islands and canals grew steadily into the lake. At Xochimilco, the vegetables for Mexico City are grown today by peasants on chinampas made and tended by the ancient technique. Over large areas of Lake Texcoco that have been exposed by modern drainage work, the outlines of ancient chinampas may still be seen.

While rivers make for unity, lakes preserve isolation. The Mexicans remained scattered in separate city-states, making only transient alliances. Sometimes powerful cities exacted tribute from weaker ones. But none of the dominant cities ever ruled a bureaucratic empire beyond its own borders. Within each city-state, however, the Mexicans developed most of the characteristic features of hydraulic civilization. They had priest-bureaucracies with kings at their head, huge pyramidlike buildings erected by mass labor, ideographic writing (which they may have taught the Mayas), and an impressive command of practical sciences such as astronomy. But their isolation left surprising gaps: they met the firearms of the Spanish invaders with weapons of the Stone Age.

While the surplus from their "floating gardens" encouraged them to build cities and civilization, the Mexicans still relied, outside the lakes, on swidden farming, which many of them practice to this day. They were thus at a halfway stage between the two systems. The resulting mixed societies had a population increase of the hydraulic kind, but an agricultural base inadequate to support this increase. As a result, they experienced a most serious population problem, with the following results. The Toltecs, or Master Builders (as their successors justly called them), began to build the greatest Mexican civilization in the sixth century A.D. By the end of the tenth cen-

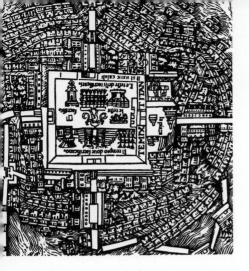

tury, it had gone the way of the Early Mayan Empire (see Chapter 4), probably for similar reasons. But the population problem built up again, and land exhaustion drove the tribes around in restless migrations. In the fifteenth century A.D., the city-states of the Aztecs, a group of recent immigrants into the valley, became dominant and levied tribute on the rest. By this time, there had evolved a system of perpetual wars between city-states, fought not for conquest but for the capture of victims for holocausts of human sacrifice. On the grisly skull-rack that towered over the city of Tenochtitlan, a Spanish soldier counted several thousand human skulls. A Mexican manuscript records the deaths of 20,000 victims at a single ceremony. These massacres certainly controlled the population, at the cost of untold suffering and the steady decay of Mexican civilization. In the sixteenth century, the Spaniards, aided by the rebellious vassals of the Aztecs, brutally finished it off.

In South America, on the western slopes of the Andes, irrigation took a more conventional and successful form. It was widely spread, and involved elaborate terracing of the hillsides, and water control in many small valleys, dominated by the high central plateau of Peru. Throughout the first millennium A.D., a number of city-states emerged to make important advances in technology

Left: Mexican map of chinampas—floating gardens formed by linked artificial islands. Human figures indicate occupied individual plots and footprints mark roadways. Cities like Tenochtitlan (above) were also built on this plan, surrounded by water. In the center is the skull-rack for the relics of human sacrifice. Below: Mexican warriors in their elaborate and decorative armor with stone-age weapons—obsidian blades fixed into spearheads.

(notably metallurgy) and civilization. Then, around the twelfth century A.D., on that strategic plateau, the Inca. people emerged as a conquering power.

Our knowledge of Inca history is almost entirely derived from chroniclers writing after the Spanish conquest, such as Garcilaso de la Vega, son of a Spanish knight and an Inca princess. But the accounts are supported by the condition of the country when the Spaniards arrived. The Incas were entirely specialized for war and for the control of hydraulic agriculture. They overpowered tribe after tribe, bringing them large-scale irrigation and efficient farming methods at the price of unconditional submission. They sent out exploring parties to find new peoples with useful technologies, and systematically conquered them. The Inca Empire spread like a cancer: progress in other directions stopped dead wherever they ruled, for all other peoples were reduced to slavery.

The Inca nobles, who made up the imperial bureaucracy, ran the imperial economy with impressive efficiency. Canals of hewn stone hundreds of miles long, tunneled in places through the mountains, brought irrigation water from glacier lakes to the driest areas. The distribution of the grain surplus in their granaries, along magnificent roads, amply insured against local crop failures. Their subjects were probably better, and certainly more regularly, fed than they have ever been since. The emperors are even said to have controlled the birth-rate, by regulating the number of recruits to the corps of sacred (and compulsory) virgins. But all this was achieved by creating the nearest possible approach to a human ant-hill. Men and women were divided into ten age-groups, each with its allotted

Above: Inca terracing in Peru. Their highly efficient agricultural system allowed the Incas to build up surpluses against famine and store them in huge granaries. Photo above right shows ruins of a large rectangular granary. An old irrigation channel runs from bottom right of picture, around one side of granary, disappearing top right.

1st to 4th Inca

5th to 6th Inca

7th to 8th Inca

9th Inca

10th Inca

Right: Three farming scenes from a Peruvian manuscript. From left to right: September, corn is planted in fields divided by neat irrigation channels; November, the shoots are irrigated from a reservoir; July, the crop is stored away in the granary.

Left: Map illustrates spread of Incas in South America, showing how the successive emperors (who were also called "Incas") added to the empire.

### TRAVAXO
**ZATARPVMITAN**

setienbre uyaraymiquilla

sienbrador de mays zaratarpoi

### TRAVAXA
**ZARACARPAIIACOMVC**

chay tupaypacha

nobienbre ayamarayquilla

cochayaio agua delpozo para uegar

carpai zipas como mitac mitacepuc ta riega

### TRAVAXA
**ZARAPAPAAPAICVIAIN**

ray julio shacra concaisyquilla

cullcacamayoc suyo ntiuo

tasks. Parents were permitted to care for their children up to the age of two. The job was then assigned to little girls just old enough to walk. Once full-time work began (at nine, for the boys) it continued till death. Food and clothing were prescribed in detail, and virtually everything that was not compulsory was forbidden.

In this mechanical and dreary bureaucracy, there was no writing. It seems that the invention of writing was a joint product of hydraulic agriculture and trade. The people of Iraq, who invented it in the Old World, had to trade for the timber, metal, and other raw materials their valley lacked. In the New World, the Toltecs and Early Mayas (who both used writing) traded profitably with each other. The Incas had no use for trade—they only conquered. They kept all their records by means of the *quipu*, a kind of computing apparatus, made of a long rope with 48 cords attached, and a further 39 cords of different colors attached to these. Knots were placed at intervals, according to a highly elaborate code of programming and the whole contrivance could store extremely complex administrative or military information. It was probably even harder to learn than ideographic writing. It could not be used for composing literature. But literature, or any other product of the individual imagination, had no place in the Inca Empire.

The ninth emperor, Pachacutec (late fifteenth century), was given to making maxims, which his officials were expected to learn by heart. "The peace of a nation," he is said to have pronounced, "comes from the obedience of all its subjects." An inveterate tendency of peasants to work harder on their own land than on the state's was dealt with by the penalty of hanging. Overt rebellion (especially prevalent among more civilized peoples, recently conquered) was generally punished by burning or stoning. But Huayna Capac (the last emperor before the Spanish invasion) varied this by impaling everyone on the rebel

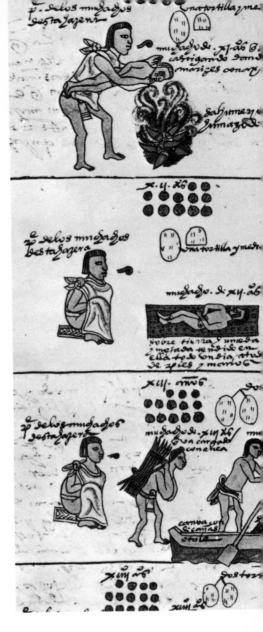

Above right: The training of children in the American hydraulic societies was very strictly organized. Dots at top of pictures indicate child's age. Ovals indicate corn cakes a child was allowed per day. Top line: Children punished by being held over smoke. Second line: Boy bound naked on damp ground as punishment; girl sweeping floor. Bottom line: Boy carrying rushes and punting canoe; girl learning to make corn cakes.

120

island of Puna, and drowning another 2000 rebels in a lake.

When Francisco Pizarro landed at Tumbes (opposite Puna) in 1529, he told the local chiefs that he had come to bring them the law of his king, the most powerful in the world. They made no comment: they had heard that story before, less than a century earlier from the envoys of the Inca Empire. Now every year their young men were drafted to the Inca mining camps in the mountains. The Incas were so hated by the recently subdued coastal peoples that the Inca Emperor Atahualpa, when he heard of the Spaniards' arrival, dared not send his army down to deal with Pizarro on the coast. Instead, he offered to receive the Spaniards at his capital, "like brothers" (an unfortunate phrase, for Atahualpa killed his own half-brother the legitimate Emperor Huascar, after making the victim watch his wives being tortured to death). On November 15, 1532, in the Inca city of Cajamarca, 164 Spaniards (with horses, muskets, and artillery) defeated some 30,000 Inca soldiers and captured Atahualpa (whom they later killed). The empire of several million people promptly accepted its new masters.

The Spanish conquerors of Peru were essentially robbers. The priceless gold art treasures of the Incas, the loot of centuries, went into a melting pot. On June 18, 1533, more than two tons of gold and silver were split among the Spanish invaders, their backers at Panama, and their boss back in Europe, the Emperor Charles V of Hapsburg. By the time more responsible administrators arrived from Spain, the agricultural system of the Incas was in ruins. The people had lost their economic security, and had acquired private masters in place of the Inca State. But the invaders cannot be held responsible for halting human progress in this area: that had already happened. It was the tragic destiny of mankind in a dry region, commanded by a central plateau, where a hydraulic empire evolved in total isolation from the rest of the world.

Far left: A quipu—long rope with a series of colored cords attached, knotted in different places—used by the Incas for calculating and keeping records.
Left: Quipu in use outside a granary.

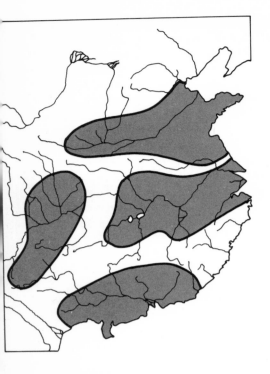

Map shows successive main areas of Chinese agriculture—around the Yellow River, lower and upper Yangtze, and the river valleys near Canton—where hydraulic civilization flourished using rivers for irrigation. The rice needed by the cities was produced on estates like the one shown below.

## Mandarins and Mongols

In the dry belt of the Old World (see p. 90), the hydraulic societies had the benefit of repeated exchange of ideas and materials with each other and with the lands outside the belt. But they also had nomads to contend with. By the sixteenth century A.D., when the European breakthrough was beginning, the western zone of this belt was already in ruins, as we shall see in Chapter 7. In the eastern zone, however, the Chinese were still technologically far in advance of Europe. Nevertheless, they too were already on the downward path.

The land of China is a great continuous mass, uniformly fitted for hydraulic agriculture. On the Yangtze River and farther south, irrigation provides rice agriculture in subtropical conditions. On the northern plains, rainfall is limited and irregular, but the Yellow River and its tributaries supply perennial waters for the irrigation of wheat and millet. But as you go northwestward and northward, into Turkestan and Mongolia, rainfall declines further. Instead of the rivers draining perennially into the sea, you find seasonal streams running inland to become lost in the sands of the desert. Except in oases separated by great tracts of desert or steppe, river irrigation is not feasible. Thus the farmers of China and the herders of the steppe confronted each other for thousands of years across the blurred border between two adjacent regions, each uniform for hundreds of miles. Supported in depth by her huge resources of food and manpower, China was bound to prevail in the end. But her compact mass also engendered a self-sufficient pride that made her civilization rigid and (on the world scale) almost parochial. In the eastern zone, Cain the farmer finally conquered Abel the herdsman, but it was a costly and a sterile victory.

The modern Chinese historian Chi Chhao-Ting has made sense of much Chinese history in terms of certain key areas of food production. The first of these is the tract of loess soil on the upper Yellow River. On this soil, as in Europe, Chinese agriculture began. For the irrigation and flood control that make up hydraulic agriculture, loess had a special advantage in the early stages. It was soft, and easily banked up or dug into canals with quite primitive tools. As the Chinese gained increasing mastery of hydraulic engineering, they were able to tackle the problem of regulating the devastating floods of the lower Yellow River. Once controlled, this flood plain was richly fertile. Once water control was perfected on the wheat and millet plains of the north, it could be extended to the rice region on the lower Yangtze, potentially the most productive of all. Later, it could spread to the Szechwan plateau on the upper Yangtze, and last of all to the Canton region in the far south.

In the early first millennium B.C., Chinese civilization had already reached the Yangtze River. This China was divided into little hydraulic states, each busy completing the water control system within its own borders. Everywhere the same pattern grew up, of identical "cells" of irrigated land (several in each state), each controlled by a walled city as its nucleus, housing the collected grain surplus to feed its laborers and garrison. The states were so similar that a class of professional literate bureaucrats arose, able to move around offering their services to one prince after another. The greatest of these was Confucius (551–479 B.C.), who composed the philosophy of life that was later to govern China for two millennia and more. Democracy and progress had no place in the Confucian scheme, but it found room for human feelings and the arts of civilized life. Its founder was himself a humane and civilized man.

As each prince completed the irrigation of his domain, he sought to develop larger schemes of water control,

Above: Modern Chinese peasants tilling the soil near Nanking on the Yangtze. The rich loess soil (see map on page 47) is easy to work and only light tools are necessary to turn it. For this reason, cave-dwellers in the northern area around the upper Yellow River have been able to dig out chambers in loess banks and inhabit them, from the Neolithic Period to the present day.

which would bring him more grain, peasants, soldiers, and power. In centuries of war, state swallowed state. By the end of the fourth century B.C., the few princes left began to build great walls around their territories. It was futile. China was now so uniform that the process of unification had to reach its logical conclusion. At last there were only two great rival states in the field, Ch'in on the western loess part of the northern plain, and Ch'u on the lower Yangtze. That great rice area still had to develop its full productive potential, and the long-established hydraulic agriculture of Ch'in gave it victory. In 221 B.C., the king of Ch'in became Shih-huang-ti, first Emperor of All under Heaven.

In the increasingly bloody last phases, the state of Ch'in had taken the lead in organization for total war. After each successful campaign, the Ch'in set a price on the head of every member of the defeated state's armed forces. In 364 B.C., for instance, they took 60,000 heads; in 318 B.C., 82,000. The Ch'in left a name cursed for millennia in China. It is ironic that we know the country by their name. The architect of the Ch'in state system, which they eventually imposed upon all China, was the professional bureaucrat Kung-sun Yang, Lord of Shang. He expounded the system very clearly in his *Book of Lord Shang*. This book reads like a satire, but he meant every word. He defined "virtue" as unquestioning obedience to the state. The worst deviations from virtue, according to him, were care for old people, not working (at farming or war—nothing else counted as work), personal ambition, a taste for beauty, and love. The people were to be adjusted to total obedience by suffering severe punishment for even the slightest deviation. Thus the really serious crimes, like art or love, would never occur. When actually executing a criminal, it was important to find out what death he most feared, and then inflict it. Anyone failing to denounce a friend for lawbreaking was sawed in half.

Human beings (and even the higher animals) cannot in fact be trained to this extent by punishment without resisting or breaking down. The Ch'in had the additional problem of demobilizing the colossal army that they had used to conquer their neighbors. The Ch'in system, born of war and water control at their most exclusive and extreme, lasted exactly one year after the death of Emperor Shih-huang-ti in 210 B.C. The people rose as one man. After a destructive civil war between rival candidates for the empire, a former village official called Liu Pang disposed of all his rivals. In 202 B.C. he founded the Han dynasty, destined to endure for over 400 years.

The followers of Confucius at once emerged from hiding. The (relatively) humane and flexible bureaucracy they formed was able to survive all onslaughts for over two thousand years. Confucius had dreamed of allotting

Above: Map shows the base areas of the states of Ch'in and Ch'u, which absorbed all the others. By 221 B.C. the king of Ch'in had conquered Ch'u, and he became Shih-huang-ti, the first emperor of China. The thick dark lines within states represent walls.

Below: Extent of the empire of the Han dynasty, founded 202 B.C. by Liu Pang. After the death of Shih-huang-ti, the peasants revolted and the Han eventually introduced a more humane bureaucracy.

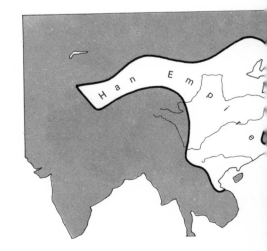

posts in the government on merit alone, by public examinations open to all. The Han began this system, perfected later by the T'ang dynasty. Only those fully accepting all the Confucian precepts passed their examinations and became officials, and when some of them later became examiners, they naturally saw to it that only those . . . and so on. The system was inflexibly resistant to any kind of fundamental change. The examinations were open to all in theory. In practice, nobody had time to learn written Chinese except the sons of the land-owning gentry. So the gentry and the bureaucrats fused into one class, which ruled China—the Mandarins.

Once established, the system survived through the rise and decline of the Han, the T'ang, the Ming, the Ch'ing (Manchu), and many lesser dynasties. Each dynasty rose and fell in a population cycle. The Mandarins wanted more land to be cultivated and more peasants to work it. This would yield them rent as owners and taxes as officials, both paid in grain. They wanted no long-distance trade or industry to disturb the bureaucratic routine, still less labor-saving machinery. The peasants were encouraged to raise large families solely for land and water labor. For a while, the reclamation of land and repair of water works, ruined in the civil wars, supported a growing population. Then the labor force began to outgrow the food resources. The state increased taxes, but began to lose its authority. The Mandarins, in their double role of landlords and bureaucrats, became corrupt and falsified returns, squeezing out more in rent and less in taxes. The government weakened further. The combined rent and taxes became so oppressive that peasants deserted the land and began to revolt. Finally the government collapsed. There was an interval of destructive civil wars, and a new dynasty arose to start the cycle all over again.

When the Han collapsed in A.D. 220, China was not yet solidly unified and there was still room for development. For a long time the country was divided between the northern plains and the now fully developed regions of the Yangtze River. Then the Sui dynasty (A.D. 581–618), almost as brutal and short-lived as the Ch'in, linked the Yangtze and the Yellow River by the Grand Canal. The grain wealth of the rice region could now be brought to a capital in the north, and the ensuing T'ang dynasty (A.D. 618–906) raised Chinese civilization to its greatest heights, particularly in poetry and the visual arts. After that the system was complete and closed, and each succeeding population cycle eroded the civilization and left it more feeble than before.

The T'ang capital had to be in the north (despite the greater wealth of the Yangtze region in the south), because by this time the nomads were on the scene. According to

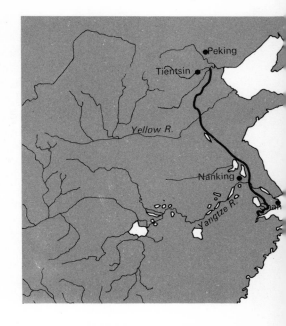

The Grand Canal (marked on map, above) was built during the period of the Sui dynasty (A.D. 581–618) to link the Yangtze and the Yellow rivers. Improved communications simplified political control, and rice from the prosperous lower Yangtze could be transported to the north to support new capitals near the border.

Below: Ink drawing of a horse, a fine example of T'ang art (A.D. 618–906).

the patriotic historians of the Han, civilized China had always fought in self-defense against barbarian hordes, and the Great Wall was built to keep them out. This picture has been demolished by the much-traveled and Mongol-speaking American geographer, Owen Lattimore. By careful analysis of the Han histories themselves, he has shown that Chinese civilization called its own worst enemies into being.

Chinese civilization could spread southward without impediment, for that way irrigation was easy because of the permanent rivers. Northward, where the streams dwindled, came a zone where irrigation failed. Mixed farming was possible here, but we have seen (p. 103) that a hydraulic society in extreme form (as it was in China) could not tolerate large herds of stock. Chinese governments therefore tried to draw a line beyond which Chinese civilization stopped. The people of the border—in fact not a line but a broad zone—were constantly tempted to indulge in the un-Chinese activity of herding. Partly to occupy his oversized army, but mainly to discourage this temptation, Shi-huang-ti combined the northern walls of several former states into the Great Wall of China. It was not built to keep the nomads out. It was a Stone Curtain to keep his subjects in, under the full control of the state. Meanwhile the border peoples had been driven out—China wanted no part of these mixed farmers. They had no option but to take to the open steppe, and develop a nomadic life as specialized in its way as China's.

Scarcely was the Great Wall built, when the nomad horde took shape. The herders of Central Asia are divided by language into the Turks in the west and the Mongols in the east. We do not know the language of the first nomad neighbors of China, the Hsiungnu. Their first known leader, Tumen, retired to the steppe in the reign of Shih-huang-ti. Disliking his son Modun, he sent him as a hostage to another steppe people farther west, and then attacked them. Modun escaped and became a popular hero, and his father had to give him command of 10,000 horsemen. Modun trained his men to fire at anything at which he himself fired a whistling arrow. He shot his own favorite horse, his own favorite wife, and a fine horse of his father's, and put to death all who failed the tests. He then felt ready to go hunting with his father. When he fired at Tumen, all his men fired too. All were thus guilty, and Modun became the first steppe emperor. Modun's whistling arrow shows how much importance such rulers attached to human life.

The Han and the Hsiungnu waged hot or cold war for centuries. Even in Modun's time, the nomads became such a problem that at one point the Chinese attempted to appease them by giving Modun a Han princess in marriage.

Above: The Great Wall of China at Nan Kon pass near Peking. This fortified wall, 1400 miles long, was first completed by Shih-huang-ti to contain his subjects rather than to keep out the barbarian hordes. Below: The Great Wall and other walls at various times in history, showing how the effective border continually changed.

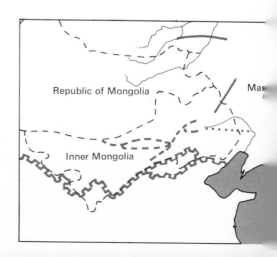

Republic of Mongolia

Inner Mongolia

From that time on, steppe chieftains claimed a right to the Chinese throne. Nearly all the later dynasties came from outside China: the founder of the T'ang dynasty, greatest of the Sons of Heaven, was descended from the Sons of the Wolf (the Turks). But the successful conquerors, who took over in the chaotic civil wars of the Chinese population cycle, were usually border chiefs. In the border zone, nomad leaders settled down as Chinese allies, and Chinese generals deserted to become steppe raiders. This zone was always a focus of disturbance, because it could never fit in with either the Chinese or the nomadic way of life. The Great Wall was repeatedly rebuilt along different lines, enclosing more or less of the border zone. Conditions here began to determine the timing of both Chinese and nomad cycles. The establishment of the Ch'ing dynasty (A.D. 1644–1911) was a typical border operation. The Ch'ing (Manchus) were Manchurian chieftains who made their successful bid for China with the support of some Mongol tribes and the traitorous Chinese commander-in-chief, Wu San-kuei, who had estates in the Chinese part of Manchuria.

The nomads themselves, even in hordes, were often prepared to trade rather than raid. The substantial Mongol horde of Altan Khan earned him the Chinese

Below: A Mongol horseman, painted on a 14th-century silk scroll. The army of the Emperor Modun consisted of such warriors, equipped with strong bows and sturdy horses.

title of "Obedient and Loyal Prince" by this change of habits. But the Mandarins disliked trade. Exporting grain was a waste of good rent, and importing anything but luxuries would unsettle the Chinese way of life. They generally denied the nomads trade, forcing them back on their own resources, with all the dangers of overgrazing that this entailed (p. 110). In A.D. 1162, the resulting time-bomb was ready to go off.

That year a boy called Temujin was born, son of a minor Mongol chief. He died in 1227 as Genghis Khan, Emperor of the Earth. He had acquired the largest empire in history, stretching from Iran to Korea. He did this by uniting the Mongols, and eventually most of the Turks, into one vast horde. Under his orders, they turned large agricultural areas of Asia forever into "pastures of the wilderness" (see p. 107); for instance, the whole northern half of Afghanistan, then the empire of Khwarizm. There was no immediate population problem in these areas, for the population was annihilated. The Mongol horde found a way to redress the balance of numbers between nomads and hydraulic civilizations. The great cities of Merv and Herat, for instance, were depopulated to the last child (after inducing the citizens to lay down their arms by promising to spare their lives). The whole of northern China would have suffered the same fate, had not the Mandarin Yehlü Ch'uts'ai convinced Genghis of the advantage of leaving it cultivated and taxing it to finance wars elsewhere. As it was, in the course of their conquest and occupation of China, Genghis and his successors are said to have reduced its population by 40,000,000.

Every former conqueror of part or all of China had been unable to govern without the Mandarins, so China had always remained culturally Chinese, wherever its emperors

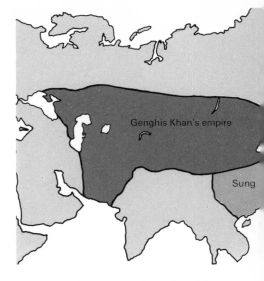

Map shows Genghis Khan's empire at his death (1227), stretching from the Black Sea to northern China. The Sung empire in southern China was finally conquered by his grandson, Kublai Khan, in 1279.

Hulagu, another of Genghis Khan's grandsons, carved out his own empire after ravaging Iraq and Syria. Below: Illustration of an anecdote told to Marco Polo. On taking Baghdad, Hulagu locked up the avaricious caliph with his huge store of gold and left him to starve, reproving him for not spending more on defenses. In fact Hulagu massacred caliph and citizens after promising not to kill them.

came from. Genghis and his grandson Kublai (who had conquered all China from the Sung dynasty by 1279) made a serious attempt to destroy Chinese civilization. They imported Turkish and Persian bureaucrats, and even a roving European, Marco Polo of Venice. Literate Turks were ordered to construct a Mongol script. In his 27 years of high office in China, Marco Polo never encountered the written Chinese language.

But the Mandarins were invincible. The Mongol Empire soon split apart. Mongol rulers lost touch with the steppes, and those who remained nomads could not rule settled lands. In 1368, a former Buddhist monk called Chu Yuan-Chang drove the Mongols out of China, and founded (for a change) a Chinese dynasty, the Ming. The Mandarins reappeared at once and remained in charge until the twentieth century. Under the Ch'ing, in the eighteenth century, they finally tamed the Mongols. They succeeded in bribing the Mongol chiefs to settle down. Then they imported the monastery system from Tibet into Mongolia. Each monastery was given some land, and was supported by a Mongol tribe, which was thus anchored to a fixed territory. In this way, the nomadic pattern was finally broken. The Mongol common people ceased to own any sheep and became virtually serfs of princes or monks. Once the flocks were fixed in position, they needed fewer people to look after them, and widespread unemployment followed. By the time of the twentieth century revolutions, over 40 per cent of the Mongol males had become monks, while princes, abbots, and Chinese immigrants ruthlessly exploited the rest. Numbers had finally won out. But by this time the civilization of China itself, originally shaken by Genghis and Kublai, and later eroded by its own population cycles, was in the last stages of decay. Europeans, arriving (at their most destructive) in the breakdown phase of the Ch'ing cycle, inflicted further suffering on China. But China, unlike Peru, is enormously *big*—too big for any kind of total conquest by a small group of foreigners unfamiliar with the working of a decentralized civil service dispersed through every town and village. Nevertheless, European technology finally broke the age-old pattern and introduced China to the modern world.

Modern industrial societies have room for all kinds of food production, and the old feud of Cain and Abel is finally being resolved, as the obvious solution of mixed farming brings prosperity to large areas of the steppe. Strangely enough, the technological breakthrough owes something to Genghis Khan, the Emperor of the Earth. The Mongol Empire gave Central Asia the only peaceful century it ever knew. And in that century, along the Khan's splendid military roads, flowed the Chinese discoveries that made Europe's achievement possible.

Genghis Khan built up a fantastic network of communications across his vast empire, and Kublai perfected it. Messengers changed horses at posting stations every 25–30 miles and covered 250–300 miles in a day. Above: Messenger arriving before the Great Khan. Detail from an illustration to Marco Polo's account of his travels, in a medieval French manuscript.

# 7    The Wastes of Abel

In the last decades of the fourteenth century A.D., a Turkish noble called Timur the Lame (Tamerlane) got control of the remains of the Mongol horde. In the old nomadic tradition he combined his forces with infantry. He turned southern Afghanistan into wilderness and did his best to smash the civilization of India. At 19 (according to his *Memoirs*) he vowed never to injure a living thing because his foot felt paralyzed once when he accidentally trod on an ant. But this was a passing phase that he made up for later, when he built a pyramid of 90,000 human skulls on the ruins of Baghdad. Unlike Genghis, he built no empire. He only looted, killed, and passed on.

Early in 1401, Timur was encamped outside the city of Damascus, engaged in the usual procedure of offering reasonable terms in order to disarm the citizens before sacking the city. He received in his tent an envoy from the Mameluke Sultan of Egypt (then the overlord of Damascus). The man who had "volunteered" for this very uncomfortable mission was an eminent professional bureaucrat of mixed Arab and Berber descent, called 'Abd-ar-Rahman ibn Muhammad ibn Khaldun al-Hadrami of Tunis. He had served, successively, the Sultan of Fez, the Emir of Granada, and the Sultan of Boujie, before entering his present employment. The interview of Timur and Ibn Khaldun is recorded in the latter's autobiography. The Berber gave his host a learned but flattering lecture on nomad conquests, and the Turk asked for a detailed gazetteer of North Africa. With his rare gift for survival (he had left Fez, Granada, and Boujie just in time to avoid ruin by court rivals), Ibn Khaldun got out of Damascus alive (and even saved the lives of a few citizens of Damascus). He saved his skin at the cost of a mule, which Timur, with the meticulous attention to detail of the really great looter, had offered to "buy." Ibn Khaldun tactfully gave it to Timur, declining a sale. He relates: "Timur said, 'I meant only that I would requite you for it with generosity.' I replied, 'Is there any generosity left beyond that which you have already shown to me? . . .' He was silent; so was I. The mule was brought to him while I was with him at his council, and I did not see it again."

## Bureaucrats and Bedouin

This Ibn Khaldun was the first person to work out in detail the influence of man's relations with nature on human history. Despite a visit to Pedro the Cruel, King of

Castile, he knew virtually nothing about Europe. So he naturally assumed that *all* human history was cyclical and unprogressive, in the manner of the dry belt (which he knew intimately). But his analysis of dry-belt history is astonishingly modern, and the principles set out in our Chapter 5 can almost all be found in his books. Many of his generalizations, too, are true of all human societies.

He showed that human behavior is a product of environment and culture, and not of race. He did not know about the Chinese and the Mongols (racially identical, culturally so different), but he had an excellent example in the Arab people. He observed that when Arabs were settled in farms and cities, they created some of the greatest achievements of civilization. But when they were roaming the desert as nomadic herders, or *Bedouin*, despite many useful qualities, they were among the most destructive forces on earth, just like their fellow-nomads—Turks, Mongols, Kurds, or Berbers. Step by step, he analyzed the course of events in a hydraulic society. He showed how a

In the 14th century Tamerlane, a Turkish nobleman, swept across the Arab world with the remnants of the Mongol horde, looting and killing. Left: The pillar of skulls he built after the battle of Baghdad. Below: Tamerlane receives the captive sultan Bayazid of the Ottoman Turks.

Above: The western zone of the dry belt was usually composed of numerous small states—hydraulic societies surrounded and penetrated by desert (gray). Their need to trade made contact inevitable.

In the western zone, desert and farmland, nomads and farmers, have often been side by side. Below: Bedouin tents (foreground) near the settled "beehive" mud houses of the peasants.

king cannot rule without a bureaucracy. He noted how population rises, and how at first this makes for a greater civilization. But then come higher taxes and general oppression, including forced labor drafts, followed by a weakening of state authority. "Famines increase because many people begin to give up cultivation owing to the increased burden of taxation and the insecurity of property . . . the stocks of agricultural produce begin to fall . . . this will lead to expectations of famine and a rise in the prices of agricultural produce. . . ." And then, as the state weakens and revolts break out, nomad invaders pour in. They easily conquer, because the nomadic life gives them great solidarity. But when they become rulers of civilized states, they lose this quality, and the whole cycle starts all over again. In his own North Africa, the Almoravides and Almohads had provided two especially clear-cut cycles. These desert groups, part Arab, part Berber, invaded the coastal strip, became civilized, declined, and were invaded in turn. All his conclusions, indeed, were based on the collection and comparison of facts about different societies known to him. He had studied both sides at first hand, too, thanks to a spell of exile among Berber nomads.

Ibn Khaldun knew little of China, yet his analysis clearly fits the cycles of Chinese history. Yet Chinese agricultural civilization, although more and more decadent, did persist, while the civilizations of the western zone (see map left) were everywhere in ruins by the twentieth century A.D. By that time—with the sole exception of Egypt (uniquely favored in its narrow valley and the perennial Nile flood)—every country in the western zone was predominantly pastoral. Their populations had shrunk accordingly. The empty deserts of North Africa are dotted with the ruins of populous Roman cities. In the time of the great Abbasid caliphs (eight to ninth centuries A.D.), Iraq had a population of over 30,000,000; by the twentieth century, it had less than 5,000,000. Afghanistan was the seat of great empires like the Ghaznavids (eleventh century A.D.). According to an F.A.O. report, less than three per cent of its land was under crops in 1964. Everywhere Abel conquered Cain and destroyed the foundations of civilization.

The eastern zone, as we have seen, is divided into two great blocks, roughly China and Mongolia. But in the western zone, as the map shows, there are many scattered regions of easy irrigation, which are divided, surrounded, and interpenetrated by deserts. This had the advantage of making long-distance trade a necessity. The western zone was never so uniform as China, and mutual trade brought a certain flexibility and variety to its civilized societies. One of Ibn Khaldun's most interesting studies, his analysis of price movements and business cycles, finds no application in the world of the Mandarins. They would have been outraged by his belief in the dangers of overtaxing private business enterprise. The western zone societies never had quite the withdrawn parochialism of China, and their literature has a glamour and excitement unknown to "the Empire of All under Heaven."

But the nearness of the wilderness meant that Cain and Abel were everywhere close neighbors. The hydraulic societies of the western zone were terribly vulnerable. Nomadic tribes prowled around, always ready to encroach with their flocks. Worst of all, the Near East civilizations were between two fires—Bedouin in the south, Turks and Mongols in the north. The climate was fiercer, hotter, and drier. The desert was always near in that sense too, ready (as we shall see) to encroach on the heels of the herders. The Bedouin has been called, not the child, but the father of the desert. An F.A.O. survey in 1962 reported that all the deserts in Iraq are man-made. With his customary insight, Ibn Khaldun noticed that a country (in the dry belt) that has been depopulated becomes drier. We shall see why later on. In the western zone, the scales were weighted against the farmer Cain.

Only for a brief century (around A.D. 700) has the whole western zone bèen under one empire (the Umayyad caliphate), although ever since then it has shared a common culture: Islam. At all other times it has been a kaleidoscopic pattern of states and empires, with continually changing rulers and frontiers. But we can sample its history by studying one typical region, the Levant (Israel, Jordan, Lebanon, and Syria), where the story of man and nature has been pieced together by the Israeli archeologist A. Reifenberg.

Agriculture began early here (at Jericho, for instance— see p. 32). By the tenth century B.C. King Solomon of Israel was buying timber and hiring technicians from Tyre (in what is now Lebanon) by the annual export of 150,000 sacks of wheat. In the eighth and seventh centuries B.C., from their central position on the upper Euphrates, the Assyrians united Iraq, the Levant, and Lower Egypt with a brutality worthy of the Incas or the Ch'in. The Assyrians were equally efficient in extending irrigation. The more civilized Persian Empire (sixth century on) keenly encouraged agriculture. The Greeks, who ruled most of the Levant under the Seleucid dynasty (fourth century B.C. on), introduced advanced agricultural science and a network of populous cities. Meanwhile the Nabataean Arabs covered Jordan with fertile farms. Under the Romans, who took over in the first century B.C., cultivation pushed out into the deserts and reached its widest extent in the history of the Near East. Hebrew agricultural writers, a couple of centuries later, knew that soil is progressively more exhausted by beans, barley, wheat, and flax. Hebrews used

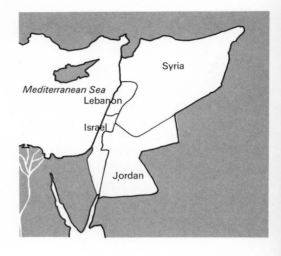

Map above shows modern divisions of Levant—Israel, Jordan, Lebanon, and Syria. Their history typifies that of the western zone of the dry belt.

In the second millennium B.C. the Levant was a prosperous agricultural region, partly covered by cedar forests. Below: Chiefs of Lebanon felling the cedars, used extensively for building, at the command of their Egyptian overlords.

Above: Bronze Roman coin struck to commemorate the Bar Kochba War, A.D. 132–5, in Israel. The datepalm symbolizes the region's fertility in Roman times.

Below: Modern dam at Kurnub, on the site of an older Byzantine dam, visible further upstream. This was one of a series used to collect flood water and trap silt before it clogged irrigation channels.

the most exacting crop (flax) in field trials to estimate soil fertility in different places. From the fourth to the seventh centuries A.D., the Byzantine Empire maintained Levantine water control and agriculture in excellent condition.

Archeologists have brought out the contrast between the flourishing condition of the Levant in these ancient times, and its ruinous state by the twentieth century A.D. The plain of northern Syria has been called "the Land of Dead Cities." Near Qul'at Sim'an (capital of the district in the fifth century A.D.), the ruins of 42 ancient towns lie scattered among the 14 villages still occupied. The plain is littered with ruined oil- and wine-presses, now standing forlorn in the desert. There is one whole ruined factory for olive oil production. (The hill of Testaccio on the banks of the Tiber in Italy is made up of remains of huge broken jars that once contained the wine and oil imported to Rome from this now deserted region.) In the valley of the Jordan, a wilderness by the 1900's, ruins of more than 70 ancient settlements have been found. Early in the second millennium B.C., as we read in the Book of Genesis, "Lot lifted up his eyes, and beheld all the plain of Jordan, that it was well watered everywhere . . . even as the garden of the Lord."

The wealth of the ancient Levant was based on splendid works of water control, most of them now ruins. The rapid spread of the Hebrews over the uplands of Israel (in the late second millennium B.C.) was achieved by the invention of a waterproof mortar, for lining the walls of great cisterns to hold rainwater. The spread of cultivation into the desert in Roman and Byzantine times was achieved by new devices, like the complex damming of wadis (as at Kurnub in the Negev) to control floods, fill reservoirs, and trap silt in special compartments. Most ingenious of all were the *foggaras*, or chain-wells, which gathered many small trickles of water into a great flow, and were used to irrigate desert settlements for opening up caravan trade across the Negev and Syrian deserts. A foggara system at Qadeym in Syria delivered enough water to irrigate 625 acres. These desert stations are ruins today.

At the confluence of the Jordan and Jezreel valleys stood the city of Scythopolis (Beisan), the seat of a bishop in the fourth century. Around it grew palms, fruit-trees, and flax for linen, thanks to aqueducts bringing water from springs in the hills to a reservoir 13 feet deep and 60 square miles in extent. A report to the (British) Mandatory Government of Israel describes this region in 1931: "Large areas . . . were uncultivated and covered with weeds. There were no trees, no vegetables. . . . The fellahin's [peasants'] lot was an alternation of pillage and blackmail by their neighbors, the Bedouin. These latter occupied the other part of the sub-district in similar conditions;

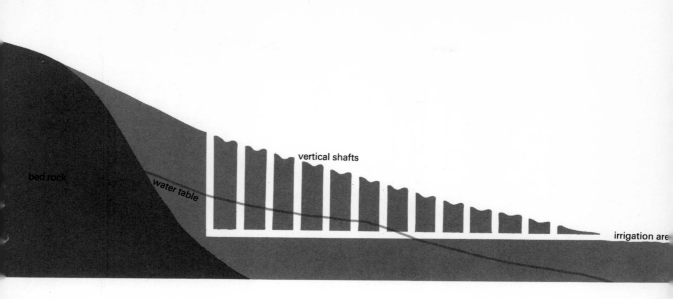

bed rock

water table

vertical shafts

irrigation are

except that cultivation by these nomads was even more scanty. In the spring the countryside was a mass of wild flowers; at other times of the year a waste of weeds and thorn bushes. Only the roughest tracks existed, and these became impassable in winter. . . . Raids and highway robberies formed [the Bedouin's] staple industry."

In ancient times, extensive forests, now vanished, covered much of the Levant. There is no trace today of the great oak forest of Ephraim, where, in the battle between King David and his son Absalom, "the wood devoured more people that day than the sword devoured." The Dead Cities of the north Syrian plain were built with so generous a use of timber that the area must have been covered with woodlands: it now has none at all. Most famous of all were the great cedar forests of Lebanon. Forty ships brought this weatherproof timber from Lebanon to Egypt in the reign of the Pharaoh Snefru (third millennium B.C.). By the fourth century B.C., the Greek botanist Theophrastus was talking of a scarcity of timber for ships in the eastern Mediterranean. But there were enough cedars left for the Roman general Pompey to build a large fleet with them in the first century B.C. In the reign of the Emperor Hadrian (second century A.D.), there was still a great state forest in Lebanon. Many of its boundary stones have been found, but between them today lies only a treeless, eroded waste. All that remains of the mighty cedars of the Lebanon Mountains is a single grove (sacred, as usual) of about 400 trees. Less than one per cent of the Levant is woodland today.

The forests clearly survived ruthless exploitation for timber by the ancient peoples. What finished them was, without doubt, the encroachment of the Bedouin. As over-grazing turned more and more land into desert, the herders

Above: Diagram of a foggara. Many vertical shafts were sunk below the water table (level of water in the ground). Trickles from all of the shafts were collected in the underground channel connecting them, producing a sizable flow. Although many foggaras are now choked with silt, some have been cleared and are in use today.

Victims of Bedouin overgrazing, the cedars of the vast Lebanon forest have been reduced to a single sacred grove.

moved in on the forests (whenever they could) and cut
down the trees to provide more pasture. Even here, the
grass withered every year at the end of the dry season, so
sheep and goats brought further destruction by eating the
young tree shoots. The Hebrews of Roman times knew the
connection between sheep and goats and the destruction of
forests. "Those who rear these small cattle," wrote
Rabbi Akiba, "and cut down good trees . . . will see no
sign of blessing." Once denuded of forest, the land was
soon turned into desert by overgrazing.

Forests prevent violent runoff, erosion, and floods, and
store water for gradual release down slopes (see p. 82).
The removal of vegetation brought severe erosion and the
eventual drying-up of large regions, where there was no
longer enough soil to hold the storm-waters after the wet
season had passed. Soil erosion was further unleashed by
the destruction of the terraces so carefully constructed to
control it. Destruction of the larger irrigation works was
still worse, resulting in severe floods and the silting up
of the wadis into marshes. The ancient Hebrews well
understood the perils of erosion. When their prophets
envisaged real catastrophe, they foretold the fall of
terraces. In the Book of Proverbs an oppressor of the poor
is likened to "a sweeping rain which leaveth no food."

The effects of soil erosion can be seen all over the Levant
in the loss of soil in the uplands and the accumulated
deposit of silt that has raised the level of the lowlands. An
air photograph of Khirbet Hass, one of the Syrian Dead
Cities, shows the boundary walls of many fields, now
completely eroded. The foundations of the upland church
of Musabbak, obviously completely buried when it was
built, are now exposed to a height of four and a half feet.
The now desert country of Jordan is covered with the ruins
of terraces, some of them in places where almost all soil
has been washed away since they were ruined. In Israel,
where terrace relics also abound, five feet of earth have
been deposited by floods on the low-lying Roman road
near Tell ed-Duweir. The Roman theater at Beit-Shan is
covered by silt to the top seats. It has been estimated that,
since Roman times, enough soil to make over 1,500 square
miles of good farmland has been washed off the western
slopes of the Judaean hills.

The ruin of the Levant, typical for the whole western
zone, took place in several stages. Ibn Khaldun's population cycle was well into its last stages by the end of
Byzantine rule in the seventh century A.D. The tax on a
peasant's annual produce was one-fifth in the first century
B.C., one-third in the first century A.D., and one-half by the
fourth century A.D., and forced labor drafts became more
and more oppressive under the Byzantines. The peasants
began to desert the land, and the government seriously

Above: Ruined terraces in Israel.
Many were destroyed, and their soil
eroded, following the Arab invasion of
the 7th century A.D.

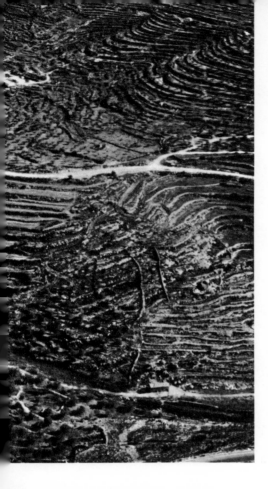

Below: Crusader castle at Byblos in the Lebanon. By the time of the Crusades, the supply of wood had been exhausted and the Europeans had to build in stone.

weakened. In the sixth century A.D., a terrible catastrophe (see Chapter 11) drastically reduced the population, and by the next century the stage was set for a nomad invasion. In due course, the nomads appeared from Arabia.

The coastal strip of southern Arabia had been a prosperous agricultural region since long before the days of Solomon's ally, the Queen of Sheba. The vigorous sea trade of the coastal cities encouraged the pastoral Bedouin of the hinterland to raid less and to take up caravan trade across Arabia. This delayed the development of a typical nomad cycle. Much of this prosperity (and the rising population it encouraged) was based on the Marib Dam, on the uplands of the south coast. This dam, probably the greatest in the ancient world, was built by the Arabs in the eighth century B.C. In A.D. 450, the Marib Dam broke, and within a century the coastal irrigation systems were totally dislocated. The result was a major population crisis. Peasants turned Bedouin, and trade broke down. The Arabs began to look elsewhere for a living. In A.D. 636, the desperate Bedouin horde overran the Levant, and the next year they overthrew the second Persian Empire.

The Arabs soon established a civilized empire from the Atlantic to central Asia, ruled from Damascus by the Umayyad caliphs who at once became typical hydraulic potentates. But the invasion itself had been devastating, and much destruction dates from that time. The Kurnub Dam in the Negev was wrecked and the whole Negev was permanently overrun by the Bedouin. The Dead Cities of Syria were abandoned. The forests began to dwindle. By the time the Crusaders reached the Dead Cities region, they had to build in stone. The sudden outburst of soil erosion is well illustrated at a place near Jisr Jindas. The position of a ruined Roman bridge here shows that more than 13 feet of silt must have been deposited before an Arab bridge was built above at the same spot.

This was, however, by no means the end of Levantine agriculture. Under the Umayyad caliphs, much was done to repair the damage to irrigation works. The Abbasid caliphs, who destroyed the Umayyad dynasty in A.D. 750, ruled a somewhat reduced empire from Baghdad in Iraq. Much influenced by their Persian ministers, the Barmakids, they raised Near East civilization to new heights. The greatest of all the caliphs was Abdallah al-Mamun (A.D. 809–833), who performed a supreme service to humanity by financing the translation by Syrian experts of the surviving literature of the Greeks. The caliphs devoted special attention to irrigation works on the Euphrates, in Iraq and the Jezire region of Syria. The district of Raqqa, in the Jezire, was famous for its oil, its gardens, and a favorite palace of al-Mamun's father, Harun al-Rashid of *Arabian Nights* fame. The Arab writer Ed-Damishqi described it as one of the world's most beautiful places.

The Euphrates runs between high banks well above the level of the plain, and is dangerously liable to flood at the wrong times. Irrigation therefore had to be based on permanent canals, mainly concerned with flood control. The canals leaked, and too much water entered the soil. The water level in the soil rose, bringing various minerals, dissolved in it, to the surface layers. Here the water evaporated, leaving a poisonous accumulation of mineral salts in the surface layer of soil used by the crops. This process, called *salinization*, is said to have ruined three million acres of land on the Indus River in Pakistan, where conditions are similar. It probably began to affect Iraq and the Jezire region by the time of the Abbasids. But there were plenty of other troubles in store besides this one.

The Abbasid caliphate collapsed into insignificance with the infiltration of Turks into Persia. From the later ninth century A.D. onward, the Near East collapsed into a chaos of transient and shifting kingdoms, engaged in perpetual wars. An Arab geographer of the tenth century A.D. put his finger on one serious consequence; he wrote that southern Jordan was still fertile and rich, but added ominously that the Bedouin already had the upper hand and were ruining everything. When the Crusaders took over most of the Levant at the end of the eleventh century, it was still rich in wheat, vines, and sugarcanes (introduced by the Arabs), There was even a forest at Sharon in Israel big and thick enough to delay the advance of Richard, King of England. The Crusaders (few and exposed) conciliated their peasant subjects by lowering taxes—to one-half of the annual produce! But the wars became fiercer now. Saladin the Kurd, the Crusaders' chief enemy, devastated Israel in 1189. The end was near.

In 1258, Hulagu the Mongol, grandson of Genghis Khan, sacked Baghdad and advanced into the Levant. This is probably why Raqqa is a wasteland, and why, of 4,000 square miles of cultivable land in the Jezire, only 20 per cent is cultivated today. Over the rest of this land, Bedouin now graze (or overgraze) among the silted-up canals. The Mongols, however, were halted at last by the Turk Baybars, general of the army of the (Turkish) Mameluke Sultan of Egypt. Hulagu and Baybars met, appropriately enough, at the Pool of Goliath near Jerusalem. The Turkish giant beat the Mongol one, and Hulagu retreated to Persia. The Mamelukes, having thus saved the Levant from one destroyer, utterly ruined the coastal areas themselves, in the course of expelling the last of the Crusaders. In 1280, the German pilgrim Burchardus still found some crops growing in Israel. But by the end of the fifteenth century, after a raid by Timur the Lame, the pilgrim Felix Fabri reported that Israel was a desert.

Ancient systems of agriculture restored to use today. Above: Experimental runoff farm at Avdat in the Negev desert. Below: Heaps of gravel have been removed to allow the soil to harden into a crust, thus encouraging runoff.

The Ottoman Turks took over the Near East in 1506, when there was not enough of civilized society left to turn them into normal hydraulic rulers. Their taxes were a new experience even for that suffering region. By the late eighteenth century, the peasants were handing over two thirds of their annual produce. They steadily deserted what was left of the farmland. At the start of the Turkish occupation, there were more than 3,000 taxable villages in the pashalik (province) of Aleppo; 300 years later, there were only 400. By the eighteenth century, Israel was so overrun by Bedouin that it was impossible to travel in safety from Gaza to Acre. Incredibly, taxes continued to rise till the end of the Turkish Empire in 1918. By that time the last forests had been cut down, to escape a severe tax on growing trees.

The coming of European technology has begun to show that the tragic retreat of agriculture in the western zone is not irreparable. It is interesting, and a tribute to the early civilizations, that modern development schemes so often follow in their track. The Tunisians are finding that the most promising sites for irrigation development are those around the ruined Roman cities. In 1938 the French restored a great dam on the Orontes built by the Egyptians in the second millennium B.C. But the most intriguing example of applied archeology comes from the Negev desert in Israel. A team of Israeli scientists (an archeologist, two botanists, and an engineer) examined about 100 sites, some as old as the tenth century B.C., but most of Roman or Byzantine date, where the ancients had established runoff farms. Just as the chain-well collects small trickles of water from the ground, so the runoff farm collects small trickles of water down slopes on the surface. Each farm needed a catchbasin of about 20 times its own area. The farms were placed among hills covered with a kind of loess soil that forms a crust when wetted, so that nearly all the rain runs off and does not sink in. The ancient farmers carefully cleared gravel away to expose the soil, to ensure crust formation. The water trickled down the channels from all around the farm, and was concentrated onto walled terraces in the farm area itself. In 1958 an ancient farm at Shivtah (Sbeita) was reconstructed, with terraces, walls, and channels and in 1959 the same thing was done at Avdat (Abde). In two drought years, young trees planted at Shivtah made excellent growth. In the exceptionally severe drought of 1960, large acreages of barley suffered total crop failure in areas further north with twice as much rainfall. Yet a respectable crop of barley (half a ton per acre) was grown at Avdat. Both farms are still thriving, typical of a renaissance of agriculture that allows us to end on an encouraging note the painful story of man and nature in the dry belt.

Modern agricultural experiments on the sites of ancient farms have shown how primitive methods of water control once made the Levant a fertile area. Above: Resulting crop on the farm near Avdat (see picture opposite). Neglect and overgrazing destroyed the fertility of the Levant, but such experiments prove that redevelopment could restore former agricultural prosperity.

# 8   The European Adventure

"No free man shall be taken or imprisoned or deprived of his estates or outlawed or exiled or in any way impoverished, nor will we go against him or send anyone against him, except through the legal judgment of his equals or the law of the land." These are the words of Clause 39 of Magna Charta, the Great Charter, signed by King John of England, in 1215. He had no intention of abiding by this charter, which was extorted by a group of powerful landowners who wanted a free hand to plunder and terrorize everybody else. Yet it has captured the imagination of the English-speaking peoples, who celebrated its 750th anniversary with great pomp on June 10, 1965. This kind of

Right: King John of England out hunting. But his subjects had a harder life. The so-called justice being meted out to them in the drawing below (from the historian Matthew Paris), was one aspect of the king's power that the Magna Charta (A.D. 1215) sought to limit, in protecting the individual against arbitrary arrest and punishment.

document has no counterpart in the history of the dry belt.

The major features of Clause 39 of the Magna Charta are the assertion of two old ideas in Europe—the jury system, and the supremacy of secular (as opposed to ritual) law over the state. The first English parliament, summoned 50 years later by the cruel would-be dictator Simon de Montfort, asserted another old European principle: the right of subjects to control the making and changing of the laws binding on the state.

All three principles made their first appearance in the empire of the Hittites (eighteenth-twelfth centuries B.C.) in Asia Minor (modern Turkey). Significantly, torture and mutilation were absent from Hittite judicial penalties —except for slaves. Asia Minor is intermediate in climate between the dry belt and Mediterranean Europe. In the international agencies of the modern United Nations, Turkey figures as part of the Near East in some contexts, as European in others. The Hittites (Indo-European invaders) seem to have practiced mixed farming. A typical Hittite farm, occupied by five people, had pastures as well as vineyards and orchards, and carried 2 oxen, 22 sheep, and 23 goats, as well as the 6 oxen used for draft. The typical hydraulic society did not develop in Asia Minor until it was absorbed into the Persian Empire in 546 B.C. But the Hittites were too near the dry belt to develop for long in the direction of greater freedom.

When we come to Europe proper, we find all three principles of European law fully realized in the democracy of Athens. In 621 B.C., the people compelled one of their ruling nobles (Draco) to write down a law-code. This Code of Draco was said to be written in blood, so many offenses carried the death-penalty. But not long after (about 594 B.C.), the laws were changed by the great statesman Solon, acting on a mandate from the whole Athenian people. Here, we may say, democracy was born.

A body of carefully worked-out and reliable laws (as opposed to the whims of a king or his officials) was the only possible basis for large-scale private business enterprise. In the critical centuries of the breakthrough in late medieval Europe, it was the businessmen who had the greatest incentive to launch modern technology. But this is not all. Different attitudes to law in society affect the way in which people think about nature. In Europe, by A.D. 1665, the term "law of nature" already appeared as a cliché in the first volume of the *Philosophical Transactions* of the Royal Society. The modern scholar Joseph Needham has traced the metaphor back through the European Middle Ages to Athens in the fifth century B.C., where the word *astronomy* (star law) was already in use. If nature had laws, then man was not subject to her whims. He could promote his own interests (just as in a human society)

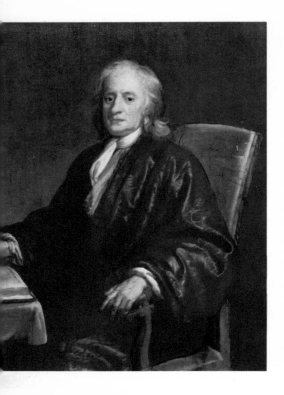

From the 17th century A.D. onward, Europeans explicitly tried to discover and manipulate the "laws of nature." Newton (above) established basic principles of physics. In America, Franklin (below, experimenting with kites in a thunderstorm) was one of the pioneers in the study of electricity.

by discovering these laws and manipulating them. It was in this spirit, explicitly, that scientists like Boyle and Newton, in the seventeenth century A.D., set about establishing the fundamental principles of chemistry and physics. It was this systematic science that accomplished the technological breakthrough.

In the nineteenth century, systematic science began to pay off in a spectacular way (for instance, in bringing electricity under human control). It was then often thought that progress in human societies was inevitable. In a sense this is true, provided that stresses in the society's relations with nature do not *either* reduce it to chaos *or* force it to specialize—that is, to remain fixed at a particular level. The tropical forest societies were forced, by heat and excessive rainfall, to specialize at a technically simple, tribal level. The hydraulic societies were forced, ultimately by restricted rainfall, to specialize at a much higher technical and cultural level, but one that stopped short of modern technology. The Europeans, forced into neither blind alley, inevitably went on to the technological breakthrough. The natural factors that stopped advance outside Europe have been relatively easy to define. The factors that permitted continued advance in Europe are much more complex.

Since the drought of 1959 (serious by European standards) every country in Europe has taken to practicing some irrigation. But this is a refinement to ensure the very high yields of modern intensive agriculture, and it is done with modern labor-saving machinery. Europe has always had enough rain in the crop-growing seasons to make farming perfectly practicable without irrigation in all but a few years. Indeed the occasional disastrous crop failures in Europe (as in 1594–7) have often resulted from *too much* rain at the wrong time.

The successful invaders of Europe, from the Battle-ax folk to the Germans (see Chapter 2), either were already mixed farmers or became so at once. Europe has practiced mixed farming since Neolithic times, and has produced no nomad hordes. Her story is that of Cain *and* Abel, brothers in successful partnership. Mixed farming gives scope for a great diversity of farming systems, varying in the ratio of stock to crops, and in the kinds of animals and plants raised. It can thus be adjusted in detail to fit changing circumstances in space and time. The most obvious visible difference between Europe and such countries as Egypt or China was always the extraordinary diversity of the farming landscape. With this went a diversity of behavior that made for vigorous local institutions and continually resisted the uniform bureaucratic order so easily imposed in the dry belt.

Divided by mountain chains, but crisscrossed by rivers

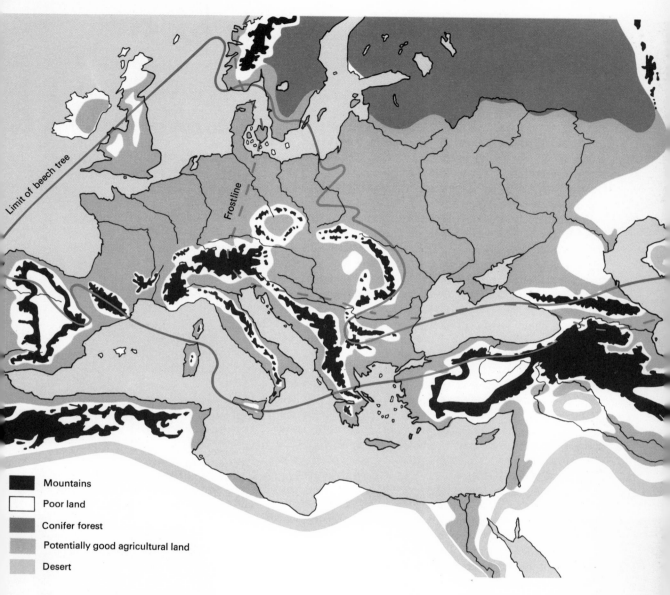

Limit of beech tree

Frostline

| | Mountains |
| | Poor land |
| | Conifer forest |
| | Potentially good agricultural land |
| | Desert |

and bounded by a very long coastline, Europe was well-equipped for trade. Each small region, with its special form of mixed farming and associated industries, had something different to offer the others. The division of the continent into many separate and diverse units, whether small tribes or great modern nations, generally favored the freedom of merchants, technicians, and scientists. They were welcome everywhere and could pack up and move on if they felt oppressed. They evolved a sense of comradeship that often led to the pooling of different technical experiences, and hence to the rapid progress of techniques. Gordon Childe (p. 12) has observed that all

Bounded by a long coastline and crisscrossed by rivers, Europe is an ideal area for trading. Beech-line encloses area where farming is easiest, with plentiful rainfall and not too much frost. Mediterranean Europe, to the south of this line, is warmer but drier. Eastern Europe, beyond the frostline, suffers continual frosts for at least one month of the year.

this can be traced at all epochs: among the technicians of Bronze Age Europe (second to first millennium B.C.), who were more inventive and original in tool design than their civilized contemporaries in the Near East; among the traders and thinkers and technicians who circulated between ancient Greek cities and between medieval or Renaissance states; and finally among "the natural scientists who from the days of Galileo and Newton to A.D. 1945 freely exchanged information and ideas by publication, correspondence and visits, regardless of political frontiers." British and French scientists, for instance, were calmly cooperating with each other throughout the Napoleonic Wars.

Wars between all its territorial units have been a major interruption to European progress. They sprang from the relative infertility of Europe. The soils were generally not badly leached. Their fertility was relatively easily maintained by alternating crops with different demands, by using legumes in these rotations, by animal manure from the stock, and by resting the fields as bare fallows. Most European land slopes too gently for serious erosion risk from the moderate rainstorms, and it is too broken up and sheltered for serious wind erosion. So Europe was better off than the tropical forest peoples. But, without every resource of modern agricultural science, European land could not begin to compare in fertility with the irrigated valley fields of the dry belt. Hence Europe before the technological breakthrough could not afford large cities. Her problem was to produce the large surplus that the hydraulic societies easily acquired—but only by mass labor, and hence at the cost of flexibility and freedom.

The surplus was won, in part by the gradual improvement of farming methods, and in part by living off the neighbors of Europe in the dry belt, through a combination of trade and predatory exploitation. This made for a highly unstable economy. A prey to repeated population problems whenever her numbers outran her own resources, Europe has always vibrated with social tensions, engendering bloody class conflicts and predatory wars. Besides these endless distrubances, Europe has had major population cycles. But, in the north of the continent, the temperate climate has caused no irreparable damage in the troughs of the cycles. After the human collapse, the forest came back. But unlike the desert, it was easily cleared again when things improved. Nor was there any unchanging social order like Confucian bureaucracy, to which the cycles incessantly returned. So, whereas in the dry belt technology declined at every cycle, in Europe it advanced. As Gordon Childe has put it, in Europe "no trough ever declines to the low level of the preceding one, each crest out-tops its last precursor."

Above: The Emperor Henry VI besieging Naples (A.D. 1194). European states attacked each other and neighboring dry-belt states in the search for more land when their own proved insufficient to feed rising populations. Europe abounded in fortified castles like the one (below) at Bingen on the Rhine.

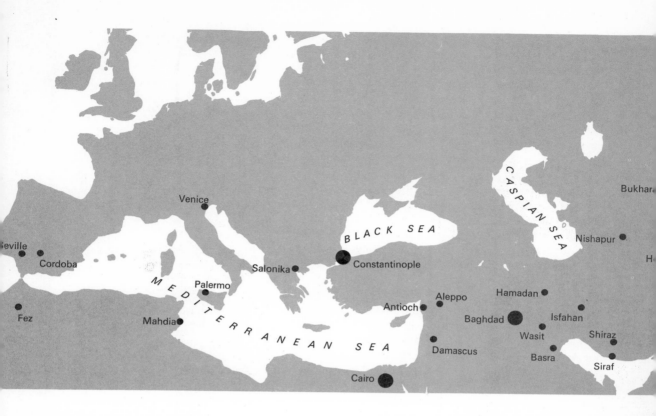

The map contains the following labels:

CASPIAN SEA

BLACK SEA

MEDITERRANEAN SEA

Venice

Bukhar[a]

Nishapur

Seville
Cordoba

Salonika

Constantinople

Palermo

Aleppo
Hamadan

Antioch

Fez

Mahdia

Baghdad
Isfahan

Wasit
Shiraz

Damascus
Basra

Siraf

Cairo

By climate and geography, Europe is divided into three regions: northwestern, eastern, and Mediterranean. Eastern Europe can roughly be defined as that region deep in the continent where frost prevails for at least one month of winter. Mediterranean Europe is the part that lies south of the southern limits of the beech tree. It has a dry summer and is intermediate in climate between the dry belt and the lands to the north. But the winter and spring rains persist long enough for growing one winter crop, harvested at leisure in the warm, dry summer. Irrigation, including terracing, was introduced into Greece, Italy, and Spain in the first millennium B.C. But it was neither indispensable nor widespread, and did not dominate these societies as it did those of the dry belt. Northwestern Europe (including northern Italy) enjoys relatively mild winters and rain throughout the year. Here irrigation was hardly used until modern times.

Eastern Europe was exposed to the nomad hordes of Central Asia. This and Byzantine influence distorted its history and retarded its development. Mediterranean Europe suffered in various ways from its nearness to the dry belt. As we shall see, it was in a serious decline by the seventeenth century A.D., just when the breakthrough was beginning. Creative individuals from eastern and Mediterranean Europe made great contributions to the subsequent

Above: Map of Europe and the Near East, marking largest towns in 11th century A.D. Significantly, all are situated in, or near, the dry belt. European towns remained limited in size compared with those created and supported by hydraulic societies—like Baghdad and Cairo. The first large towns in medieval Europe, such as Venice, grew up as trading centers.

advance of science. But today these regions are inter-mediate in technological development (and in average income per head of population) between the advanced countries of northwestern Europe and the now relatively poor countries of the dry belt and the tropics. It was left for northwestern Europe to take the second step and make the breakthrough. But this region began its civilized career very late in the day, and the story of European adventure really begins in the Mediterranean.

## Glories and Grandeurs

In the early sixth century B.C., there lived in the Greek city-state of Miletus, on the west coast of Asia Minor, a prosperous trader called Thales. On his business trips abroad, he made a point of collecting scientific informa-tion—geometry from Egypt, astronomy from Babylon. Back at home, he had plenty of leisure to think about these things. He worked out the theory that everything is made of water. This sounds primitive, but so will Einstein's relativity theory 2,500 years from now. Thales worked out his theory in sufficient detail for others to disprove it, and so improve on it by further observations. His signifi-cance is that he was the very first person known to have

Greek pure science formed the basis of modern European thought. The foundations of modern geometry were laid by thinkers like Pythagoras and Euclid. Their work first reached European civilization via the Moslem world. Below: Two versions of Pythagoras's theorem—(left) page from an Arabic commentary of about A.D. 1250 on Euclid's *Elements*; (right) page of an English textbook of 1888.

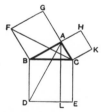

82                                        EUCLID'S ELEMENTS.

### PROPOSITION 47.   THEOREM.

*In a right-angled triangle the square described on the hypotenuse is equal to the sum of the squares described on the other two sides.*

Let ABC be a right-angled triangle, having the angle BAC a right angle:
then shall the square described on the hypotenuse BC be equal to the sum of the squares described on BA, AC.

*Construction.*   On BC describe the square BDEC;   I. 46.
and on BA, AC describe the squares BAGF, ACKH.
Through A draw AL parallel to BD or CE ;   I. 31.
and join AD, FC.

*Proof.*   Then because each of the angles BAC, BAG is a right angle,
therefore CA and AG are in the same straight line.   I. 14.

Now the angle CBD is equal to the angle FBA,
for each of them is a right angle.
Add to each the angle ABC:
then the whole angle ABD is equal to the whole angle FBC.

engaged in what the Greeks called philosophy, and what we call pure or fundamental science. That is, he tried to understand the basic workings of nature, with no immediate practical application in mind.

As we now well know, pure science is not a waste of time, but this was naturally less obvious to the friends of Thales. The story goes that one of them asked him what was the point of this kind of thinking. Thales did not reply, but he began to concentrate his new orderly way of thinking about nature on some problems of weather and plant growth. A few years later, during the winter, he quietly bought up every oil-press in the territory of Miletus. That summer the olive crop was a record one, and Thales made a fortune. In his love of pure science and the ruthless logic of his business methods, Thales well represents "the glory that was Greece and the grandeur that was Rome."

The nation we now know as ancient Greece was formed by groups of Indo-Europeans, invading from the north in several waves during the latter half of the second millennium B.C. They fused with the native inhabitants of mainland Greece, the Aegean and Levantine islands, and the west coast of Asia Minor. Greece, a miniature of Europe, is split by mountains into many small regions. In these, as well as on the islands and on the peninsulas of Asia Minor, many small city-states evolved. They acquired a share of the Near East surplus by piracy and, increasingly, by trade. The territories of these city-states were small and the land poor, so that the Greeks had a persistent population problem. From about the eighth century B.C., they began partially to solve it by founding "daughter-cities," or colonies, all around the coasts of the western Mediterranean and the Black Sea.

In the sixth century B.C., the continuing population problem in Greece itself caused increasing social disturbance. The city of Athens took the lead in a new kind of solution. She abandoned hope of feeding herself entirely

Above: Olive gatherers, on a Greek vase (6th century B.C.). Olive oil and pottery were the vital exports that enabled Athens to import wheat.

The Greeks tried to solve their population problem by founding colonies all around the Mediterranean (black dots on map below). The Phoenicians, from the Levant, did the same, and built a great trading empire on their network of ports (white dots).

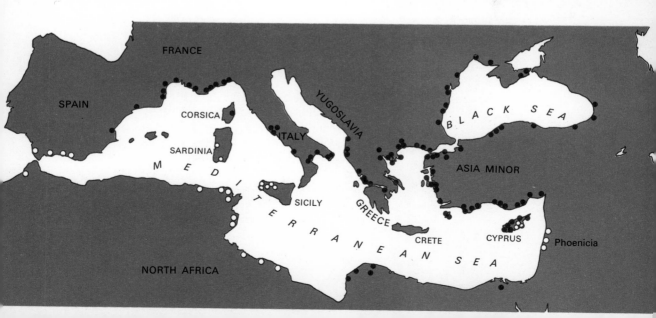

The Phoenicians were the first to use efficient alphabetic writing (top line, above). This was adapted by the Greeks for their own use. They added letters for vowels. Next two lines show parts of two Greek alphabets.

In the first millennium B.C. the Phoenicians dominated trade in the Mediterranean. Below: Phoenician ship, and map of their trade routes. Solid lines indicate known trade routes, and broken lines probable ones.

from her territory of Attica, and became the first mainly industrial city. Athens produced manufactured goods, especially cheap pottery, for export to the civilized Near East and to lands as far away as central Russia, western Germany, and northern France. With this and lucrative oil exports from her olive crop, she was able to pay for imports of wheat, chiefly from south Russia.

Through the creative work of Solon and of the still more inspired statesman Cleisthenes (active in the last decade of the sixth century B.C.), Athens became a civilized democracy. In the fifth century B.C., attracting gifted people from all over Greece, the city achieved the greatest concentration of creative activity (in science, literature, history, drama, and the visual arts) in the history of mankind. The democratic system, involving paid official posts and the responsibility of officials to paid juries (both open to all), soon spread to other city-states. It lasted longest in Athens (until 261 B.C.). The city's vulnerable position (its dependance on food imports from far away) was eased by the presence at Laurion in Attica of the richest silver mines in the ancient world, which paid for a powerful war fleet.

The progress in Greece was made possible by the development of two inventions made outside Europe—the alphabet and coinage. Trade is the joint result of diversity in nature, such as the uneven distribution of metals on or near the earth's surface, and the organization of human societies. Within China, for instance, once the country was organized in uniform hydraulic style, there was no point in the peasants exporting cereals to each other. In the Near East of the second millennium B.C., by contrast, the developing societies were not yet highly uniform, and the volume of trade steadily expanded. This necessitated a more flexible and easily-learned method of writing. By the end of the second millennium, after many experiments in various parts of the Levant, an efficient alphabet was in use in the Phoenician cities on the coast of Lebanon.

The Phoenicians were the first sea-traders and the greatest navigators of the ancient world. They were at first tolerated (as neutral traders) but were later dominated by the great inland empires. Their basic insecurity must have arisen from their dependence for food on the very narrow strip of land between the Lebanon Mountains and the sea. They became totally specialized for trade, employing other people both to grow food and to fight. Their population problem (far worse than that of the Greeks) left them with a primitive addiction to human sacrifice. These traits persisted in the colonies they planted on the Mediterranean coasts at about the same time as the Greeks, especially in the great city of Carthage in Tunisia (founded about 800 B.C.). By about 600 B.C., Carthage had assumed leadership over all the Phoenician trading cities in the western

Mediterranean. But though Phoenician civilization became static, their alphabet writing was recognized by other states as a great innovation, and quickly spread to other languages. The Greeks, in particular, added letters for vowels (necessary in Indo-European languages) and had developed several alphabets by about 700 B.C. In 403 B.C., they finally agreed on one standard alphabet for all Greek-speaking peoples. In the seventh century B.C., writing had already ceased to be a prerogative of bureaucrats: Ordinary Greek mercenaries (with the age-old vandalism of tourists) were scratching their names on the ancient statues in Egyptian temples.

During the eighth century B.C., a state called Lydia had appeared in western Asia Minor. The area was rich in gold, and the gold-bearing river Pactolus crossed the center of its capital city, Sardis. For their foreign trade, the Lydians invented the gold coin, a small unit of uniform weight and purity, while at the same time they may have begun to use cash, instead of barter, in retail food transactions. For cash they used handfuls of gold dust, just as was done up to modern times in the marketplace of Bida in Nigeria, where gold was also plentiful. The new idea of coined money was eagerly adopted by the Greeks, who (during the sixth century B.C.) introduced cheaper coins of silver and bronze. This had far-reaching effects. One was an entirely new feature of town-planning, first fully developed in Athens—a central space, where scientists and travelers strolled and chatted, and where one could buy or sell anything from a ship's cargo to a quick snack. This was the marketplace.

Gordon Childe has pointed out the analogy between breaking down ideographic characters into an alphabet and breaking down costly ingots into coined money. Together, letters and coins brought literacy and business within the reach of many, and made both political and social democracy conceivable. In a society dominated by money, some people at least could have leisure and freedom from state and social pressures. If many squandered the opportunity, some used it to develop pure science.

The invention of coins, together with alphabetic writing, boosted development of trade in Mediterranean Europe. Above: Ten-drachma piece from Syracuse in Sicily, 5th century B.C., showing head of Arethusa, and, on the other side, a charioteer. In Greek cities, the market place became a focal point, where all commodities were bought and sold at prices varying according to supply and demand. Right: Reconstruction of the market place in the city of Assos, Asia Minor.

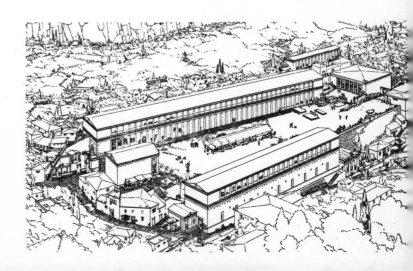

The marketplace brought with it a fundamental change in the relations of human societies to nature. The civilized societies of the Near East had long been using relatively small quantities of precious metal (because of its rarity) to symbolize larger quantities of food surplus. But American scholars have recently been reinterpreting the writings of the ancient Near East. They have concluded that, until Greek times, merchants made their living by taking fixed commissions for their work, and not by buying cheap and selling expensive. In the Greek market places, prices were free to move up or down instantly, as demand or supply increased. From the fifth century B.C. to the nineteenth century A.D., the history of Europe was largely influenced by the price of food, especially of grains. The Greeks were alarmed to find that prices rose steadily with rising population (and hence food demand) in the fifth and fourth centuries B.C. Prices were also affected by the amount of precious metal in circulation as money. They rocketed at the end of the fourth century, when Alexander the Great looted the treasure-hoard of the Persians and put it into circulation. The Greeks themselves never understood what had happened.

The problem they failed to solve was their dependence on the dry belt societies, whose food they needed to feed their expanding population. Greek civilization failed, in part, because it rested on the institution of slave labor. The wealth of Athens was derived from the foreign slaves who worked, until they literally dropped dead, the silver mines of Laurion. Slavery rotted the Greek societies in several ways. It supplied a constant temptation to make war on each other. (They sometimes hesitated to enslave their fellow Greeks, but not when it came to the pinch.) The permeation of the Greek states by cheap slave labor prevented the free laborers (who worked side by side with slaves, for instance, to build the Parthenon at Athens) from effective bargaining for wages. The one modern social institution conspicuously lacking in the Greek and Roman world (otherwise so much more modern in spirit than any other time and place) was the labor union. Instead, the use of slaves made manual work (other than farming) seem more and more degrading. The free lower classes lost interest in wage increases, and struggled only for landed property. The result was a ceaseless and bitter class war within the city-states, encouraging ideological wars between them.

Cheap slave labor also meant a lack of interest in the application of science to labor-saving machinery or the development of new sources of power. Contempt for manual labor prevented Greek scientists from tackling the one science where they would have had to dirty their hands—chemistry. Ignorance of this crucial subject set an

Above: Coin shows the head of Alexander the Great, the Macedonian ruler who conquered the Near and Middle East. Map above right shows extent of his empire.

Like the Greeks, the Romans depended on slaves for most manual labor. Below: Part of a Roman funeral monument dedicated to Publius Satur of Capua. The three figures at the foot represent the selling of a slave (central figure), and were probably a reminder that this public figure started life as a slave.

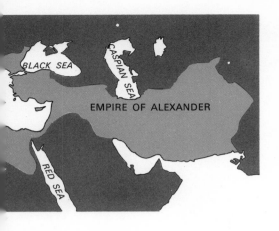

EMPIRE OF ALEXANDER

absolute limit on Greek scientific advance and caused it to stop short of the breakthrough. The lack was remedied later, partly by the Arabs, and partly by medieval European scientists, who simply loved getting their hands dirty.

Once thoroughly infected with slave labor, Greek democracy withered. The Greeks ended by succumbing completely to the dry belt way of life. In the fourth century B.C., after a long succession of wars, the Greeks were forcibly united by Philip II, ruler of Macedonia, a half-Greek state of landowners. His son Alexander the Great used both Greeks and Macedonians to conquer the Near and Middle East as far as Pakistan. On the conqueror's death in 323 B.C. his Macedonian marshals fought each other for his empire. The territory was finally divided into the great Kingdoms of Macedonia, Syria, and Egypt, several smaller princedoms, and the surviving independent Greek city-states, notably Rhodes. All the city-states were by now oligarchies with a democratic facade, but voting rights were firmly restricted to the rich.

Mainland Greece was on the wane. Other peoples had adopted the industries of Athens and Corinth, and made their own pottery, so the privileged position of those cities was lost. (The same thing could happen in due course to the developed societies of the present day.) Greeks poured into the new Near East states to staff their bureaucracies,

Desire for more slaves and more silver, and inability to feed their growing populations, drove the Greek city-states to make war on each other. Below: Vase-painting of Greek warriors fighting with swords and spears.

founding many cities but becoming completely absorbed by hydraulic civilization. Even the free Greek cities were now quite prepared to worship allied kings in their temples, a thing unthinkable before.

Under royal patronage, especially in Egypt under the Ptolemy dynasty, the traditional dry belt sciences (such as astronomy and agricultural science) were pursued with spectacular success, thanks to the insights of the new pure science. We have already seen that they raised Near East agriculture to its zenith by the time of the Roman Empire. But pure scientific activity gradually dwindled, finding a last glory in the work of Archimedes of Syracuse in Sicily (287–212 B.C.), often considered the greatest physical scientist in history. Painting and sculpture flourished through the third century B.C., but literature and drama, more sensitive to the loss of democratic freedom, decayed at once.

The Greek states, large and small, settled down to a condition of limited but almost permanent mutual warfare. At a congress of Greek states in 217 B.C., amidst the usual halfhearted planning for a United Greek Nations Organization, one delegate (Agleaus of Naupactus) advised his colleagues to watch out for the "cloud in the West." Here a total war was on between Carthage and a league of Italian peoples headed by the city of Rome.

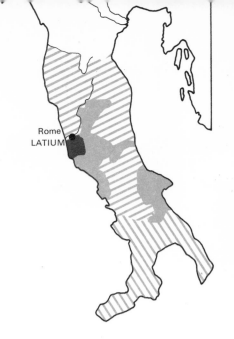

Rome
LATIUM

| | |
|---|---|
| ■ | 500 B.C. |
| ▨ | 300 B.C. |
| ▨ | 290 B.C. |
| ▨ | 275 B.C. |

Map opposite illustrates spread of Roman League in Italy between the 5th and 3rd centuries B.C. The Romans subdued neighboring states and then treated them as allies in wars against fresh foes. By 275 B.C. Italy was thus welded into one strong unit.

Commanding cheap slave labor, Greek and Roman factory owners alike were uninterested in machinery. Processes thus remained simple, as in the Roman bakery below left (depicted on a baker's tomb). Lower strip shows animals grinding grain and bakers who kneaded the dough by hand. On upper strip workers weigh and dispatch the bread.

The dark areas on the map below show extent of the Roman Republic at the height of its territorial expansion in the 1st century B.C.

Italy is the Mediterranean country most favored by nature, with a broad plain running down the west coast, in places very fertile by European standards. In the center of this belt, a new kind of society of farmers was emerging: the city-state of Rome. Around 509 B.C., this community of mixed farmers threw out their Etruscan overlords and formed the Roman Republic. From the beginning, the governing council, the "Senate," was monopolized by the biggest landowners. But their subjects retained all the independence of farmers owning their land. The Republic combined iron discipline in war with unusual personal freedom from state control in all other contexts. The smaller farmers pressed stubbornly, but with remarkably little violence, for practical reforms. The most spectacular move of this unusual lower class was in 449 B.C., when they set up their own Republic, ignoring the old one. The Senate gave in, and accepted some of the new officials (the tribunes of the people) as permanent elements in its state. In general, the Senators resisted every change, but as each reform became law, they abided by it. The people, in return, never embarrassed the Senate when the Republic was in danger.

When the Romans defeated another Italian people in war, they used similar principles. The losers became their allies, accepting the authority of the Roman Senate in war, but absolutely free from interference in civil matters, and

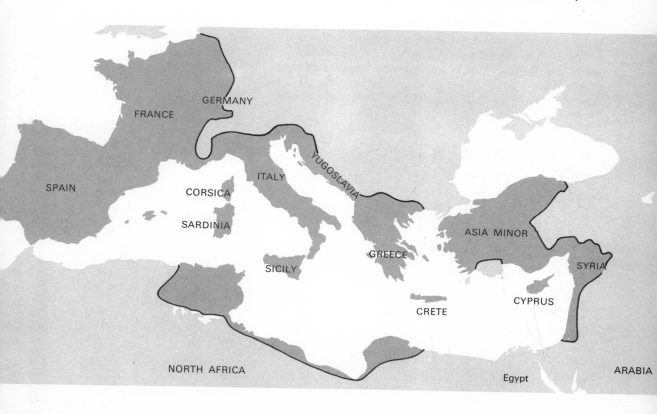

entitled to their share of loot from the next losers. It is not surprising that during the fourth century B.C. the Romans united all Italy into an invincible league.

In the third century B.C., the Romans wiped out the Carthagian Empire. In the second century B.C., they gained control of the entire Greek world. In or soon after the first century B.C., they conquered northwestern Europe. Vast quantities of loot had gathered in Rome, and Roman war contractors had made fortunes. The Romans proceeded to invent the business corporation (a legal "person" independent of the actual people composing it) and the stock market (where the public could buy shares in, for instance, shipping companies). Free private enterprise was without limit, and not even in the nineteenth century A.D. was the power of money so absolute.

Meanwhile Rome had caught the virus of slavery from the Greeks and the dry belt. After the wars with Carthage, the new tycoons invested in slave-run plantations, growing vines or olives or raising stock for export. The swelling city itself was fed increasingly on wheat imported as an imperial tax from Sicily, North Africa, and the Near East. Eventually the very destructive conquest of the East Mediterranean was nearly completed, and the supply of war-slaves dried up. The Roman Senate then found a technical reason for demilitarizing Rome's most faithful foreign ally the Rhodian Republic, which had until then kept down the pirates of Asia Minor and Crete. By simple kidnapping, the pirates now kept the slave-trade going for Rome till 67 B.C., when the Romans finally destroyed them for going too far and interfering with the wheat-importing fleets. Julius Caesar replenished the slave-market in the course of conquering France (58–49 B.C.). In the first

Rich in precious metal plundered from other societies, Roman civilization was entirely organized around money. Even peasants in the provinces, like the ones above, paid their rents in cash. (From a stone sarcophagus of the 3rd century A.D., found in northern France.)

and second centuries A.D., the slave supply dwindled, and it was found that slaves did not breed. Slavery began to decline in Europe. But, long before, Republican Rome had ceased to exist (30 B.C.).

## Decline and Fall

It was Rome's misfortune that the flowering of her civilization, which produced some wonderful poetry and a vigorous prose literature, coincided with a prolonged and bloody revolution (about 135–30 B.C.). There was a furious struggle for the loot of the empire. The struggle was partly between Rome and her Italian allies (especially the hill-folk), and partly between the noble politicans (who paid heavy bribes to the voters for their lucrative posts, so that they were often heavily in debt, and therefore kept debasing the coinage) and the businessmen (who wanted a stable currency and stable rates of interest on loans). Having shaken off a wild fringe of speculators who were ruining the empire by extortionate exploitation, business won, with the help of a new professional army.

In the first to second centuries A.D., with moderate, stable interest rates for investment, business ruled the Western civilized world, but (because of the tradition of slavery) without any attempt to develop new machines. The rule of business was as drearily unprogressive as any bureaucracy; literature soon decayed. The empire became virtually a federation of city-states each run by business-men, paying and controlling a common army and police force led by the emperor at Rome. Prolonged peace and large-scale production of cheap goods, like pottery (by cheap labor, not machines) raised even the peasants' standard of living, but not enough by comparison with the

Two stone carvings from Trajan's column in Rome. Trajan (A.D. 53–117) typifies the imperial ideal of a ruler working hard for the glory and wealth of the business empire. Below left: Trajan addresses Roman army. Below: With his staff, he receives barbarian chiefs.
Treated here as equals, the barbarians were to infiltrate the Roman Empire and build new societies on its ruins.

affluent society in the cities, which took little interest in the welfare of those who produced its food. The peasants recruited into the army finally got out of control. Throughout the third century A.D. they proceeded to wreck civilization in a series of senseless civil wars, in which they raised one general after another to the throne, murdering him when he tried to restrain them from looting the cities. Some sort of order was restored in A.D. 285 by the Emperor Diocletian, who was born a slave and rose from the ranks of the army, but only by imposing a bureaucratic regime of extreme hydraulic pattern, in which everyone was bound to a hereditary occupation.

From the beginning, the Roman Empire was divided into a Latin-speaking Western half (the western Mediterranean and northwestern Europe) and a Greek-speaking Eastern half (the eastern Mediterranean and much of the Near East). During the peaceful first to second centuries A.D., as agriculture, industry, and trade revived in the Eastern half, the unrealistic status of the Western half became glaringly obvious. The food surplus in the West was still totally inadequate for supporting so elaborate a civilization. This had been achieved only because money, symbolizing the surplus of the Eastern half (largely its dry belt regions), had accumulated at Rome in the form of loot. But the Romans did not realize this, and continued to import both food and luxuries on a grandiose scale. Their gold and silver flowed into the Eastern half of the empire,

Below: Map marks extent of the Roman Empire in A.D. 476. The Western Empire, weakened by years of overdependence on the Eastern Empire for food supplies, had shrunk to a small fragment (center). Its former territories were being reshaped by barbarians.

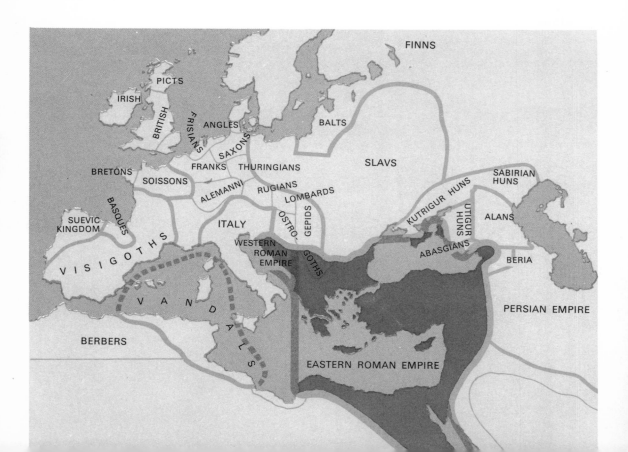

By A.D. 771, the Eastern Empire had become the shrunken Byzantine Empire, based in Constantinople, and was as rigidly organized as any hydraulic society. Expanding Islam was overshadowing Europe.

The Emperor Theodosius I (379–392) formally divided the Empire between his sons, who reigned at Rome and Constantinople.

and some of it went on to India and Afghanistan, to pay for spices, jewels, and Chinese silk. The real importance of Rome steadily declined. Emperors were at first Romans, then Italians, then Westerners, then (throughout the third century A.D.) generals from the region of modern Yugoslavia and Albania, with a few Syrians and even an Arab. Diocletian (born in Yugoslavia) ruled chiefly from his palace at Nicomedia in Asia Minor.

In A.D. 330, Constantine I took the logical step of expanding the city of Byzantium, on the borders of Europe and Asia, into the great new fortress-city of Constantinople (modern Istanbul) as a new capital. When he was fighting his way to the throne (A.D.312), the armies of Italy, sensing his attitude, put up their last great fight. Normally, in these times, a beaten army simply went over to the winner. The desperate Italians refused, and the emperor had to forge their weapons into chains.

In the Western Empire, the cities shrank and civilization steadily declined to a level more in keeping with the very small food surplus of Europe. The region split into fragments, which were eventually forged by the Germans into the new kingdoms of Visigothic Spain, Lombard Italy, Frankish France, Belgium and western Germany, and Anglo-Saxon England.

The failure of Greece and Rome was a result of a premature attempt to civilize Europe, whose own food surplus was still minute, by drawing on the huge surplus of the dry belt. It could not last. Rome and the West sank into the Dark Ages. Greece and the East were finally absorbed into the dry belt and shared its final ruin under the Turks. But this premature attempt had permanent results. The Romans had codified their new business contract practices, and much else, into a set of laws, which the Church preserved in the West. In the later Middle Ages, this Roman law aroused great interest among a rising (and characteristically European) class of lawyers, who used it to lay the foundations of modern enterprise that organized the technological breakthrough. The pure science of the Greeks, transmitted via the Islamic peoples (who had made important additions) taught Western Europeans to become scientists themselves, and made the breakthrough possible. Her great statesman Pericles said that Athens was the school of Greece. Ancient Greece and Rome were no less the school of modern Western Europe. Finally, it used to be thought that the ancient Greeks and Romans had ruined their natural surroundings in the Mediterranean. But this is far from true, as we shall see when we next consider the history of the European farmers. The ultimate fall of Mediterranean Europe still lay far in the future, when in A.D. 476 the (Western) Roman Empire came to its inevitable end.

# 9  Toward the Breakthrough

A time-traveler from the modern world might feel much more at home among educated Romans of the first century B.C. than he would among the Italian barons or even the Roman clergy in the seventh century A.D. High civilization had collapsed in the western Mediterranean area, because the local surplus there was quite inadequate to support it. But this does not prove that the resources of the region were already destroyed. The Greeks were undoubtedly brilliant as agricultural scientists, and the Romans, as a result of their peasant origins, took the keenest interest in farming. We have seen what they achieved between them in their territories in the dry belt.

In Greek Egypt in the third, and in Italy in the second and first centuries B.C., sophisticated field experiments were in progress. Elaborate crop rotations were devised, and the relationship between legumes and soil fertility was well known (although it could not be *understood* without modern chemistry). The engineers of the Ptolemies in Egypt reclaimed a polder some 200 miles square by draining a lake in the Fayum region. Part of it was sown with selected grasses and clovers for pasture. Agricultural textbooks by ancient Greeks and Italians were common, and some survive, including the *Georgics*, a popular book in verse by the north-Italian poet Virgil.

Below: Italian bronze model, from around 1st century B.C., of plow and oxen used in traditional peasant agriculture. The animals' manure was carefully applied to the fields.

Prosperous ancient Italians lived in graceful houses like the one below, excavated in Pompeii (from 1st century B.C.). As the Western Roman Empire crumbled, its highly civilized society was superseded by barbarians, like the Lombards, who "smelled of horses." Above: Bronze figure of a Lombard knight.

The Ptolemies' experts invented a form of what is nowadays called *seed certification*. They selected varieties of each kind of crop, and distributed their seed to the peasants, who were forbidden to sow anything else. Such procedures could not be applied to the free farmers of Italy, and their traditional farming methods were little influenced by the scientists. However, these old methods, although not very productive, do not seem to have been destructive. Erosion was carefully controlled, legumes were grown in some places, and animal manure was copiously applied to keep the land fertile.

It is true that the whole of Mediterranean Europe, with its perilously long, dry summers, has suffered severely from erosion and the drying-up of the land through widespread destruction of forests and their replacement by useless, patchy shrubs. Many modern conservationists have assumed that the ancient peoples were responsible for deforestation on a grand scale throughout the Mediterranean, although, as we have seen (p. 135), the deforestation of the Lebanon Mountains was certainly done much later. One reason for this assumption was the fact that some of the ancient writers were keenly interested in forest conservation, and complained bitterly of the effects of deforestation in certain districts (chiefly the eastern Mediterranean). Plato, for instance, in the fourth century B.C., declared that the land of Attica around Athens had been dried up and eroded by the destruction of forests in the hills, which had formerly trapped water in their soil to issue in springs

and streams. A number of ancient sanctuaries in his time had been built where there had once been sources, which had dried up. From such examples, the view gained currency in the nineteenth and twentieth centuries A.D. that the whole Mediterranean had been ruined in a similar way. Great stress was also laid on the consequences of overgrazing by goats.

The goat has acquired an evil reputation in Europe. His cloven hoof has become the mark of the Devil. A mobile upper lip and a gift for climbing enable him to eat the young shoots and leaves of bushes and trees, which other livestock cannot easily tackle. It seemed to follow logically that overgrazing by goats must destroy both grasses and shrubs or trees, leaving bare soil to be eroded. But the goat is not the only animal with a cloven hoof, and he may have been made a scapegoat—perhaps because goats usually belong to peasants, who can safely be accused of anything, while herds of sheep (which graze very close to the ground) and herds of cattle (which trample plants heavily) have often belonged to the rich. In 1936, the British agriculturalist H. E. Hornby suggested that, since goats will eat the last shrubs left after sheep and cattle "have departed with the last of the grass," they are "merely

Goats feeding on an argan tree in Morocco. Unlike cattle and sheep, goats are well fitted for climbing trees and feeding on them. But they are not necessarily more responsible than sheep and cattle for destroying vegetation.

completing the destruction wrought by sheep, cattle, donkeys and man."

In the whole history of agricultural research, only three experiments have apparently been made to determine the relative destructiveness of heavy grazing by goats and by cattle in regions with long dry seasons. All three were reported during the 1940's, two at Mpwapwa (in Tanzania) by Hornby himself and colleagues, and one at Warmbaths in northern Transvaal, South Africa. In all these experiments, the goats failed to destroy forest or scrub, and did much less harm to grass than cattle, which could leave the soil quite bare in three to four years. In world history, in numbers and economic importance, sheep and cattle have certainly been of overriding importance. Cattle, introduced on a grand scale in the nineteenth century A.D., were the main agents of erosion in the New World. Sheep have dominated the history of both zones of the Old World dry belt, and we shall presently see that the same is true for the western Mediterranean.

The fact that the ancient peoples did *not* ruin this region might be suspected from its subsequent history. Throughout the Dark and Middle Ages, the western Mediterranean was often the most advanced part of western Europe. Naples and Amalfi in southern Italy were the first cities to revive. Brilliant civilizations emerged in the twelfth century A.D. in Provence (southern France) and under the Norman kings of Sicily and southern Italy. Spain made vital contributions to the progress of medieval Europe. The climax of the Middle Ages, the Italian Renaissance, had its center in northern and central Italy, on the borderline between the western Mediterranean and northwestern Europe. It was not until the seventeenth century that the Mediterranean became a backwater.

Provençal civilization was the victim of brutally destructive aggression by its neighbors in northern France: barons in the thirteenth, royalists in the seventeenth, and finally revolutionary leaders and their business associates during the French Revolution at the end of the eighteenth century. But the peoples of Spain and southern Italy really did ruin their own resources, and not in ancient times either. There are many indications from Spanish writers that the deforestation and devastation of once-fertile Spain occurred at the end of the Middle Ages. In southern Italy, the question has been settled decisively by factual evidence from an unexpected source—the Royal Air Force. Aerial photography has become a useful archeological technique, because the outlines of ancient fields, invisible at ground level, are clearly shown in air photographs. The RAF aerial survey of Italy was made during World War II for reasons that had nothing to do with archeology. But the study of the photographs since the war, confirmed

Statuette of goat feeding in a thicket, a common motif in Sumerian art, from a royal tomb in Ur, *c.* 2500 B.C.

161

In the 10th century A.D., the Moors ruled over most of Spain (top map). But by the 14th century the kingdoms of Castile and Aragon had expanded and driven the Moors into a small area in southern Spain—Granada (above).

Below: Alphonso the Wise of Castile dictating his book on chess, from a 13th-century manuscript. A patron of science and scholarship, he assembled a team of translators and made Arabic works accessible to the rest of Europe.

by excavations and forgotten documents, has been most illuminating. The pattern of fields under cultivation in southern Italy can be mapped back to the Bronze Age, and it shows that the cultivated area never shrank in ancient times, even in the places most desolate today. A retreat in the sixth century A.D. (as everywhere in Europe) was soon made good again, and the whole of southern Italy was covered with small peasant farms until the fourteenth century. Then, and only then, did the ruin of southern Italy begin.

## The Spanish Tragedy

The course of events in southern Italy and in Spain seem to have been very similar, and the two countries were politically related from the fourteenth century onward. Their story is a tragic one, for they began by playing a crucial part in transmitting ancient science to western Europe. In the eighth century A.D., the Moors (Arabs and Berbers) overran nearly all Spain and much of Provence. The civilization of the Moors in Spain shared the typical cycles of the dry-belt civilizations of north Africa. At the peaks, it was magnificent. Al-Hakam II, who became emir of Cordoba in A.D. 961, had a library of 400,000 volumes, with a catalogue that filled 44 registers of 50 pages each. He encouraged active research into astronomy, medicine, and agriculture. But at every trough in the Moorish cycles, the Christian kingdoms of Spain (especially Castile, Aragon, and Portugal) pushed back down the peninsula, and by the fourteenth century had recovered nearly all of it.

During the centuries of intermittent warfare, a cosmopolitan spirit of tolerance often prevailed on both sides. Hence, by the closing years of the tenth century, the first translations of scientific works from Arabic into Latin were compiled at the Benedictine monastery of Santa Maria de Ripoll in Catalonia. From then on, the Christian kingdoms of Spain led the way in making available to western Europe the scientific work of the Greeks, to which Arabs, Persians, and Moors had by now made important additions, either original or derived from India or China. This activity culminated in the court of Alfonso X (the Wise) of Castile, who reigned from 1252 to 1284 at Toledo. Here a team of Christian, Jewish, and Moorish scholars worked together in perfect harmony under this prince. Among the works translated under his auspices was an important eleventh century textbook by the Moor Ibn Bassal on agricultural science. Alfonso was as enthusiastic a patron of practical agriculture as of science and scholarship. He took pains in his decrees to conserve the forests, which in the fourteenth century were still described (in a book on hunting) as "extensive" all over Castile.

Three centuries later, by the mid-sixteenth century, Castilians and foreigners, such as Venetian ambassadors, were describing Castile as a treeless waste. The agriculture of Spain was in ruins, her economy rotten, her civilization decaying. Her people were in the grip of the Spanish Inquisition, a system of government reminiscent of the Ch'in, which modern Catholic historians have viewed with as much horror as their non-Catholic colleagues. The agent of this terrible change was the Merino sheep. Through a deadly combination of European and dry-belt factors in this intermediate region, Abel ruined Cain—not by fire and sword, but by money and the law.

The fiercely dry summers of Spain and Italy produced in ancient times a system of transhumant stockraising (see p. 107), almost entirely of sheep, in the midst of the

Merino sheep bred in England. Until the 18th century, the Spanish prevented the export of this breed to the rest of Europe, thus preserving a monopoly of its excellent wool.

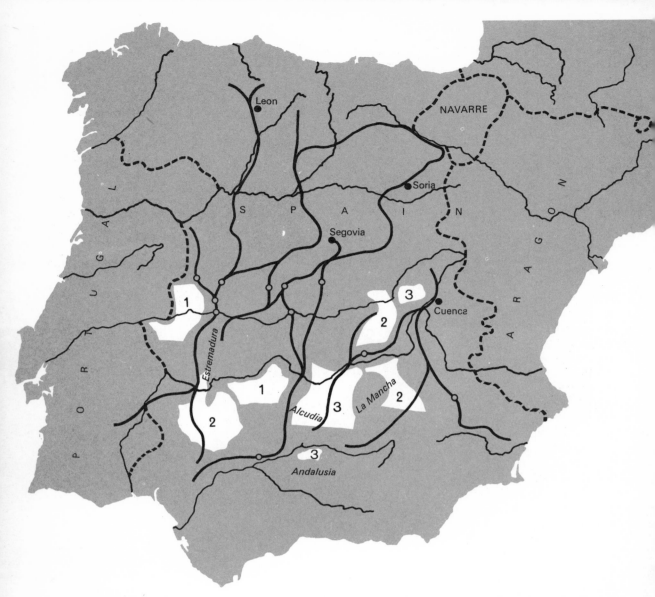

Map shows sheepwalks granted to the Mesta and guaranteed by Alphonso the Wise of Castile in 1273. Sheep grazed on pastures of Estremadura and other southern regions in winter, and in summer were driven to the hills of northern Spain. White patches mark winter pastures owned by military orders of (1) Alcantara, (2) Santiago, and (3) Calatrava.

Mediterranean civilization of mixed farming. The sheep were grazed in winter on rich level pastures in Estremadura and Andalusia (Spain) and on the coastal plains of southern Italy. In the dry summer they were driven hundreds of miles into the hills of northern Spain and central Italy, along well-marked tracks or sheepwalks. Most Spaniards, even in the sixteenth century, did not realize that transhumance had anything to do with climate. They thought the march merely kept the sheep fit—and, anyway, it was the traditional thing to do. They actually tried at that time to introduce a transhumant industry on the Caribbean island of Haiti, which has no vast stretches of pasture extending between different climates, and were surprised when it proved a failure.

Ever since the Visigothic kings of Spain (fifth to eighth centuries) the transhumant practice had been protected by royal decrees. The Moors then came along and introduced the Merino sheep, with its especially excellent wool. The division of the peninsula between Christians and Moslems cut the transhumant routes in half. But in 1212, at the battle of Las Navas de Tolosa, the Castilians conquered the pastures of southern Spain. In 1273 Alfonso the Wise gave a charter to the Honorable Assembly of the Mesta of the Shepherds, commonly called the *Mesta* (a word of uncertain meaning). This Mesta was a corporation of all the owners of transhumant sheep (as opposed to those kept all year round on the same pastures). Alfonso guaranteed them their three great sheepwalks (each 250 feet wide), but he strictly guarded the rights of the settled farmers along the routes, besides taking pains to ensure conservation of the forests. The importance of the industry lay in the export of Merino wool, which in the early Middle Ages began to replace linen as the main textile for north-western European clothes. From 1303 the customs reports of Southampton, Sandwich, and Portsmouth show Spanish wool imports almost every year.

In the fifteenth century (for reasons we shall see later) the price of bread fell, and the mixed farming of north-western Europe began to shift its emphasis from crops to stock. In Spain the Mesta began to gain ground and abuse its privileges. Its big chance came with the reigns of Ferdinand of Aragon (1479–1516) and Isabella of Castile (1474–1504). They married, united Spain, conquered the last Moorish state (Granada), and launched a determined policy of destroying local privilege and extending the power of the central government. In November 1476 Rodrigo Manrique died. He was the acting Grand Master of the military Order of Santiago, which owned much of the southern winter pastures and also the income from all taxes on transhumant sheep (by which the Mesta paid for their sheepwalk privileges). Queen Isabella heard the news at Valladolid. She rode at once to the Order's headquarters at Uclès, and proposed her husband as Grand Master. From then on the Mesta and its wool-export trade provided the main revenue of the Crown. But this was not its only attraction for Ferdinand and Isabella. During the reconquest of Spain from the Moors, both the Mesta and the settled landowners and towns on their routes had been bribed with ambiguous and incompatible land-use privileges. Until the fifteenth century the two parties had a fair working arrangement. But now Ferdinand and Isabella had backed the right of the Mesta, a nation-wide corporation, to encroach on privately owned or town lands, including cropland and woods. The monarchs were able to break down the privileges of local bodies and to impose everywhere the authority of the central government. With merciless thoroughness, they set out to destroy Spanish

Above: Ferdinand and Isabella, whose marriage united the kingdoms of Castile and Aragon, entering Granada, the last Moorish state to be reconquered in Spain. In strengthening the Mesta, they extended the power of the central government, destroying local privileges.

Above: Jakob Fugger (1412–96), a member of the powerful family of German bankers who leased the southern pastures of Spain as security for loans. Below: Frederick II, Holy Roman Emperor, who promoted the transhumant sheep industry in southern Italy.

(especially Castilian) agriculture for the benefit of the Mesta. A decree of 1489, for instance, greatly widened the borders of the sheepwalks, and prescribed death for peasants who tried to preserve their old land boundaries. Bringing new land under crops was prohibited.

The next king, Charles I, 1516–56 (the Holy Roman Emperor Charles V), was interested in Spain only as a source of money for his endless wars elsewhere in Europe. The wool trade gave him quick returns, and he leased most of the southern pastures to his chief financial backers, the German banking house of Fugger. He gave the Mesta a free rein. The number of transhumant sheep rose from 2,694,032 in 1477 to a peak of 3,453,168 in 1526. By now the Mesta almost ruled Spain. It had close links with the Spanish Inquisition. One of its presidents was also Grand Inquisitor. In 1492, to secure a monopoly of Spanish commerce, the Mesta used its influence at court to obtain the expulsion of the Jews, a mortal blow for Spanish culture as well as for Spanish banking. In 1609–11 the Mesta arranged for the expulsion of the remaining Moorish peasants, who had tried to protect their cropland. In 1639 and 1655 they finished off the Spanish forests by obtaining royal permission to use tree shoots for fodder "in every dry season"—the very time when it did most damage.

By this time, however, the Mesta had lost its grip. From about the mid-sixteenth century, when the population and the price of grains were rising steeply, the towns and farmers rallied and eventually forced the government to withdraw practical support from the Mesta. As early as 1501, a delegate from the town of Caceres at the High Court of Valladolid was complaining bluntly of the Mesta's abuses. "Such things," he said (with remarkable courage), "cannot be called just or honest, since they are not for the public good but for the private interest of a favored few." There was special resentment against the army of legal officials who accompanied the flocks to enforce their privileges. "There is no grandee of Spain," wrote a Spaniard later, in 1616, "who has so many judges and sheriffs to defend him as has the sheep." From about 1550 the numbers of sheep steadily declined, but the tide had turned too late: Spanish agriculture was ruined. Many Spaniards emigrated to the American colonies from the desolate lands, especially Estremadura. The settled landowners themselves, who had been so fiercely discouraged from growing crops, turned to settled sheep-farming, and destroyed the last woodlands.

In southern Italy the pattern of events had been similar, although here the tax on the transhumant flocks had been the main factor. Frederick of Hohenstaufen (the Holy Roman Emperor Frederick II, 1212–50) probably began to enlarge the industry. Alfonso V (1416–58), a Spanish

Above: Charles of Parma, enlightened ruler of southern Italy, who became Charles III of Spain in 1759. He opposed power of transhumant organizations in both countries and worked to bring more land under crops.

Below: Map of Europe and the Near East in A.D. 737, marking principal towns, trade routes, and products for export. Northwestern Europe was conspicuously devoid of large towns and natural resources on which prosperity might have been built through trade.

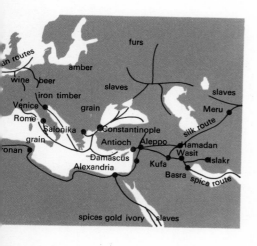

ruler of southern Italy, continued the process. The vastly lucrative tax was one of the chief baits that lured France and Spain to fight for possession of Italy during the early sixteenth century. In the process they destroyed the Renaissance civilization of northern and central Italy. The Spaniards, who won, naturally continued the system on Spanish lines.

In 1734 Charles of Parma became ruler of southern Italy, and in 1759 he became Charles III of Spain. He gave both countries their first competent government since the Middle Ages. He finally disposed of the transhumant organizations in both countries and did his best to bring more land under crops. The price of grains was rising again. In a series of patient investigations and reports (1771–83), Charles and his minister Campomanes unraveled the sad story of the ruin of agriculture and civilization in southern Italy and Spain. Their conclusion is summed up in Campomanes's verdict on the powers conferred by governments on the supreme legal officials of the Mesta and its Italian counterpart. It was, he wrote, "a grant of extraordinary jurisdiction, equivalent to placing a sword in the hands of a madman." The sword had been used. Dry summers and big business had between them finally ruined the western Mediterranean.

## The Rise of Northwestern Europe

We have seen the regions of the world eliminated, one by one, from the race toward the technological breakthrough. It happened not through any inherent defects in their peoples, but through the limitations imposed by their natural surroundings. And so we come finally to northwestern Europe. In the eighth century A.D. this region was the most backward, and apparently the least promising, in the world. Its towns had been shrinking steadily throughout the decline of the Western Roman Empire. Autun, for instance (in what is today eastern France) covered 500 acres in the second century, and 25 acres in the fifth. Precious metals, symbols of surplus, had drained away. By the ninth century, gold coins were no longer minted in northwestern Europe.

The Scandinavians benefited sporadically from trading and raiding in wealthier eastern Europe. Britain still exported a little tin. The Frankish empire of Charlemagne (A.D. 800 onward), which covered almost exactly the area of the modern Common Market, was poorest of all. The stockraising Friesians of the northern Netherlands did enough trading to preserve a money economy. But elsewhere commercial transactions relapsed largely into barter, each district producing barely enough for its own needs. Charlemagne could pay for his wars, and for his more constructive attempts to recivilize his empire, only by capturing Slavs and Saxons for export as slaves to Islam, which had access to African gold. In the ninth and tenth centuries, devastating raids by Vikings, Magyars, and Moslems further destroyed towns and sapped civilization.

But the turn of the millennium was the turn of the tide for northwestern Europe. From then on, unlike all other civilized parts of the world, it never again suffered devastating invasion from outside. The Vikings were tamed, and their descendants became part of the European culture. Financed by the trading cities of Venice and Genoa, northwestern Europe even began to thrust back into the Moslem world, in the expansionist wars called the Crusades. Increased trade, and the scientific ideas learned from Islam in peaceful interludes, restored both the money economy and science to Europe. In 1252 gold coins were minted at Genoa—northwestern Europe was back in business.

The central problem for the region was that of increasing its own agricultural surplus as a necessary base for any other developments. This was achieved by a series of technical advances that together produced an entirely new farming system. So diverse were European conditions that these advances occurred at different times in different places, and in several orders and combinations. Nevertheless, there is one main sequence that was common to large areas and must have been critical for the progress of Europe. This sequence begins with a new kind of plow.

The Mediterranean peoples continued to use the original dry-belt plow, a light instrument that merely scratched the surface of the soil, leaving undisturbed earth between each furrow. The farmers plowed first in one direction and then at right angles across the first furrows, breaking up the dry clods and keeping the earth as damp as possible. They generally had small, squarish fields, convenient for this cross-plowing. The early farmers of northwestern Europe used the same methods, including small, walled fields. These methods worked fairly well on light, well-drained upland soils, but were almost useless in the damp but much more fertile valleys. Here the soil was heavy and difficult to scratch, and the minerals needed by crops were leached some way below the surface (although not out of reach, as in the tropics). A method was required that would provide better drainage and bring minerals to the surface by deeply disturbing the soil. Because no such method was at hand, both the early European natives such as the Celts and the Italian colonists of northwestern Europe could clear and cultivate only the upland soils.

The problem of heavy soil was solved by the invention of a heavy, fixed-moldboard plow, and its use on very long strip-shaped sections of huge "open fields." The new plow had three parts: the colter, which cut vertically; the share, which cut horizontally; and the moldboard, which

Top: Moldboard plow especially suited to turning heavy soils of northwestern Europe (from the 14th-century Luttrell Psalter). Farmer plowed once down center of field and then around clockwise, the moldboard turning each slice of earth inward. This produced a field with raised center and troughs at side, as cross-section above.

In upland areas of Europe where soil was poor, peasants adopted the infield-outfield system, as still seen at Ashleam in Ireland (below). The outfield, beyond the straggling village, is used for shifting cultivation and for grazing animals whose manure is used to enrich the soil of the infield (foreground) divided into strips.

turned the whole slice of earth over on its side. It was usually wheeled and needed several draft animals to pull it. The farmer plowed down the middle of the strip of field, and then clockwise on alternate sides, always turning the slices inward toward the middle. The result, in course of time, was a raised ridge along the middle of the field and troughs along the sides. This system provided good drainage and some insurance against weather fluctuations. The crop on the ridge did well in wet years, the crop in the troughs in dry years.

Changes in plow construction seem to have been going on in northern Europe since the early Iron Age, and all combinations of plow and field-shape are found, but the fully developed heavy plow, in use on strips in open fields, first appeared among the Slavs of eastern Europe in the sixth century A.D. In 643 the Latin word *plovum* appears in a northern Italian document (the old scratch-plow was called *aratrum*). By this time the new instrument was probably widespread in northwestern Europe. Meanwhile the open fields with ridged strips were also appearing. In places (e.g. in the Netherlands) they simply replaced the old Roman square fields; but they also appeared extensively in valley lowlands now cultivated for the first time—for instance, in Britain, where the ash layer (which shows the original clearing of forest by burning) can be dated (by means of radioactive Carbon 14) to around A.D. 650–750. Hence the second wave of forest clearance in Europe.

With this new development, the uplands in many places became backward areas. In Ireland, Scotland, and parts of France and Germany, upland farmers evolved their own system, called *infield-outfield*. The outfield was used only for shifting cultivation and mainly left as wasteland for grazing animals. The manure of these animals was collected and heaped on the infield, which was cultivated without pause, year after year. This system was certainly the best that could then be used with poor upland soils. It meant a considerable emphasis on stock, and a modified form of it survives in parts of Ireland to the present day.

Now that the rich valleys were opened up, however, the outlook for northwestern Europe as a whole was becoming brighter. And on this new land, a way was found to achieve an impressive increase in crop production. The Mediterranean peoples had normally used (and continued to use) a simple cropping system called the *two-year rotation*. A winter grain (wheat or barley) was sown in autumn and harvested early the following spring. The land was then left fallow until the next year's fall, when it was manured and another crop sown. Generally the farm was divided into two parts, with their rotations staggered. This meant that in any one year only half the land was in use, so the surplus produced per unit of area was small.

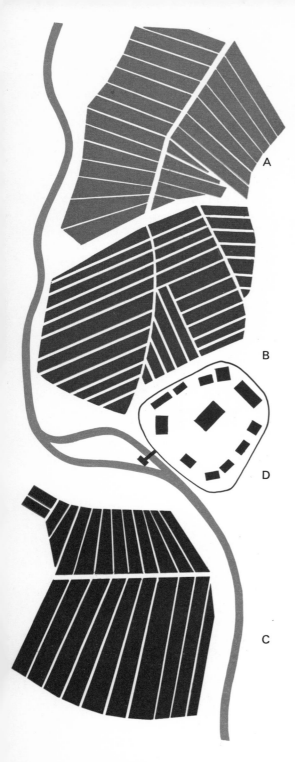

Grain crops could not be sown in spring and harvested in summer because there was not enough rain during this period in the Mediterranean region.

When the Italians colonized northwestern Europe, they took their traditional two-year grain rotation with them, not realizing its connection with climate. The Italian naturalist Pliny (A.D. 23–79) tells of an odd accidental discovery by some farmers near the German town of Trier, on the Moselle River. Their winter grain crop failed. In desperation, they sowed another crop in March, and to their surprise they got a harvest. But nobody dared repeat this experiment.

At about this time, however, as pollen studies have shown, Scandinavian and Baltic peoples were practicing a two-year rotation with the crop sown in the spring instead of in the autumn of alternate years. Here there was plenty of rain in spring, but cold winters discouraged autumn sowing. This system persisted throughout the Middle Ages in the colder regions of Finland and eastern Sweden. In the eighth century A.D., the peoples of the formerly Roman part of northwestern Europe came into closer touch (in part, through their Christian missionaries) with those farther north. It may be, as the American historian L. White has suggested, that as a result "the Baltic-North Sea spring planting was married to the Mediterranean autumn planting to create a new agricultural system." Certainly a new system, the *three-year rotation*, did appear about this time. It is mentioned in records of the Swiss monastery of St. Gall in 763.

In the three-year rotation, wheat or rye was sown in autumn and harvested in late spring. The next year oats, barley, or legumes were sown in early spring and harvested in summer. Then the land was left fallow for a little over a year, and the cycle started again. Usually (although not invariably) three big open fields were used, each being in one of the three states in any given year. Such a farm was worked by a group of peasants, living nearby and contributing draft animals for the heavy plow. Each peasant had a set of strips in each field. Some give-and-take was involved, especially for plowing, but in general each peasant could choose his crops to suit himself. Draft animals and other stock, for meat or wool and to supply manure for the fallow, were grazed on common pasture between or around the fields. The surrounding woodland supplied timber, firewood, and acorns for pigs.

The three-year rotation spread widely on the open fields during the next three centuries. Although some areas adopted it as late as the eighteenth century (or never at all), enough farmers changed over to make a very substantial difference to food production. Instead of one half of the land being used in any one year, two thirds were now

Above: Diagram of a medieval village using the system of crop rotation over three years that was frequently practiced in northwestern Europe. Agricultural land surrounding the village (D) was divided into three large "open" fields, each one divided into narrow strips cultivated by individual peasants. In a year when field A was left fallow, field B was plowed in the autumn and sown with wheat or rye, while field C was sown with barley, oats, beans, or peas in the spring.

In the 8th century A.D. the idea of a rigid wooden horsecollar was imported into Europe. Above: Part of the Bayeaux Tapestry showing a horse wearing this type of harness. It allowed an animal to pull four or five times as much weight as did a harness of soft neckstraps like the ones worn by the straining oxen below. These often tended to choke the animal.

producing crops. Moreover, since the fallow was generally plowed twice, whereas cropland was only plowed once, in each year, the same amount of plowing labor would cultivate more land. The inclusion of legumes varied the peasants' diet, and the diversity of crops and growing periods lessened the risk of total crop failure from bad weather. Finally, the new system could be used to produce an annual crop of oats, a very satisfactory diet for horses.

This oat crop would have been of little use but for the arrival in northwestern Europe, some time in the eighth century, of a crucially important invention from Turkestan (perhaps originally from China). Up to this time, horses had been harnessed (for pulling) with a yoke and neckstraps so arranged that every time the animal took the strain it nearly choked. The new invention was the rigid wooden horsecollar. Modern experiments have shown that a team of horses can pull four or five times as much weight with collars as they can with neckstraps. The new invention made both horse-drawn plows and horse-drawn wagons really practical. Land transport became more than three times as cheap as in Roman times, which encouraged the growing of crops for distant markets. Horsepower is about one and a half times greater than oxpower, and horses can work faster and longer hours—a vital point for plowing and harrowing operations in the uncertain weather conditions of northwestern Europe. The feeding of plowhorses was made possible by the oat crop in the three-year rotation.

The difficulty of changing over from the two-year system slowed the advance somewhat, but horses were plowing in

Yellow areas on above map of northern Holland indicate land reclaimed from the sea during the 16th and 17th centuries by draining polders and building dikes.

Right: Two pages from a 15th-century Shepherd's Calendar. Top: July, peasants making hay, with insets of the month's Zodiac signs—Cancer and Leo. Below: August, harvesting the wheat, with insets of Leo and Virgo, signs for August. Improved farming methods brought new confidence, and man began to mark the seasons by his own changing activities in controlling nature.

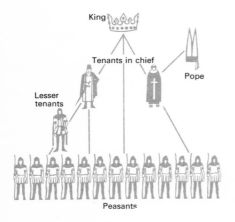

Above: Diagram of structure of medieval society. Some peasants were directly responsible to the king, some to lesser tenants, and some to the clergy. But all were well aware of their legal rights.

Norway by the late ninth century. By the eleventh century the whole new system—heavy plow horses, oats in a three-year rotation on open fields—was common throughout northwestern Europe. One effect of the greater speed of horses was that farmers could live farther from their work. By the eleventh century many hamlets were being abandoned and the farmers assembled in villages.

The profound change in farming methods between the fifth and tenth centuries meant a spectacular increase in production for a given amount of labor. One result was the mounting wave of forest clearance (p. 42), together with reclamation of marshes and (in the Netherlands and Belgium) polders from the sea. Another was the surplus that made possible the rise of many new towns and the revival of trade and industry on a greater scale than ever. Most momentous of all was the exuberant confidence and excitement that made the early Middle Ages in northwestern Europe the occasion of a profoundly new approach to man's relations with nature (see Chapter 2). Ancient illustrated calendars, for instance, had tended to mark the months with symbols of nature in the different seasons. From the eighth century A.D. onward in northwestern Europe, as the historian L. White has put it, "the pictures change to scenes of plowing, harvesting, woodchopping, people knocking down acorns for the pigs, pig-slaughtering. Man and nature are now two things, and man is master." Man was on his way. Given enough know-how, nothing could stop him.

The soldier-landlords and the clergy, who were the masters in the early Middle Ages, lacked the lavish supply of cheap and docile labor available to the hydraulic bureaucrats or the Greek and Roman slave-owners. At this stage their food surplus was much too small for mass labor. Slavery persisted throughout the Middle Ages, but only as a vestige. Since the later Roman Empire, many, if not most, of the people had been serfs, bound to the land. The knights and clergy often usurped local judicial functions from the royal officials who would otherwise have heard peasants' complaints. This double power led to much oppression: "Injustice stalks the highroads," wrote the German poet Walther von der Vogelweide at the end of the twelfth century. Nevertheless, the northwestern European peasants were never as docile as those of the dry belt. True heirs of Rome (thanks partly to the Church, whose power offset that of the feudal knights), the peasants were obsessed with their many legal rights.

Many peasants remained free from serfdom throughout the Middle Ages. Forest clearance made for freedom (p. 44). So did the growth of towns, encouraged (as a source of taxes) by the lords. A serf who could escape and avoid being caught for a stipulated period (generally about

Above: Carving on a pillar base in the cathedral of Mainz, Germany, symbolizing the burden borne by the lower classes who supported medieval society. But this patient resignation was sometimes exhausted. Below: The Swiss Confederacy of free peasants and citizens developed new fighting techniques and often defeated feudal hosts like the Austrians at the Battle of Sempach (1386).

a year) in a town, ceased to be a serf: "town air makes free" was a medieval German proverb. Even those who remained serfs benefited from the existence of these loopholes. Where stockraising predominated, the peasants were fairly rich (since stockraising needed more capital than crop farming), and this made them surprisingly independent. City-states, with more or less freedom, emerged in the industrial and trading regions of Italy and Belgium. Independent peasant federal republics, like the old Roman league, emerged in the stockraising regions of Switzerland and the northern Netherlands. Against such a background, cheap mass labor was out of the question, even when the population rose steeply from the eleventh century onward.

The result was that the peoples of northwestern Europe showed an enthusiasm never seen before or elsewhere for power technology and the mechanization of industrial processes. If the Greeks were the first pure scientists, the medieval Europeans were the first wholehearted technologists. They made few completely new inventions, but they showed astonishing energy and versatility in improving processes and applying them on a large scale to a great diversity of purposes. The existence of the wheelbarrow (known in the third century in China, but quite possibly re-invented in Europe, and widely used there) is a homely but significant difference between the medieval and ancient worlds. The watermill is probably a Greek invention (about the first century B.C.), but the Greeks, Romans, and Chinese never used it on a large scale or for anything much besides milling grain. In northwestern Europe it is mentioned in the law-codes of the Franks, Visigoths, and Alemanni (of Switzerland and southwestern Germany) by the sixth century. In 1086 the *Domesday Book* (William the Conqueror's inventory of English resources) lists 5,624 watermills in about 3,000 English villages or towns. The town of Troyes (France) had 11 watermills in the eleventh century, and 41 by the fifteenth century.

The windmill derives from the Tibetan prayer wheel (used only for ritual) and was used for milling grain in Afghanistan in the early tenth century. Northwestern Europe had numerous windmills in many places by the twelfth century at least. During the next century, 120 were built around the Belgian town of Ypres alone. Perennial streams favored watermills in Europe, but the variable winds made windmills difficult to operate. Nevertheless, the highly efficient rotating-roof type was developed by the fifteenth century.

But more striking than the number of mills is the variety of uses for water- or wind-driven machinery in the Middle Ages. It was used in the most important industry (textiles) by the tenth century. During the next five centuries, mills,

Above: Engraving (*c.* A.D. 1588) of an early type of windmill. The whole building turned with wind direction. Windmills, invented in Asia, were in use in Europe by the 12th century.

174

Left: Drawing in a 13th-century manuscript by Matthew Paris, showing a man pushing a wheelbarrow—a modest illustration of medieval technical advance over ancient Europe.

Power from windmills and watermills was harnessed to more and more mechanical uses, as shown in the two 16th-century engravings on this page. Right: Waterwheel turns a shaft with pegs that raise and drop a series of hammers. These might be used for crushing or grinding anything from grain to metal ores. Below: Revolving shaft with grindwheels for polishing armor.

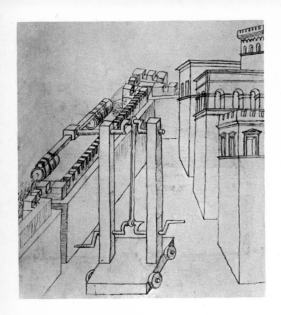

Above: Francesco di Georgio's drawing (about 1500) incorporating the principle of parallel crankshafts. Turning a handle at the foot rotated a mechanism on a higher level.

Throughout the Middle Ages, men were searching for an accurate method of recording time. Below: Sketch of an escapement mechanism for a clock, drawn by Villard de Honnecourt. This 13th-century technologist traveled widely, sketching and making notes on new inventions wherever he went.

lathes, trip hammers, and such machines were adapted for tanning, laundering, sawing, crushing anything from olives to ore; for working bellows in blast furnaces, the hammers in forges, and grindstones for polishing armor; for use in brewing and in the paint and paper industries. Nor were the engineers content to stop at water and wind. They looked eagerly for other sources of power, and by the thirteenth century had developed the steam bellows.

A similar enthusiasm for the applications of driving machinery led engineers to find endless new uses for cranks and cams, and above all to tinker with clockwork (gravity- or tension-driven machinery). This may have arisen independently in China and Europe around the twelfth century, but the Chinese did little with it. The Europeans, however, were fascinated. The spirit of these early technicians is summed up in a textbook written by Robert the Englishman in 1271. No clock, wrote Robert, is astronomically accurate, "nevertheless, clockmakers are trying to make a wheel, or disc, which will move exactly as the equinoctial circle does; but they can't quite finish the job. If they could, however, they would have a really accurate time-piece." After untiring experi-

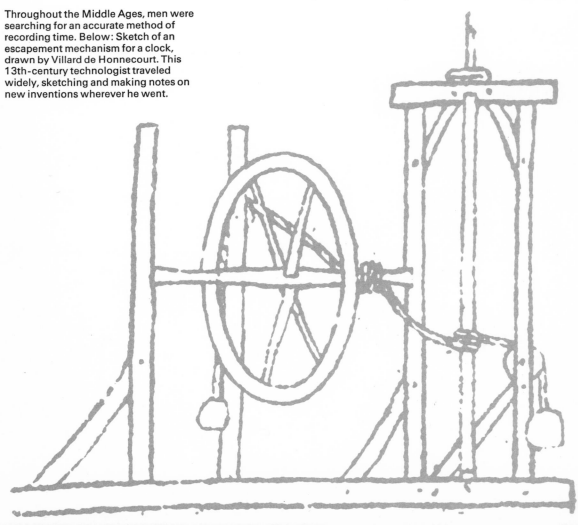

ment, they cracked the clock problem in the fifteenth century by inventing the escapement. And the resulting chronometers made possible the long sea voyages that turned the world into Europe's treasure chest.

The technologists of those days enjoyed unprecedented prestige. Alfonso the Wise himself wrote proudly about his own back-room wizards, such as Samuel Ha-Levi Abulafia, a Jewish engineer specializing in hoisting devices. The great master-engineers of the Gothic cathedrals were invited all over the continent and treated as VIPs. But it was not only the big names who traveled. A foreman in a saltworks at Salins, in eastern France, during the early fifteenth century had studied industrial processes in Burgundy, Lorraine, Provence, Poitou, Germany, Italy, and Spain. Traveling technologists, such as Villard de Honnecourt during the thirteenth century, kept notebooks on their travels, full of sketches and notes on how to do this and that. Know-how was valued above all. Pure science returned from Greece and Islam, *via* the Spanish translators, and fused with this exciting new technical tradition. There occurred a series of Renaissances, from that of the twelfth century to that of the fifteenth and sixteenth centuries.

Troubles were in store for Europe and were to lead to dreadful sufferings and convulsions, but the foundations of modern technology were firmly laid by about the twelfth century and from then on progress was steady and ever faster. The authentic voice of the Middle Ages echoes down to us in the words of Roger Bacon (1214–94): "Machines may be made by which the largest of ships, with only one man steering them, will be moved faster than if they were filled with rowers; wagons may be built which will move with incredible speed and without the aid of beasts; flying machines will be constructed . . . machines will make it possible to go to the bottom of the seas." The technological breakthrough had begun.

Gothic architecture represents one of the greatest achievements of medieval technology. Engineers learned to build graceful structures that were also strong. Above: Fine example of a fan-vaulted roof from Chapter House of Salisbury Cathedral, England, (about A.D. 1280).

Right: Miniature depicting the scholar Roger Bacon, from a 15th-century manuscript. This medieval scientist realized the significance of the technological breakthrough that was beginning.

# 10  The Modern World

Europe's new farming system caused, in the eleventh to thirteenth centuries, not only a technological spurt, but a dramatic rise in population that considerably overstepped the rise in production. By the thirteenth century, this began to have serious consequences. The Crusaders in the Near East were halted by Saladin the Kurd and expelled by Baybars the Mameluke, and northwest Europe began to be overcrowded. The resulting tensions led to ferocious wars, like the Hundred Years' War with England, which devastated France; and bitter social conflicts, like the civil war between businessmen and skilled workers that raged in the towns of Flanders (Belgium) from 1297 to 1328.

Frightful mass lynchings began, the first victims being religious nonconformists, or heretics. In 1231–3, the Chief Inquisitor of Germany, Conrad of Marburg, without the knowledge of the pope, stirred up the German masses like a medieval Hitler and conducted a reign of terror. In the fourteenth century A.D., the chief lynch victims were Jews

Overpopulation in 13th-century Europe led to internal wars and persecution of minority groups. In this relief at Naumberg, Germany (below), the high priests paying Judas his 30 pieces of silver wear the special hats that Jews were compelled to wear in the 13th century as a distinguishing mark.

and "witches" (mostly women). The craze for lynching witches persisted on a considerable scale until the eighteenth century. In the meantime class barriers hardened, while thought and speech, hitherto remarkably free, were increasingly censored.

As the settled populations grew denser, farms were subdivided and became smaller. In Martham (Norfolk, England), for instance, there were 107 tenant farmers in 1101, and 935 in 1292, with 2021 little plots of land. Such small farms were quite vulnerable to a run of bad harvests. New class distinctions appeared between well-to-do farmers and the layers of poorer peasants beneath them. Meanwhile the clearing of new land became so urgent, to feed the growing numbers, that areas of poor soil were brought into use, and after a few years crop yields on these began to fall.

Since the nineteenth century, farmers have generally harvested more than 10 times the amount of wheat grain they have sown. In the ninth century, the ratio was three to one or less. By the twelfth century, it had risen to about four to one. When this ratio is low, small changes in it make a big difference. Thus the twelfth-century farmer could use three-fourths of his (cropped) land for growing food (leaving one-fourth for next year's seed), as opposed to two-thirds in the ninth century. He also got the higher yield on the one-twelfth of land saved for food production. This is even more important if a large part of the land is fallow, as it still was even under the three-year rotation. That is why the new farming system made such a huge difference, although still not very productive by modern standards. But, by the same measure, a slight fall in yield was still disastrous. Hence many of the farms on the later and poorer clearings went bankrupt and were abandoned. In Germany literally hundreds of pioneer settlements are known to have been abandoned. This process began before the great disasters that drastically reduced the population after about 1300.

Even on good and long-settled land, drastic changes occurred. The swelling population demanded more staple food, and therefore more grain production. The result was a spread of cropland at the expense of pastures and hay meadows, while at the same time more horses and oxen were needed for draft. One result was a modified form of the three-year rotation, which appeared in the twelfth and thirteenth centuries. The animals were allowed to graze the

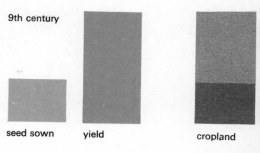

9th century

seed sown    yield                      cropland

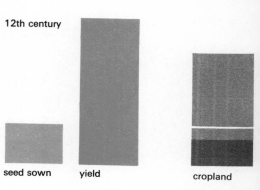

12th century

seed sown    yield                      cropland

19th century

seed sown    yield

Improved farming methods brought increased yields, as shown in these diagrams. Red columns show the yields produced by same amount of seed in 9th, 12th, and 19th centuries. Columns at right show increasing proportion of cropland that could be used to grow food (as opposed to growing seed for next year). By 19th century, farmers sold the whole crop and bought seed.

179

fallow field and the stubble on the cropped fields after harvest. Since the individual peasants each owned many small unfenced strips of land, their operations now had to be synchronized. Their freedom to choose their own crops and timings disappeared, a uniform plan being dictated by a manorial or village council.

Northwestern Europe shows so many differences in local history that it is not too surprising to find one survival into the twentieth century of this curious medieval farm system—the village of Laxton in Nottinghamshire (England). In 1952 it was taken over by the Ministry of Agriculture (acting as Lord of the Manor) to be a living museum. Its three open fields are worked today by 22 farmers. They meet annually at the "Court Leet of the Manor" and form a twelve-man Jury to decide on dates, inspect boundaries, and ensure that their few stretches of permanent pasture and meadow are not infringed on by the plow. The controlled three-year rotation on open fields, with most of its traditional techniques, can thus be observed in actual operation with horses today. Open-field farming has probably been practiced continuously at Laxton at least since the time of Tochi, son of Outi, Lord of the Manor just before the Norman Conquest of 1066.

Above: Aerial view of Laxton showing the three open fields, still farmed today: (1) West Field, (3) Mill Field, and (4) South Field, set around village (2).

Above: Members of the Jury of Laxton, who are responsible for administration of the three open fields, meeting in South Field (see above) to re-stake boundaries, as they do regularly.

Even the grazing of stubble and fallow did not solve the problem of the lost pastures and meadows. Hay for winter feeding became particularly scarce. In his great poem *Inferno* ("Hell"), written in 1312–14, Dante expresses the idea of utter dismay by using the image of the farmer whose fodder has run out and who looks out of his house to see the fields still white with snow. A more practical note is struck by Walter of Henley, a farm manager turned monk, who in the early thirteenth century wrote a textbook on farm management. "If you must buy cattle," he writes, "buy them between Easter and Whitsuntide, for then beasts are thin and cheap," having had little to eat during the winter. Some farmers may have had to slaughter some of their stock at the beginning of winter; this and the increasing meat shortage led to meat being stored for long periods to be eaten a little at a time. To preserve it salt was needed; to make it more appetizing, spices were added. Salt was available in Europe. The luxury trade in spices from the East Indies had flourished sporadically since the first century B.C. This trade now assumed greater proportions. Salt and spices produced a terrible thirst. By the end of the Middle Ages the average consumption of beer per head in Sweden was 40 times as great as today.

As the proportion of stock to crops declined, the resulting shortage of manure brought down yields, especially in the poorer, newly cleared lands. People also ate less meat

Below: Map of Europe and the Near East in A.D. 1212, marking principal trade routes and commodities exported. Once northwestern Europe had begun to prosper and produce a food surplus, natural resources could be exploited and trade developed with dry-belt countries. (Compare map on page 167.)

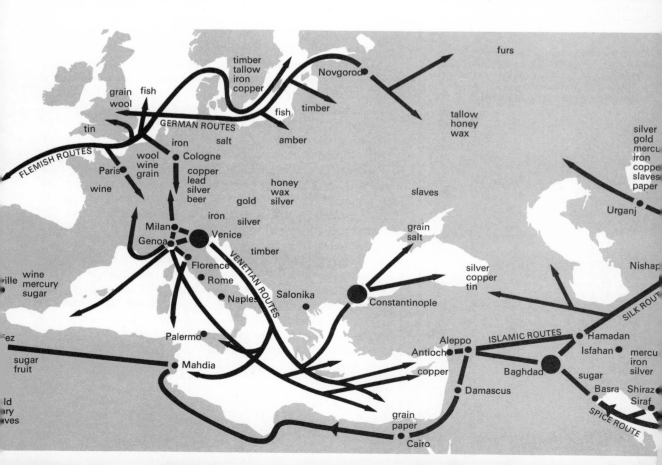

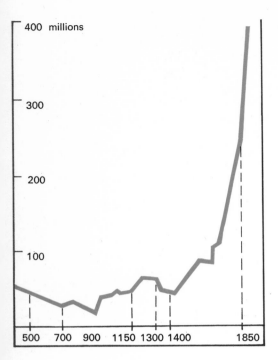

400 millions

300

200

100

500  700  900  1150 1300 1400        1850

Above: Diagram of probable population
of Europe, A.D. 400–1900. Note the
sudden drops around 1000, 1400, and
1650, when malnutrition had undermined
people's health and the death-rate
rose through wars and epidemics.

Black line shows land reclaimed in
Netherlands. Red line marks maximum, and
blue minimum, wheat prices, whose rise
made farming profitable and encouraged
reclamation. (Year 1730 equals 100.)

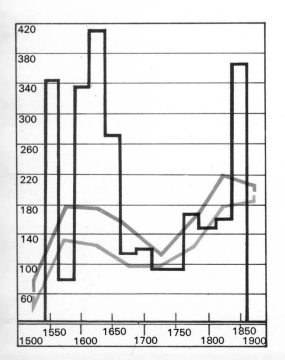

420

380

340

300

260

220

180

140

100

60

1550      1650      1750      1850
1500      1600      1700      1800  1900

and dairy products. The new emphasis on oats, together
with the controlled choice of crops, may have meant less
production of legumes as spring crops—though the spring
crop field at Laxton has, as it happens, always been called
the Bean Field. There must certainly have been a lack of
protein in the diet, and hence malnutrition, which undermined the people's health. In 1315–17, there was a disastrous famine: Overpopulation was exacting its price.

The population of northwest Europe reached a trough in
about 1400, and then began to rise again. It continued to
rise until the mid-seventeenth century, stabilized until about
the mid-eighteenth century, and then rose more rapidly
than ever until the twentieth century. We can ascribe the
rise to a gradual improvement in agriculture. It took place
almost entirely in the countryside, which supplied a steady
flow of recruits for the growing towns. Its interruption in
the seventeenth century (like that of the fourteenth) can be
traced to a deterioration in diet. On the manor of Grips-
holm in Sweden, the number of calories (energy supply
from food) dropped by about a third between 1555 and
1653. In the course of these big fluctuations in numbers a
sequence of linked changes occurred. They have been
assembled into a connected story by the Dutch economic
historian, B. H. Slicher van Bath.

By the thirteenth century, money and business dominated
the region's history (p. 168). Every time the population
rose, the demand for basic foods rose faster than production. The price of grains, especially wheat, rose too. In the
sixteenth century, the import of precious metals from
Mexico and Peru lowered the value of money relative to
that of grains. Since the population was also steeply rising,
the already rising wheat prices rocketed, in a convulsion
called the "price revolution." Prices of other goods
(manufactured or dairy products and meat) reacted less
sharply to population change, for these goods were not
essential to life.

When wheat prices were relatively high, it paid to clear
or reclaim more land for crops. When prices were relatively
low, crop farming paid badly and suffered a depression,
and newly cleared land was abandoned. This is mirrored in
records of polder-making and marsh drainage in the
Netherlands, and in the proportion of grains in pollen
sequences in several parts of Europe. When wheat prices
were high, mixed farming emphasized crops at the expense
of stock. When prices were low, the reverse occurred, and
formerly plowed land was converted to pasture. The
resulting increase in manure and in protein food helped to
restore crop yields and human health, and start the population rising again. In the fourteenth-fifteenth centuries,
this swing toward stockraising was most prominent in
Norway and in England. There, hundreds of farming

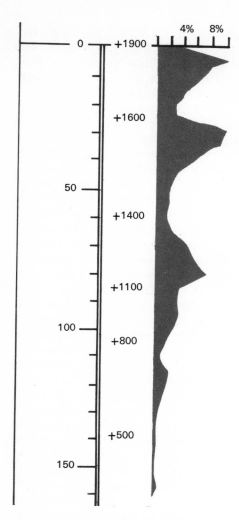

0 — +1900

+1600

50 —

+1400

+1100

100 —

+800

+500

150 —

Counting pollen grains from a section of heathland shows proportion of grains to other plants grown on the site over the centuries. This is shown on the right of the diagram (above) of a piece of land in Holland. Figures on left mark depth dug, in centimeters. Center figures give dates (A.D.) represented by each layer. The three main booms in crop agriculture correspond in time to peaks of population increase.

Diagram (right) shows the gradual development and improvement of mixed farming in northwestern Europe. From the 14th century onward, farmers cleared more and more of their land of forest and used an increasing proportion of it for growing varieties of crops for food or stock-feed in more sophisticated rotations. Eventually all land was used productively, with none under fallow.

villages disappeared altogether to make room for sheep, so important by this time was the woolen textile industry. In the late seventeenth and early eighteenth centuries, the swing from crop to stock farming was about equally extensive in Germany, Austria, Switzerland, Belgium, the Netherlands, France, England, and Ireland. But every time population and grain prices rose, the pastures were plowed up again for crops.

In Mediterranean Europe, the swings to stockraising were disastrous (p. 165). In northwest Europe, where severe summer droughts were rare, mixed farming remained flexible, and its emphasis on crops or stock could easily be reversed. When land was abandoned, some damage was caused by erosion and (in the Netherlands) floods, but no vast areas were transformed into desert. On the contrary, despite much suffering in the agricultural depressions, mixed farming showed steady progress, for each of its components was vigorously developed by turns. The result was the construction of new and elaborate systems of mixed farming, which at last produced a surplus on something like the dry-belt scale.

The pioneers, from the fourteenth century onward, were the farmers near the populous centers of the textile industry—in northern Italy, north-eastern France, and above all in Flanders (Belgium) and Brabant (the Netherlands). Their new farming system contained three new ideas. First was "ley farming" or "convertible husbandry": alternating the same piece of land regularly between temporary pasture (ley) and crops. Second was the use (in rotations) of root crops—for example turnips—which were fed to stock kept in sheds. Third was the use of pasture legumes (clovers and alfalfa), not just on permanent pastures but on

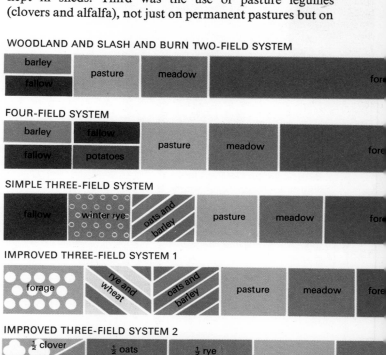

WOODLAND AND SLASH AND BURN TWO-FIELD SYSTEM

| barley | | pasture | meadow | for |
| fallow | | | | |

FOUR-FIELD SYSTEM

| barley | fallow | pasture | meadow | fore |
| fallow | potatoes | | | |

SIMPLE THREE-FIELD SYSTEM

| fallow | winter rye | oats and barley | pasture | meadow | for |

IMPROVED THREE-FIELD SYSTEM 1

| forage | rye and wheat | oats and barley | pasture | meadow | fore |

IMPROVED THREE-FIELD SYSTEM 2

| ½ clover | ½ oats | ½ rye | pasture | meado |
| ½ root crops | ½ wheat | ½ barley | | |

From the 1st to the 5th centuries A.D., India led the world as a trading center and achieved a high degree of civilization. This 5th-century sculpture of Buddha from the Gupta period (A.D. 300–600), a graceful figure in fine transparent drapery, typifies the Greek-influenced art of Classical India.

leys, mixed with grasses, or fitted into rotations. The legumes not only promoted soil fertility but (because they grew during more of the year than grasses) provided winter feed for the animals. At the same time, food legumes (beans, etc.) were emphasized again.

The new system (which provided lavish manure) had many special forms. The so-called "Norfolk Rotation" (modified from a Belgian one used in 1650) was a system of four courses (wheat, turnips, barley, clover). But much longer and more elaborate rotations, often including leys, were also developed. The fallow became shorter and at longer intervals, until it finally disappeared altogether. This left the land at all times (and therefore the whole cropland at any one time) in use to produce food, directly as food crops or indirectly by feeding animals. At Schmatzfeld in the Harz district of Germany, for instance, the proportion of cropland under fallow at a given time fell from 37.3 per cent in 1592 to 0.8 per cent in 1850. The "new husbandry" spread steadily over northwest Europe. In Austria it had a hero, Johan Christian Schubart, created "Cloverfield Knight of the Holy Roman Empire" by the Emperor Joseph II. In France it had a martyr, the unfortunate Marquise de Marboeuf, guillotined during the Revolution on the muddle-headed charge of sowing fodder crops instead of wheat to feed the people.

The fall of grain prices in the seventeenth century had encouraged investment in the new industries emerging from the new technology of northwest Europe (instead of in farming). The substantial surplus provided by the new husbandry supplied labor and capital for the industrialization of northwest Europe in the eighteenth-nineteenth century. In England, at least, this process is rightly called the industrial "revolution," for it was horrifyingly brutal. Not even Roman slave-owners had overworked children as the new industrialists did. The world now received another lesson in the horrors to be feared from unrestricted private business. But by 1850, the technological breakthrough in Europe was an accomplished fact, and it was to change the life of the whole world.

**Toward One World**

Until the breakthrough began in Europe, the interlocking cycles of the dry belt and the great currents of trade within and around it had produced a kaleidoscopic pattern. Peaks of power and/or civilization appeared in different places at different times. Ethiopia was a great power in the sixth, Tibet in the eighth, Lithuania in the fourteenth century A.D. The world was still divided by shifting but formidable barriers on land or sea.

At almost every period since the Bronze Age, some great region has maintained human progress. After the Greek and Roman decline began, it was India's turn. The history of this great subcontinent has been intermediate between those of the western and eastern zones of the dry belt. But in the first to fifth centuries A.D., India broke this pattern to become the trading center of the world. It had great merchant cities where Roman and Chinese wares mingled, and from which expeditions set off east to tap the resources of Southeast Asia and Indonesia. Some of these Indian cities were even republics. This civilization, known as Classical India, was brought to an end by a nomad invasion from Central Asia, and India relapsed into the old cycles. The trade of the Indian Ocean returned to the Arabs and Persians, who maintained it until the final decline of the Near East eroded their base. Once Chinese civilization embraced the enterprising coastal peoples of southern China (around Canton), the hatred of the mandarins for private trading enterprise (p. 125) met considerable resistance. In the fifteenth century A.D., Chinese trading fleets, with the best ships then made, were visiting Africa. But by 1500, the iron bureaucracy had finally won, recalling the Chinese from the mastery of the world's oceans.

Indians, Arabs, and Chinese had great hydraulic civilizations. In Africa, south of the Sahara, there were no great fertile food plains to provide the surplus for such development (p. 74). Nevertheless, the rise of impressive native African empires was achieved by means of a trade surplus. This was true both in the western Sudan, where flourishing textile industries and universities of scholars were to be found, and in eastern Africa. In 1415, at the peak of Chinese enterprise, the Kenyan port of Malindi sent ambassadors (with gifts that included a giraffe) to the Ming emperor in Peking. In the African hinterland, from Kenya to the Transvaal, lived the miners and technicians, creating—thanks to the trade—a nonliterate but architecturally magnificent native civilization. This culminated in the colossal city of Zimbabwe in Rhodesia.

In 1488, the Portuguese explorer Vasco da Gama rounded the Cape of Good Hope. Four years later Columbus sailed. From this time on, the kaleidoscope of world

Above: Chinese painting of the giraffe sent to a Ming emperor in Peking by the East African port of Malindi in A.D. 1415 as a gift, when trade flourished between the two countries.

Rich mineral deposits—particularly of iron—and great skill in exploiting them, enabled cities of eastern Africa to build up a food surplus through trade, and to support a magnificent civilization in the hinterland. Below: Ruins of the great Temple of Zimbabwe, Rhodesia, destroyed in the 17th century but once the prosperous center of an empire.

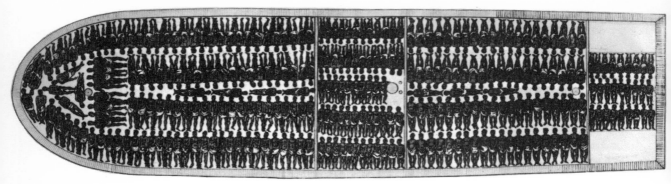

This drawing of a slave ship illustrates the terrible conditions under which slaves were sent from Africa to the New World by British traders. Packed together like cattle, many of them died on the journey.

As late as 1865 the Southern States of America still exploited slave labor to work their plantations of tobacco and cotton, and as domestic servants. Below: Engraving of a typical slave sale at Charleston, South Carolina, at that date.

history steadied into a consistent pattern. Europeans dominated the world, but in so doing they brought it together into one system, all of which is now adopting the new technological civilization. The European expansion was in two stages. From about 1500 to about 1850, the Europeans used their technological equipment mainly to control the rest of the world for purposes of trade, loot, and plantation agriculture using slave labor.

Thanks to great sea power combined with an ample home surplus, Britain finally obtained the lion's share of the trade. This, together with her resources in easily mined coal and iron, made Britain the pioneer of the Industrial Revolution. The plantations were chiefly of sugar cane in the West Indies, and cotton and tobacco in the south of the

region that became the United States of America. To staff the plantations with a labor force accustomed to tropical climates, the Europeans (especially the British and Dutch) launched the appalling trade in African slaves, which completed the ruin of African civilizations. Everywhere during this phase the Europeans were brutally destructive and rapacious. Robert Clive, the conqueror of eastern India, wrote in the 1760's that "such a scene of anarchy, confusion, bribery, corruption and extortion was never seen or heard of in any country but Bengal." (He made a fortune himself.) And the British in India were matched by other Europeans elsewhere.

Just as wool replaced linen in the twelfth-thirteenth centuries, so cotton partly replaced wool in the eighteenth. The cotton textile industry of Lancashire, England was the setting for much of the early machine development in the Industrial Revolution. In 1794, Eli Whitney of Massachusetts invented the cotton gin, a machine for separating the cotton fibers from the seeds. By 1800, American cotton production had risen from 5 to 35 million pounds; and when Whitney died in 1825, it was 225 million pounds. The invention prolonged plantation slavery for half a century, until the maintenance of slaves became unprofitable.

From about 1850, the pattern of colonial exploitation changed. Some at least of the European powers, such as

Above: Eli Whitney of Massachusetts. In 1794 he invented the cotton gin. This machine (below) consisted of a drum with pointed teeth, rotated by hand, that tore away the cotton fibers from the seed. It did the day's work of several men in an hour. It made slave-worked cotton plantations profitable for fifty years, until erosion reduced the supply of cheap land.

Above: Painting of British emigrants leaving Gravesend for the New World. When Europe's population rose steeply in the 19th century, millions emigrated.

Arrows on map above mark the routes followed by the 55 million emigrants who left Europe during the 19th and 20th centuries. The majority (including one-eighth of the total population of Ireland) went to the lands opened up in North America in the preceding centuries. But a considerable number chose South Africa, Australia, and New Zealand. Many of the emigrants from the Mediterranean area went to South America.

the British in India, began to provide honest and competent government, and also some preparation for the introduction of industrial technology. By this time advances in transport (railways and steamships) were unifying the world and making mass trade in cheap goods (such as grains) feasible. By this time, too, the population of Europeans was increasing out of all proportion to that of the rest of mankind. It has been estimated that they made up about 22 per cent of the world human population in 1800, and about 35 per cent in 1930.

This huge increase was funneled into regions hitherto occupied only by small, scattered tribal societies (which were generally ruthlessly displaced)—above all in North America. About 377,000 people per year left Europe in 1846–90, about 911,000 per year in 1891–1920, and about 366,000 per year in 1921–9. Between 1846 and 1930, over 50,000,000 Europeans emigrated. In this way Europeans helped to form various societies outside Europe, the largest being the modern U.S.A. and U.S.S.R. Those who stayed in Europe were now fed largely by grain imports from these newly opened regions. As the American geographer Carl O. Sauer has put it, "the industrial revolution was made possible by the plowing-up of the great non-tropical grasslands of the world." The supply of space in relatively temperate climates outside Europe began to run out in the early twentieth century, when the United States began to restrict immigration. By this time the European population was leveling off, but there was enough crowding to generate two frightful wars, in which the European powers involved most of the rest of the world.

A rising population accompanied the spread of industrialization from Britain, that is, the change to a state of steadily increasing production by means of machines and inanimate power supplies. The American economist W. W. Rostow has suggested some dates for the initial stages of industrialization in some different countries: Britain, 1783–1802; France, 1830–60; Belgium, 1833–60; U.S.A., 1843–60; Germany, 1850–73; Sweden, 1868–90; Japan, 1878–1900; Russia, 1890–1914; Canada, 1896–1914.

One astonishing feature of this list is the early industrialization of one non-European country, Japan. It is a country with a unique history. Since at least the fifth century A.D., when her written history begins, Japan has practiced typical hydraulic agriculture based on rice. "Before any business else," says an old Japanese proverb, "draw water to your winter fields." But Japan has no great river systems like the Yellow River, the Ganges, or the Euphrates. Her irrigation was based on small streams in a number of districts divided by mountains or inland seas. Hence the Japanese developed the docility of a hydraulic civilization without the centralized bureaucracy.

Instead, there evolved a feudal system, in which each district was controlled by a military lord with his knights (samurai). Whereas in the European feudal system the rights of inferiors had great weight at all levels, in that of Japan inferiors had only duties. However, just as pine and poplar may provide a good nursery for beech and sugar maple (p. 20), so in the succession of human history a feudal system may provide a good nursery for a technological society. Because of its small original surplus, Europe could never have started civilization. Because of its hydraulic agriculture, and its isolation from influences other than Chinese, Japan could never have made the technological breakthrough. But Europe readily adopted and developed civilized techniques, and Japan adopted modern technology with astounding speed after 1867, when a modernizing party gained control.

Up through the first half of the twentieth century, the only fully industrialized, or developed, nations were Japan,

The British brought technological knowledge to India, and railways were built there in the mid-19th century. Engraving shows the first steam engine for the Peshawar railway being taken across the Indus by boat.

Japan was the first country outside Europe to participate actively in the breakthrough. In 1867 a modernizing party came into power and Japan started to absorb European technology at an amazing rate. Below: Opening of the first Japanese railway in 1872.

Above: Indian farmers working with
ox-drawn plows in Damodar valley near
pylons of an electrification project.
Outside finance for such projects
is vital to developing countries today.

Below: Map marks countries that made
up the Common Market (blue) at end
of 1966. Also named are countries that
had applied to join at that date but
had not been admitted.

the United States, and the countries of Europe. This situation is now changing rapidly. The European colonial empires have almost disappeared, although their economic influence is still predominant. The most powerful nations today are the U.S.A. and the U.S.S.R., who combine industrialization with great natural resources within their own large territories. Gradually the countries of the dry belt and the tropics are beginning to develop too. Rostow dates the start of industrialization in China and India at about 1952. Just as Athens lost her privileged status when ceramics industries started elsewhere, so the Europeans will gradually lose their long-sustained predominance, and cannot expect to go on importing raw materials in return for industrial products, which others will soon be making for themselves.

By that time, however, the world will probably be even more integrated than it is today. Meanwhile, the problem of speeding development in the developing countries is more urgent, and the developed countries are contributing 3.6 billion dollars a year to advance this. The problem is complicated by the peculiar financial and trading system that has evolved between nations. The modern nation itself, as a social unit, played an important part in the technological breakthrough. It was a new balance of town and countryside interests, of central and local government, which the ancient city-states had failed to achieve. National organization is spreading everywhere as a precursor of industrialization. But valuable as the national stage has been, it has features that make it increasingly unsuitable for the modern world. These include the subsidies to native producers, tariffs (high duties or limited quotas) against imports from abroad, and the strangling network of international trade balances.

There is little doubt that international organization is on its way. By the 1960's, every urban country in the world, developed or developing, had original scientists and technologists of its own. All now work together for what is no longer European but world science. The International Geophysical Year in 1957 was an impressive demonstration of a completely coordinated world program. There is already a tendency to set up longer programs of this kind, like the International Hydrological (Water Study) Decade, which started at the beginning of 1965. While tensions and confusions still obscure international politics, this ceaseless work in the background is gradually making the world one and indivisible.

## Progress and Problems

The advance of food production since the breakthrough in northwest Europe had not been without difficulties and setbacks. When the Europeans colonized North America,

they reckoned without the dangers of climates and landscapes less favorable than those they had left behind. In the Southern States of America, the planting of rows of cotton or tobacco on bare unprotected soil soon led to catastrophic soil erosion by runoff water. By the outbreak of the Civil War in 1861, usable land was already scarce and expensive, so that slave labor became unprofitable. Much of the South has been a comparatively depressed area ever since.

In the grassland belt of North America, the nineteenth- and early twentieth-century settlers often indulged in reckless overgrazing, or plowed up the grass and raised crop after crop of grain without manuring or rotation. The soil was soon exhausted, and the bare fields were unprotected from the terrible gales and cyclones of the region. Disaster struck with the dry period of 1928–37, reaching its climax with the terrible drought of 1934. Masses of soil were whirled up by the winds as dustclouds, to be deposited again in drifts up to two feet deep, smothering vegetation elsewhere. In 1934, dustclouds from North and South Dakota blew as far as Washington, D.C., bringing the problem of soil conservation visibly to the attention of the Government and Congress. By that time, according to the U.S. Department of Agriculture, out of the total area of the Continental U.S.A. of 1.91 billion acres, 1.16 billion were more or less seriously affected by erosion.

But modern technological man is extraordinarily resilient in the face of such disasters. Within a year of the great drought, both the United States and Canada had set up special areas for studying the problem, the Vale Project in Oregon and the Melita Reclamation Station in Manitoba. By 1964, both projects had shown the possibility of avoiding erosion on the dry plains and of fully reclaiming eroded land. The station at Melita was located on land actually abandoned, and has restored much of it to full productive use. Experience in North America, and in

large tracts of North America
ergrazing or continuous farming with e same crop exhausted the land. Bare lds were a prey to water erosion, aving dry barren gullies (above). metimes gales and cyclones swept away e topsoil. After droughts, such as the vere one of 1934, high winds whipped rched topsoil into huge duststorms, nothering vegetation and choking wns. Photo right shows a duststorm Kansas (1935).

New Zealand has also been faced with
problems of soil conservation. Right,
above: Section of the Tara Hills, South
Island, where effects of overgrazing
were aggravated by a plague of rabbits.
Lower picture illustrates how fertility
was restored to this land by manuring
and seeding with pasture legumes.
Serious efforts were made to control
rabbits. The success of this experiment
is particularly striking since this land
is on steep slopes.

Australia, New Zealand, and South Africa (faced with similar problems), has produced an impressive technology of soil conservation. On wind-swept plains, for instance, rows of trees can be planted at intervals as "shelter-belts" to break the force of the winds. The sowing of grasses and especially legumes can gradually reclaim bare soil for fertile cropland. These and other techniques are helping to repair the damage and ensure that it never recurs. In addition, much has been learned about the effects of grazing in dry regions, which can be applied in the overgrazed Old World dry belt.

All this work is not without surprises. After all we have seen of the effects of deforestation and overgrazing, planting trees might seem always a good idea. Yet in Arizona, carefully nurtured cedar and juniper thickets have been shown to waste the region's scarce water and hence lower the carrying capacity for cattle. The trees have to be thinned and pruned. Too many trees can be as bad as too many cattle. The one completely general rule is that too many of *anything* is dangerous.

More spectacular than any disaster has been the advance of agriculture as a direct result of the breakthrough. One obvious new gain was the introduction of more machinery (made of improved metal) and of the new sources of power. Up to and including the eighteenth century, farmers were still concerned with increasing the ratio of yield to seed. The chief innovation was the seed-drill, a machine for sowing seeds in rows instead of broadcasting them by hand, which wasted seeds. As early as 1566 the Senate of Venice granted a patent to Camillo Tarello of Lonato for a device of this kind. After about 1800, the new farming systems had greatly increased yields and the Industrial Revolution was in full swing in Britain. Interest turned to machines for harvesting and cleaning the greater amounts of grain quickly and with less labor. The American drive westward was hastened by the reaping machine, which

Invention of the seed-drill was an important factor in increasing yields, because less seed was wasted. Above: Woman using early seed-drill, from an 18th-century French print.

Below: 19th-century English metal seed-drill. Seed dropped from box straight down into the furrow.

Cyrus McCormick of Virginia invented in 1831 and began mass producing in 1845, in the (then) decaying settlement of Chicago. The reaping machine evolved gradually into the combine-harvester, which did everything from cutting to cleaning.

In 1784 James Watt patented steam-powered plowing, and by 1870 steam-powered tractors were in use. These, however, were heavy and used much fuel and water. In 1892 John Froelich built a tractor powered by an internal combustion engine, and in 1907 Henry Ford began to manufacture such tractors in Detroit. They thus shared the benefits of the system of total mass production Ford had developed by 1913. Mechanization caused an unprecedented saving in labor. In 1830, using the ordinary plow, harrow, sickles, and flails, it took 144 man-hours to produce 50 bushels of wheat. In America, this was reduced to 22 man-hours by 1896, and to 8.25 man-hours by 1930 (with tractors and combine-harvesters). A large labor force was thus freed for industry. By now in the United States there are relatively few full-time farmers left. The farmhorse, which served European progress so well in the

Above: Drawing of the first really effective reaping machine, invented by Cyrus McCormick in 1831. Finally replacing hand-scything, this invention dramatically cut down the manpower needed for harvesting.

Diagram below shows how increasing mechanization has cut down the man-hours needed to plow two and a half acres of land. Using an early type of plow with two horses, one man would take 13 hours 42 minutes. Today with a tractor and multi-furrow plow, one man can cover this area in 40 minutes.

13h 42m

12h 3m

5h 57m

4h 19m

Above: Illustration from Copeland's *Agriculture, Ancient and Modern* (1866) shows a threshing machine powered by a steam engine. This machine needed several men to operate it and would be owned by a contractor who leased it out.

Middle Ages, has had its day. In the United States between 1915 and 1940, 11 million horses and mules were displaced by tractors. By 1964, there were too few draft animals left to be counted in agricultural statistics, and there were five million tractors—more than one per farm.

Farm machines have saved mankind much tedious labor, freeing him for other work or increasing his leisure time. For raising food production, however, they have not, so far, been the most important contribution of the breakthrough. This is clear from the extraordinary story of modern Japan. Unlike Britain and the U.S.A. (or, to a large extent, continental northwest Europe), Japan industrialized without mechanizing her farms or freeing farm labor for industry. She increased her food surplus with the same quantity of farm labor, and this fed a rising population to work her industries. Her farm labor force was 15,500,000 in 1878, and 15,660,000 in 1956–60. Meanwhile her total population rose from 36,911,000 to 91,780,000. One reason for this different pattern was the very small size of Japanese farms, which averaged two and one-half acres each in 1878 and two acres in 1962. In 1879

2h 7m

1h 0m

0h 40m

the government began to manufacture farm machinery, but by 1888 the project was dropped. The machines could not be used effectively on such small farms.

Attempts to develop larger farm units and install machines in Japan have been made since World War II. But in 1950, there were still only about 60,000 small tractors in Japan, and even in 1960 only 500,000. Yet average husked rice yield, starting from the high figure of 0.8 tons per acre in 1878 (typical of advanced hydraulic agriculture), was over 1.6 tons by 1962. Of this 100 per cent increase, about 70 per cent was achieved by the 1930's, when there were still virtually no machines. This increase in yields was achieved in Japan by something else: *agricultural chemicals*. These were the fruits of that knowledge of chemistry, so lacking in Greek science. They included fertilizers, weedkillers, and pestkillers.

The first of these entirely new developments was the use of chemical fertilizers, the great contribution of the nineteenth century to agriculture. A number of European scientists established the chemical elements needed by plants. These elements—above all nitrogen, phosphorus, and potassium (NPK)—were extracted from natural products and later increasingly synthesized by purely chemical means. Supplied in suitable compounds to crops, they greatly increased, often doubled, yields. World annual consumption of NPK was already about 2 million tons by 1905–6, about 9 million by 1938–9, and about 32.5 million tons by 1962–3. Meanwhile, by the twentieth century, chemists were able to make extremely elaborate compounds, and the age of plastics and synthetics dawned. Substances such as nylon, synthetic detergents, and all the plastics now in household use are the things that make our daily life most different from that of all previous generations. By the 1930's, it had been discovered that growth patterns in plants are governed by chemical regulating substances, and new compounds were being made to duplicate some of their actions. In large doses, growth-regulating substances are lethal to plants, and in 1940 it was discovered that some of them kill certain plants more readily than others. The result, especially after World War II, was the synthesis and manufacture of a host of powerful selective weedkillers.

Weeds may include many kinds of plants (see p. 79). However, substances like 2,4-D and MCPA, which spare wild or cultivated grasses, can be used to kill many weeds of grain crop fields. TCA and dalapon, relatively lethal to grasses, can be used to kill grass weeds in non-grain crop fields, such as of peas or beets. Some recent weedkillers are even more selective. Diallate, if suitably applied, will kill wild oats, a serious weed of wheat and barley fields, without harming the cultivated plants, although the three species are

Increasing use of chemical fertilizers has been an important factor in the development of modern agriculture. Chemical deficiencies produce unhealthy plants. Plants on the right of photos above have been deprived of nitrogen (top), phosphorus (middle), and potassium (below). Fertilizers that correct the balance of these elements help produce healthy plants like those on the left.

closely related. Dicamba will kill some grass species but not others, and can be used to change the composition of grassland. Diquat and paraquat will kill everything above ground without deeply penetrating the soil or leaving residues to harm *subsequent* growth. They can be used when grassland is to be re-sown with improved grasses, without the necessity of plowing it up.

The new control of weeds is an important factor for increasing production. Even carefully cultivated crops could lose 15 per cent of their yield to weeds competing for space and the nutrients in the soil. Weeds dictated the practices of swidden farming. They have been almost as crucial in other types of agriculture. An experiment in India in 1961–2 showed that differences in plowing methods make relatively little difference to the physical state of the soil, but great differences to yield, in accordance with their effect in suppressing weed growth. Research is going on in Britain to replace plowing almost entirely by the use of such thoroughgoing weedkillers as paraquat, the more promising because chemical techniques for improving soil structure are also being developed. The need to suppress weeds may have been the main reason for the ceaseless labor of tilling the soil in the past. Perhaps one day the plow itself, so long a vital factor in human progress, will follow the farmhorse into honorable retirement.

After so much attention to man as farmer, citizen, manufacturer, and trader, we may return to man as a hunter. Hunting animals are restrained from exterminating their prey (and hence destroying their food resources) by limits on their own numbers. Also, the means they evolve for detection and attack are matched by the evolution of comparably effective means of flight, concealment, or defense. Since the breakthrough, man's increase in numbers and advance in technical equipment have been so outstanding that he has been in real danger of reducing game populations to the point where they yield less and less and eventually die out. On land, this has been of minor importance. In Neolithic times, besides developing crop agriculture, man had resolved the problem of overhunting by domesticating the most useful animals and ensuring that they kept up their numbers under his supervision.

Since so little of his food came from hunting the remaining animals, civilized agricultural man has been little troubled by overhunting on land. The principle of domestication has steadily been extended. The feeding-grounds of game in Canada and Africa are being studied with a view to systematic management, just as natural pastures are managed for cattle. Many people regard Africa's wild game as a vital source of animal protein, and by 1962 two farmers in Rhodesia had actually begun to farm game and make it pay.

Man has also used his chemical knowledge to develop selective weedkillers. Applied to a grain field (left of post, top photo) 2, 4–D destroys wild mustard (see untreated plot, right of post). Middle photo: Simazine has significantly cut down weeds in corn on the right. Below: Dinistro and CDAA have kept weeds out of soybeans (right), while untreated plot is choked with weeds.

Overhunting in the seas, or overfishing, is another matter. Fishing has remained an important means of food production without interruption since the Upper Paleolithic. The reliability of fish food from lakes may well have given man one of his first opportunities to settle long enough to grow a crop. Throughout man's subsequent career, the volume of fishing has steadily grown—more than ever in the twentieth century. The world fish catch was about 21 million tons in 1938, and about 46 million tons in 1963, when it provided 3 per cent of the world's protein food and nearly 10 per cent of the world's animal protein. The breakthrough created both the demand (by population increase) and the technical means for a much bigger world catch than ever before. The division of mankind into nations led, on the open seas, to unrestricted competition for the game. The result may be illustrated by one of the greatest tragedies in the history of man and nature, the story of whales and whaling.

Man must early have made use of whales stranded on his coasts. A carving of one in northern Norway dates probably from before 4000 B.C. To go out in open boats and hand-harpoon them was a natural step for people whose coasts were often visited by whales. Offshore whaling was apparently invented independently by several peoples, including the Basques (before A.D. 1150, when it is mentioned in a document) and the Japanese (sixteenth century A.D.). "A whale makes seven villages rich" is an old Japanese proverb. Taught by the Basques, the Dutch and English went farther afield, whaling in the Arctic from the seventeenth century onward. The great Pacific whaling grounds were opened up from 1789 by the seamen of New

For centuries men have been hunting whales for food. Above: A 14th-century seal belonging to the town of Biarritz in France shows men harpooning a whale.

"A whale makes seven villages rich" is an old Japanese proverb. No doubt the villagers in the Japanese painting (below) felt delighted as they hauled up three whales onto the foreshore and cut up the highly prized meat.

England, especially from Nantucket Island. Because of their excellence in handling small boats, men from the Azores were recruited by the New England ships; returning home, the Azoreans founded an off-shore hand-harpoon sperm-whaling industry that survives to this day and has been filmed by the British zoologist Robert Clarke. Between 1863 and 1870, the Norwegian Svend Foyn, with the help of Pastor Hans Esmark, invented the harpoon-gun for tackling the largest whales, hitherto avoided by all except the Japanese; the great Antarctic large-whale industry began in 1904. The development in the late 1920s of the factory ship, which could keep the whales afloat and cut them up on board, completed the whalers' freedom of the open seas right around the Antarctic.

By this series of whaling industries, one whale stock after another was reduced in numbers to the point where it was not worth hunting. The right whales of the North Atlantic and Arctic were so completely overhunted that the whole northern industry had utterly collapsed by 1914. In the west Pacific, 193,000 southern right whales were killed between 1804 and 1817, and 41.25 million gallons of oil from sperm whales were taken in 1830–40. Schools of sperm whales, formerly up to 100 each, shrank to about 15. The sperm whales here were only saved from total extinction by the discovery of petroleum in Pennsylvania in 1859, which replaced whale-oil. By 1868 the world whale catch is said to have shrunk to 30. The harpoon-gun and the opening of the Antarctic increased it to 25,673 in 1913, the factory ship increased it further to 54,835 in 1938. The Antarctic rorqual industry, responsible for most of these catches, had drastically depleted the humpback whale by 1913, and the blue whale by 1931, despite warnings by scientists. By 1960, 80 per cent of the world catch consisted of fin whales, the last whales to survive in numbers worth exploiting.

In 1932 the Norwegians and British, then the chief whaling nations, signed the first agreement for restricting catches, but when other nations entered the industry this became ineffective. In 1946 the International Whaling Commission was formed to control world whaling. But the spirit of competition that goes with national organization has prevented it from achieving realistic control in time. The member nations could not even agree on the quota for 1964–5. At a conference at Durham in 1960, R. M. Laws, of the British National Institute of Oceanography, once again reported that survival curves for the blue and fin whales "indicate that at the present rate of exploitation recruitment is insufficient to maintain the stocks." In plain language, the blue and fin whales were dying out.

Fishes are more numerous than whales, and overfishing had had less serious results than overwhaling. However, by

Today whales are hunted with more modern equipment than hand-harpoons. Top photo shows a whale gun—a harpoon containing an explosive charge, mounted on the prow of the ship. Lower photo shows a whale being cut up on a factory ship. Ample storage facilities on such ships make long whaling trips possible.

the twentieth century, rising population and technical advance were causing severe depletion of important commercial sea fishes like cod, haddock, plaice, halibut, and herring. The fish populations of the North Sea rose dramatically after both World Wars—during which periods fishing there was much reduced. According to the 1964 report of FAO on the condition of food and agriculture, the leading fishery nations were by this time looking for new grounds on the coasts of developing countries, which were becoming alarmed at the threat to their sea resources from these intruders. However, a new branch of science has developed to tackle the problem of how to fish at a rate that will ensure the highest possible sustained catch. Its recommendations may be applied before it is too late. The potential world fish harvest, if fishing is adequately controlled, has been estimated at about 115 million tons a year, about two and a half times the harvest in 1963.

In the long run, however, as on the land, the tendency will probably be to domesticate sea life and turn the oceans (70 per cent of the earth's surface) into a gigantic farm. The farming of freshwater fish is an old practice. In the flood plains of the Far East, freshwater fishes are actually bred as a crop in rotation with irrigated rice. Already much is being done to change the living composition of the smaller inland seas, especially in the U.S.S.R. There, not only fish but fish-food animals from one sea are used to stock another, just as crop plants are introduced from one region to another on land. In 1939–40, for instance, Soviet scientists took 61,000 specimens of the small worm *Nereis* from the Sea of Azov and put them in the Caspian. By

At Port Erin, Isle of Man, scientists experiment in fish farming. Plaice are hatched from eggs in trays (above) and then fed on shrimps. This helps a larger percentage of fish to develop than is normal and at a faster rate.

Above: British fishermen in the Baltic landing a catch of herring. Fish forms an important part of our diet today, and as rising populations increase the demand for fish, it is vital that overfishing, which might seriously threaten supplies, should not occur.

When plaice are ready to live on the sea-bed, they are transferred to enclosed bays where the water is enriched to increase growth. Below: Workers at Ardtoe, Scotland, taking fish in plastic bags from the hatchery to the bays.

1956, two or three million tons of *Nereis* were being produced there annually, greatly increasing the food supply, and hence the numbers, of Caspian fishes.

A more radical development is the artificial rearing of sea-bottom fishes from eggs. This was begun in Norway and the United States in the 1880's, but abandoned by 1952. The fish were reared to their larval stage only, then dumped into the sea. The fish spend this stage in the upper water layers. Our knowledge of conditions in the sea has been greatly increased meantime by marine biologists such as Sir Frederick Russell. The number of larval fishes surviving depends on the tiny food organisms in water (which fluctuate with currents and other factors) and is almost independent of the number of larvae to start with. In Britain, after World War II, methods were developed, chiefly by J. E. Shelbourne at Lowestoft, for tank-rearing young plaice to the adult fish stage. At this stage they normally live on the bottom, where the food supply is more constant. The numbers of plaice successfully reared to adulthood were: 1 in 1957, 100 in 1958, 327 in 1959, 1178 in 1960, 2807 in 1961—still only 3.3 per cent of the original eggs. In 1962 there was a big jump to 25,000 reared, more than 50 per cent of the eggs.

By this technique, three developments will be possible: adding adult fish to the natural sea populations, making new nursery grounds where they can grow larger, or complete fish farming up to marketable size. It should be possible to grow plaice to this size in two years under intensive farming, as opposed to four to five years in present natural conditions. Since 1947, British scientists have shown that the fish stocks of Scottish sea-lochs can be increased by applying agricultural fertilizers. In 1965, a Scottish bay was prepared to serve as the first experimental farm for complete sea-fish stockraising.

But even all this may only be the beginning. The British biologist Sir Alister Hardy has envisaged a true farming of the oceans themselves. Arthur Clarke's novel *The Deep Range* (1957) gives some idea of the possible future here, including domestication of the surviving whales. These ideas are not likely to remain science fiction for long: the sober FAO 1964 report envisages (for a "not far distant" time) such possibilities as "massive engineering operations to plow the bottom of the sea, and the fertilization of the surface waters." Thus man will extend his control of nature from the land to the sea, and realize an old prophecy. For, according to Obed Macy's *History of Nantucket* (quoted by Herman Melville in *Moby Dick*), "in the year 1690 some persons were on a high hill observing the whales spouting and sporting with each other, when one observed; there—pointing to the sea—is a green pasture where our children's grandchildren will go for bread."

# 11 Pandora's Box

Above: 16th-century French engraving of serpents flying out of Pandora's box—symbols of the evils that plague mankind. Man's cultivation of the earth released many unwanted and unexpected evils.

When man began to clear the forest, raise crops and herds, and build cities, roads, and ships, he opened the box of the Earth goddess, and out flew a squadron of merciless enemies. So far we have considered only the least deadly result of the coming of agriculture, the rise of the weeds of cultivation. Another and more serious result was the rise of crop pests, especially insect pests.

That this result is a creation of agriculture appears very clearly from Soviet studies in Kazakhstan, where much of the grass steppe is being plowed up for wheat. On the steppe before plowing, there were 199 individual insects per square meter, drawn from 330 species. In the wheat fields, there were 351 individuals per square meter, of which almost all belonged to only 19 dominant species, most of them serious pests of wheat. In the new environment provided by man, the few species fitted for eating wheat had increased to a startling degree. The population of one such species was 280 times greater after a single cropping season than it was before plowing.

Such species we call pests. Not only can they reduce a country's whole agricultural production by an average of 10–15 per cent; they can also destroy much larger percentages of particular crops, or in particular years, and thus cause devastating crop failures. The synthesis of really efficient chemical insect-killers (insecticides), which kill on contact, has been yet another gain from the technological breakthrough. Their effect on agriculture may be shown by a single example. In an experiment in 1965 at Luzon in the Philippines, spraying lindane to kill insect pests increased the yield of rice by 150 per cent. The pests had been destroying three-fifths of the potential rice yield. The first really powerful synthetic compound, DDT, known as a chemical compound since 1873, was discovered during World War II to be an insecticide. It was followed after the war by many others.

There was a big difference between the early uses of weedkillers and insecticides. If the weedkillers had not been selective, they would have killed the crops as well, and could therefore never have been widely used. Killing all insects seemed to matter less, and most of the insecticides developed in the last 30 years have been so generally poisonous that they have destroyed not only most insects but also other animals. The use of chemical insecticides, believed to be necessary for increasing food production, has thus raised a whole set of new problems. Compounds like aldrin and dieldrin leave residues in the crops themselves. Although there is no evidence that these have yet been high enough in quantity to harm man, they have caused great concern. This is not the only disadvantage, for beneficial animals have certainly suffered from these unselective killing sprays. In a number of Nova Scotia

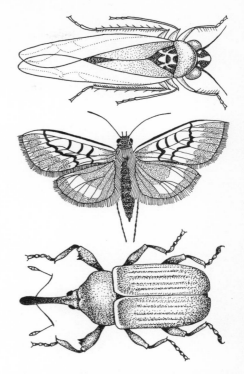

Above: Three of the many insects that can cause extensive damage to vital crops. Top to bottom: Potato leafhopper, European corn borer moth, and boll weevil (which attacks cotton).

Chemical insecticides are important weapons in the war against pests. Below: Worker in an anti-locust campaign in the Middle East is helped on with portable apparatus for spraying aldrin.

Above: Doctor with pesticide sprayers in a vine-growing village in Bulgaria. Toxic sprays demand that workers wear heavy protective clothing. But such measures will not protect wildlife.
Below: Whitethroat's nest containing a dead chick, probably poisoned by eating a caterpillar killed by pesticide.

orchards in the 1940's and 1950's, bees were wiped out by DDT. Fortunately, they regained a foothold after its use was stopped. A shortage of bees in parts of Japan has also been ascribed to the use of insecticides. Bees are vital for pollinating certain fruit-trees and pasture legumes. The Japanese have had trouble in establishing clovers as a result. Earthworms in pastures also suffer from the sprays. Since the work of Charles Darwin we know that their activities improve soil structure, and it has been shown more recently that they help to convert the nitrogen from cattle manure into forms usable by plants.

Yet another difficulty has been the effect upon wildlife of insecticides with persistent residues. The chief problem here arises from what scientists call the *food chain*. Animal A eats a plant, animal B eats A, C eats B, and so on. At each stage, the total mass of living matter from an earlier stage gets smaller. The reason is that much of it is converted into energy for food-getting or is excreted. The amount added to the body-weight of the animal in the next stage in the chain may be as little as 10 per cent. Poisonous chemical compounds, therefore, may accumulate to reach high concentrations in the hunting animals at the end of the chain, either killing them or reducing their fertility. In the north central states of the U.S.A. in the 1950's, DDT sprayed on elm trees to kill bark beetles reached the soil in leaf litter and was eaten by earthworms. The worms were in turn eaten by robins, of which very large numbers died. Another compound, DDD, was applied at the rate of one part in 50 million to Clear Lake, California, to control the larvae of gnats. It was taken up by small water plants, then eaten by fishes, then by other fishes, and finally by birds (grebes). By this stage in the food chain it had been concentrated 100,000-fold to become 2000 parts in a million, and many birds died. Such drastic effects on wildlife may have considerable, and often unexpected, repercussions (p. 21).

More directly, unselective insecticides may defeat their own object by destroying insect hunters of pests. Since the drugs are not *equally* poisonous to all insects, the complexities are formidable. In a strictly controlled experiment on alfalfa plots in the state of Washington in 1956–9, the American agriculturalist Wyatt W. Cone studied the effects of three insecticides on populations of three mite species. Two of them, *Tetranychus* (A) and *Tydeus* (B), were pests, and the third, *Typhlodromus* (C), preyed on the first two. DDT decreased B and C and increased A, because of less hunting by C. The insecticide schradan decreased A and C and increased B for the same reason. Dieldrin increased C and thus decreased A and B. In this instance, therefore, dieldrin would be beneficial, but the other two drugs would actually make matters worse.

Biological control works by importing an insect's natural enemies. Above: Australian ladybird beetles feeding on fluted scale insects (fluffy white insects in photo), which formerly did great damage to citrus trees in California.

Another modern method of controlling pests has been to encourage or introduce their enemies. This has sometimes worked extremely well. In 1868, the fluted scale insect (*Icerya*) reached California on plants imported from Australia, and by 1886 became a devastating pest in Californian citrus orchards. In 1889 its natural enemy, the ladybird beetle was imported from Australia, and by 1900 the pest was almost exterminated. By 1916 it was said that the fluted scale, previously a terrible menace, was of no importance in agriculture since the use of the ladybird beetle. In the 1940's, the use of DDT in California reduced the beetle population, and the fluted scale reappeared as a pest. Use of DDT was restricted in 1948, and the ladybird beetle regained control.

What is most striking is the speed with which all these new problems are being met. Aldrin and dieldrin came into use only in 1950. By 1955 a British government working party was reporting on risks to wildlife from these and other agricultural chemicals. It had also been studying the risks to man since 1950. By 1959, the FAO was tackling the residue problem on a world scale, spurred by the fact that nations varied in the residue levels they would permit in food—and could thus block imports from more tolerant nations. All this was long before 1962 when Rachel Carson's book *Silent Spring* caused a public uproar. There has been action in several countries to ban or restrict the use of insecticides with persistent residues, in favor of more poisonous but less persistent ones, such as parathion. By 1964, less poisonous but equally effective compounds like fenitrothion were replacing even these.

It is generally agreed that chemical insecticides are essential if the world population, even at its present level, is to be fed. There is, however, vigorous research to find more selective ones, and also to combine their use with that of natural enemies of pests. In Nova Scotia apple orchards, the Canadian agriculturalist A. D. Pickett and his colleagues have had much success since about 1950 using carefully timed applications of the relatively selective drug ryania. This is designed to leave hunting insects unharmed to help in controlling the chief pests. The result has been much better control as well as more bees (p. 203).

New, quite different, methods are continually being devised as well. One such is the use of ultrasonic or amplified sound broadcasts, which are very effective (for unknown reasons) in reducing the fertility of certain moths.

Left: Worker examining grubs of Mediterranean fruit fly stored in trays. In Mexico and southern California large numbers of such grubs are reared and exposed to radioactive cobalt-60, making male flies sterile on hatching. These are released in infested areas. A large proportion of matings consequently produce infertile eggs. This method has been very effective in cutting down numbers of these destructive flies.

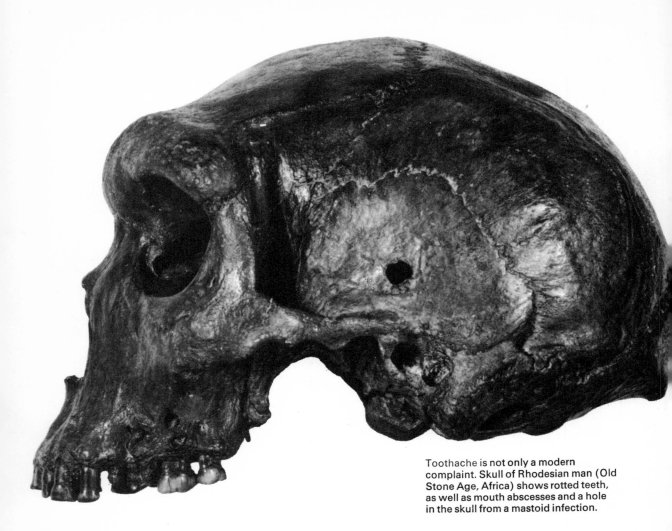

Toothache is not only a modern complaint. Skull of Rhodesian man (Old Stone Age, Africa) shows rotted teeth, as well as mouth abscesses and a hole in the skull from a mastoid infection.

Another is the use of the scent of female insects to lure males of the same species into traps. The insecticide story has shown both that man is always liable to have new problems with nature, and that he is now better equipped to solve them than ever before.

Pests, however, are by no means the worst things out of Pandora's Box. For it now seems certain that the coming of many infectious diseases was also a result of man's growing command of his natural surroundings. It is true that from earliest times man suffered from some present-day diseases, and especially from general inflammation of parts of his body, often after an injury. Sinusitis, which irritates the nose, is the result of breathing damp, smoky, or dusty air. It has been detected in skulls from all ages, in Dark Age England and France, in ancient Egypt, and even in hunters who lived in a damp cave during the Paleolithic Period.

Some diseases, while equally ancient, can be shown to have greatly increased since the coming of agriculture.

Below: Rates of tooth decay among four European peoples (3000 B.C. to present day). Note huge rise in highly urban Roman period and in modern times.

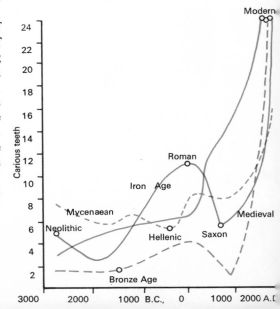

The toothache is as old as mankind. Most of the early Paleolithic human populations, known to us from bones, showed a proportion of tooth decay. One specimen of Rhodesian man, who roamed Africa perhaps 15,000 years ago, must have suffered agony from rotting teeth and mouth abscesses, before he was finished off by a mastoid infection of his left ear. Tooth decay depends largely on what you eat. Along with the new eating habits that arose with agriculture came a marked increase in the incidence of this complaint. And tooth decay has been increasingly prevalent ever since. It seems to be especially a disease of city life.

Many of the great specific infectious diseases, however, each caused by one particular type of germ or worm, are real novelties in the story of man and nature. From quite different kinds of evidence, students of parasites and experts on the diagnosis of disease in ancient bones and bodies are agreed that most human diseases have been acquired during the past 10,000 years—that is, since the coming of agriculture. From that time on, new disease problems have continued to arise, in wave after wave. It has been said that they reached their peak throughout the world in the eighteenth century, but new kinds of outbreaks have occurred even since then. The reasons for all this are complex.

Infectious diseases are due to parasites. The word *parasite* comes from the Greek *parasitos*, meaning someone who comes to dinner. There are enormous numbers of organisms that live on or inside the bodies of other animals, and this way of life is extremely old. Some of these guests earn their keep. A good example is the bacterial population that inhabits a compartment of the digestive tract (especially evolved to house them) in ruminants, such as sheep and cattle, that depend entirely on plant food. These bacteria have an ability that their hosts (the ruminants) lack: they can break down plant substances such as cellulose and convert them into easily digestible sugars. (This is what makes the ruminant hosts so useful to man.) Other organisms can at least live in the bodies of animals without killing or injuring the host, which can thus entertain them all the longer. A healthy guest in a healthy host is the ideal solution for both parties, and when host and guest have been associated over many generations, they often come to make the best of each other. But this compatibility takes time to evolve, and it often happens, especially when a parasite takes to a new host, that the ordinary life-processes of the parasite cause the host damage or even death.

We can divide parasites that are harmful to man into two main groups. The first are the worms, of which there are many kinds. In small numbers they are unimportant, and indeed all human adults entertain a few. But the presence

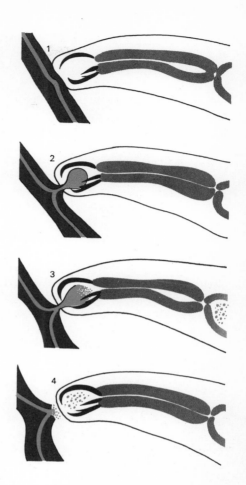

Above: Diagram of a hookworm feeding. (1) It clasps intestine walls and this, with blood vessel, (2) is sucked into mouth cavity of the worm, then disintegrated by its juices (3), and the end products are digested. Worm then releases wall (4), leaving blood vessel exposed.

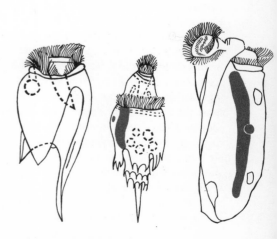

Above: Three small parasites that live in the digestive tract of ruminants. Such organisms are actually useful to their host, in helping to convert the cellulose in plant foods into digestible sugars.

of too many specimens in one individual host has serious results. Hookworms, for instance, get into human hosts through the skin and make their way to the intestine. Here they fasten on to the intestinal wall, disintegrate it, and eat the remains, sucking in blood in the process. A single hookworm does little damage in this way, but 500 hookworms can remove nearly half a pint of blood per day. People heavily infected with these parasites become listless, weak, and vulnerable to other diseases. When the people of Puerto Rico were treated intensively for hookworms, their working efficiency increased by more than 60 per cent.

The second main group of parasites consists of microscopic organisms: protozoa, bacteria, rickettsias, fungi, and viruses. These are liable to do damage in several ways, especially when introduced into a new host. First, such a parasite during its life may release substances called *endotoxins*, which poison the host tissues. ("Toxin" is merely another word for poisonous substance.) Or, second, after its death it may release other substances called *exotoxins* with the same effect. Or, finally, the parasites may breed and multiply rapidly inside the host, and simply overwhelm the host's life-processes by sheer numbers.

While a parasite may damage its host, the host body may defend itself by various means, especially by producing substances that attack the parasite or its toxins. Such substances are called *antibodies*, and each of these antibodies usually works only against a particular parasite or toxin. Sometimes they are produced only as long as specimens of the parasite are present. Sometimes they are produced in response to the first invasion of parasites and continue to be available, after the attack, for years or even for life. In the latter case, after one attack of the disease the host becomes *immune* for a longer or shorter period. During this period, fresh infection with that particular parasite will cause little or no disease.

Parasite populations may in turn circumvent the defense by developing new strains against which the original antibodies have no effect. The viruses of influenza, in particular, are constantly changing in this way. Moreover, the efficiency of the defense system varies with the general level of health in the host. It may be undermined, for instance, by malnutrition. For this reason, in developing countries where the diet is low in protein, the death-rate from infectious diseases in children 1–4 years old is 20–50 times higher than in the United States and northwestern Europe.

The virulence of a parasite (its capacity to cause disease) clearly depends in a complicated way on both host and parasite. Furthermore, its virulence may be continually changing. A microscopic parasite may be present for some time without being able to multiply in the host's body, and hence without doing harm. If a change in the host's health

Below: Upper picture shows tuberculosis bacteria in human spit (magnified about 600 times). Lower picture shows Asian flu virus (magnified about 200,000 times). This virus first attacked Europeans in 1957, then again in 1965. By the second time, the virus had modified, and those who had suffered from it in the first epidemic were no longer immune.

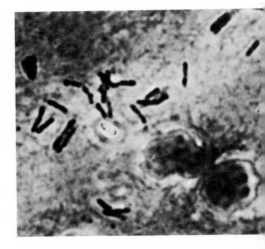

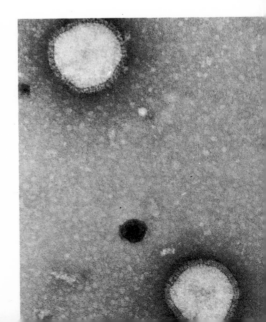

permits it to multiply, it may cause serious disease. When a parasite first invades a new host population, it may kill many. Those who survive, however, will be partly or wholly immune. If all or most of the host population go on being infected for several generations, most will suffer from the disease early in life. Thus most adults will be immune. Meanwhile a gradual process of adjustment may have made the symptoms less serious. Eventually, the disease may become a mild childhood illness, like mumps, chicken pox, and measles in human populations of the northern temperate regions. At one time in England the family of a child with such an illness would invite other children to a party, where they could all catch the disease and "get it over." But if these parasites are introduced to populations where they have not been present before, they will cause dangerous disease in people of all ages. This happened when Europeans brought measles to the Eskimo and to the people of Tahiti.

Below: Photo of *Trypanosoma gambiense* (magnified about 600 times) in human blood. This protozoan parasite causes sleeping sickness and is carried by tsetse flies from one person to another. Parasite first invades the blood and later attacks the fluid in the brain and spinal cord, thus causing death.

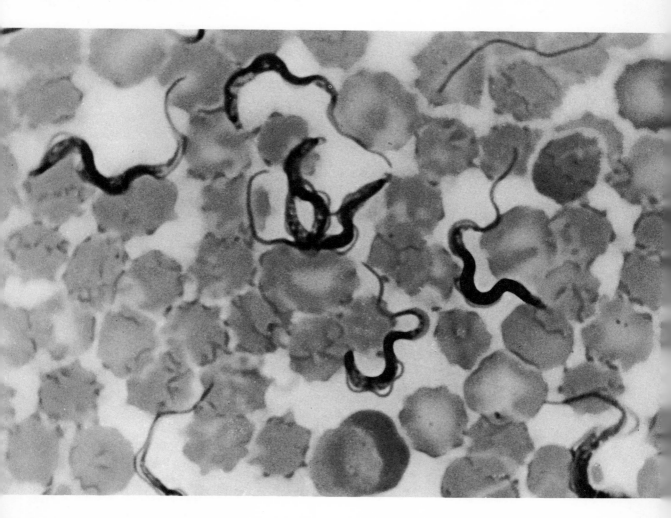

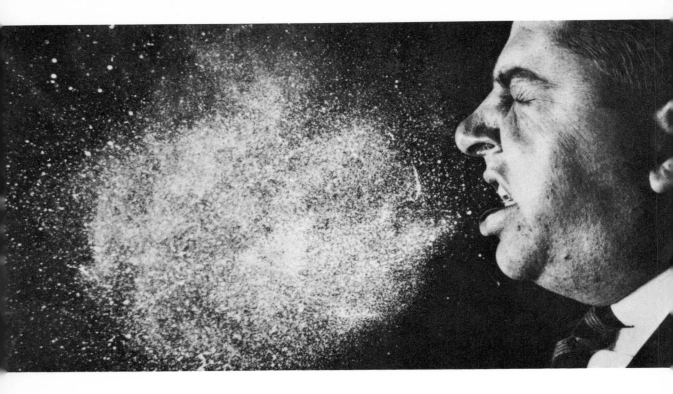

Many parasites can live in more than one host species, while others become specialized for a single host. Unless this specialization is complete, a parasite can move at need from one host species to another. With a new host, the result is likely to be serious disease. Some parasites, especially protozoa and worms, have complicated life-cycles, parts of which are spent in secondary hosts or even as free-living forms. They may move from one kind of cycle to another. Parasites have evolved a variety of methods of moving between individual hosts. Hence human infectious diseases are spread in many ways.

There are, however, four main ways. First, microscopic parasites may pass into the air when we breathe out, and get into somebody else's lungs. "Coughs and sneezes spread diseases," as the posters in England used to proclaim in World War II. This is called *droplet infection*. Second, the parasites may get into the next host when food or drink is contaminated by the corpse or excrement of the previous host. Third, they may be transmitted by close bodily contact. Fourth, they may be carried by other organisms (*vectors*), notably bloodsucking insects. The great variety of transmission methods means that spread of infection depends on an equally great variety of climatic and public health factors, and makes infectious disease a bewilderingly complex problem. Measures effective against one infection may be useless against another, and any attempt to control

One method of spreading disease is by droplet infection. Above: Man with a cold sneezes, expelling air containing microscopic germs. These may pass into someone else and infect them—a danger that the British Ministry of Health warned the public against in a poster (below) issued in World War II.

The Ministry of Health says:-

# COUGHS AND SNEEZES SPREAD DISEASES

Trap the germs in your handkerchief

the spread of disease in human populations requires considerable knowledge. Until this knowledge was gradually built up, it is no wonder man found infectious disease the most terrifying of all mysteries.

### The Perils of Agriculture

Man's troubles must have begun with his earliest successes, the improvements in hunting technique, aided by the first rudiments of agriculture. These enabled him to multiply and spread into the forest, and in the forest there lurked a terrible booby trap. As man advanced into new areas, he attracted the unwelcome attentions of more and more parasites and vectors. They had previously comfortably settled among populations of wild animals, most of which had become immune and suffered no disease. Killing or driving away the game left the parasites no alternative but to try the new host instead. Many of them were ready to do so anyway. Today, at least 80 diseases can be naturally transmitted between higher animals and man. New human diseases, introduced from the great "reservoir" of wildlife, have cropped up throughout history. Students of parasites see every reason to expect more new human diseases, particularly virus diseases, from this source in the future.

In the jungles of Africa and Middle and South America, the virus of yellow fever is a parasite of monkeys. It is carried from one monkey to another by various species of jungle mosquito. In the Americas, people who wander into the forest to hunt may be bitten by these mosquitoes and catch the virus. On their return to more populated centers, they are bitten by the mosquito *Aedes aegypti*, one of that band of bloodsuckers that now confines its attentions to human victims. *Aedes* then bites other people in the town or village, and carries the virus through the population, which is then smitten with the deadly disease. In Africa the monkeys themselves are attracted by human agriculture. They come to raid banana plantations, where they are bitten by another bloodsucker of man, *Aedes simpsoni*, which soon spreads the virus among the villagers. In human history, yellow fever, or Yellow Jack, can fairly challenge comparison as a killer with Genghis Khan or Tamerlane.

Yellow fever is a disease of the tropics only. The mosquitoes that carry it cannot live for long at temperatures below 68°F. Many (although not all) killer diseases are restricted to particular regions of the world. This is related to the way they are spread. Free-living stages of worms, and many insect vectors of other parasites, can survive only in particular climatic conditions. The differences between the tropics (where, in general, temperature is high and steady, but air moisture varies enormously between

Above: Howler monkey of South America. In America and Africa, infected monkeys form a reservoir for yellow fever. The virus is carried from monkey to monkey by jungle mosquitoes, which sometimes bite humans. *Aedes aegypti* (below, sucking blood from a human arm) transmits yellow fever between people.

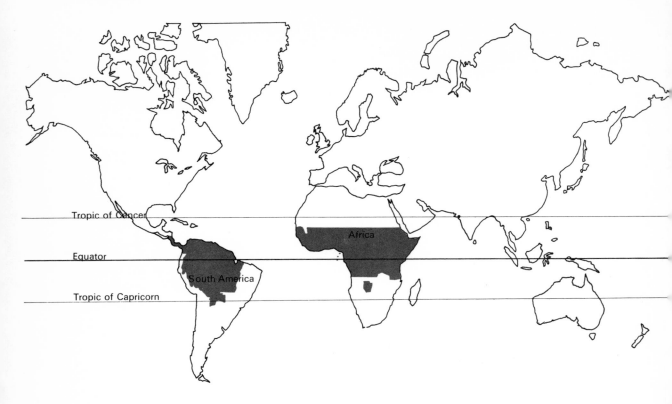

Map above marks areas of Africa and South America where yellow fever is endemic. Mosquitoes carrying this disease can survive only in the hot wet conditions of the tropics.

wet and dry seasons) and the temperate regions (where it is just the other way round) are extremely important for infectious disease. The temperate regions have a monopoly on several diseases. Those spread as droplets in the air (like the common cold) tend in tropical climates to die without reaching another host individual. Those spread by lice attack people in the temperate regions simply because lice are most comfortable at the temperature of a *warmly clad* human body. But, in comparison, the tropics have by far the worst of this bargain. Most of the 80 diseases transmitted from animals to man are tropical. And most of these are African, for tropical Africa is the worst afflicted of all.

The progress of agriculture in the wet tropics exposed the farmers to more and more disasters. It was not only a question of new diseases. In fact, the most striking example involved a disease as old as man. The picture emerges from one of the most ingenious detective stories in science, the story of malaria in Africa. There are certain hereditary conditions of the blood pigments (sometimes called "sickle-cell"), found only in human populations that have been exposed to the protozoan *Plasmodium falciparum*, the most recently evolved and the most deadly malarial parasite of man. The American anthropologist F. B. Livingstone noted the distribution of one of these

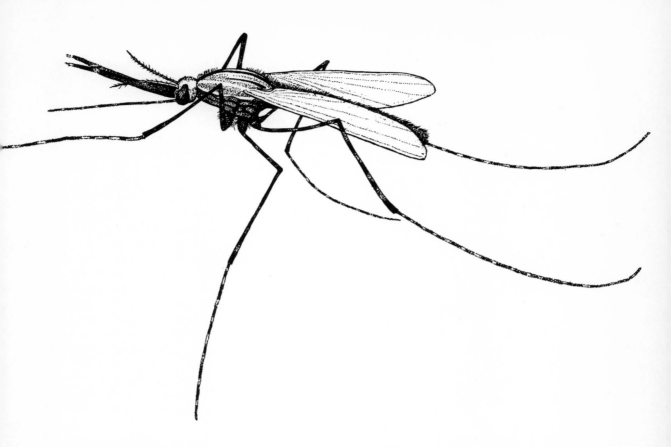

Above: *Anopheles gambiae* is the most deadly species of malarial mosquito in that it prefers human blood. These mosquitoes breed in sunlit pools, and the clearing of tropical forest created ideal conditions for them.

Below: Map shows the way people with a particular hereditary condition of blood pigments, connected with malaria, spread across Africa. In first millennium A.D. yam-growers pushed native peoples westward. In second millennium, rice-growers mixed with natives of areas further west.

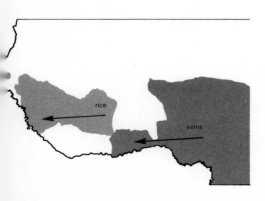

blood conditions in western Africa, and compared it with evidence about the movement of peoples in this area (chiefly from language distribution). He showed that the condition had spread into western Africa in two waves. In the first wave, migrating and invading peoples drove the original inhabitants before them to the west coast. In the second wave, incoming peoples mixed with local inhabitants and taught them their way of life. Both waves brought with them the practice of clearing the tropical forest for agriculture. The first wave brought the yam (which the Bantu meanwhile were spreading southward, p. 38), and the second wave brought a kind of rice. Later Livingstone established a similar connection in India and southeastern Asia. From this indirect evidence, it seemed to follow that agriculture in the wet tropics created the situation where *falciparum* malaria could spread among people. The villain of this "whodunit" is the mosquito *Anopheles gambiae*.

All the malarial parasites are carried from person to person by mosquitoes of the genus *Anopheles*. The most deadly species is *Anopheles gambiae*, because it shows the greatest preference for human blood. But it cannot breed without stagnant water, or in deep shade. In the forest the soil absorbs water and there are few stagnant pools. There is also deep shade. But when the forest is repeatedly cut

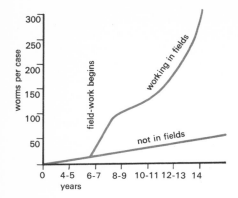

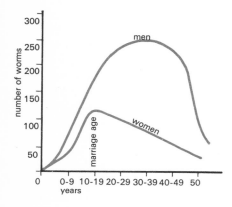

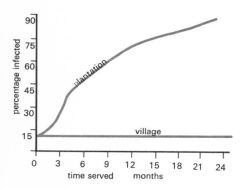

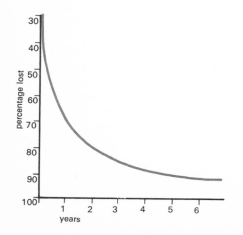

away, the soil will not absorb water so readily. After rain, puddles remain as stagnant breeding sites for the mosquito, unshaded by the missing trees. Any swamps already there are also now exposed to sunlight. Finally, the villages of the farmers abound in wet, stagnant breeding places. In various parts of Africa, *Anopheles gambiae* has actually been seen to increase after forest is cleared and to disappear if the forest is allowed to return; it is virtually confined to the neighborhood of farming villages. Malaria, which the farmers thus brought upon themselves when they first cleared the forest, has been called the greatest killer of all diseases; when it does not kill, it causes misery and inertia, and drains all the energy and initiative needed for progress.

Another penalty of agriculture in the wet tropics is the hookworm. There are several kinds of hookworm, but they all like hot climates. The few in temperate regions have occurred in mines. The worms get in through the skin, especially of the feet and ankles. These worms are a menace only when many of them enter one person's body (p. 208). This happens when they are rapidly transmitted from the excrement of one host to the skin of another. Human extrement is often used for manure, and in any case, without proper sanitation, it is liable to contaminate the fields around a village. Graphs show in detail that the heaviest infections almost invariably occur in agricultural workers at just the ages when they are busiest in the crop fields. In 1947, it was estimated that some 457 million people were infested with hookworms.

In the village of Keneba in Gambia, medically surveyed in 1950–1, most of the villagers were infected with malaria, and all were loaded with hookworms and several other

Many factors influence the incidence of hookworm disease, but one of the most important is time spent working in fields contaminated by excrement. Left: Top graph shows sharp rise in number of worms present in the body when a child starts work in fields. Second graph shows that men are more prone to the disease than women. Third graph: The high proportion of field workers who become infected in a short time compared with those working in village. Bottom graph: Length of time worms may live in body.

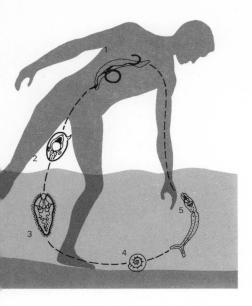

Above: Life-cycle of *Schistosoma* worm that causes bilharziasis in man. Adult worms in bladder or intestines of man produce eggs that are passed out in urine. Immature worms hatch in water and invade snail hosts where they develop into cercariae—the infective stage for man—ready to penetrate the skin.

Continuous irrigation channels, also used as watering troughs, like this one in the Sahara (below), risk being contaminated and are a constant threat to health.

kinds of disease-causing worms. In addition, they were suffering from various degrees of malnutrition from lack of the right amount and balance of protein. The authors of the survey concluded that the combined forces of malnutrition and parasitism were "limiting progress and development." This is typical of countless villages in the wet tropics, particularly in Africa.

Malnutrition and disease form a vicious circle. From the nature of the farming system, food is scarce or absent at the time of planting, when the hardest work needs to be done. This critical period often occurs during the first few weeks after the fall of the season's first rain. Not only are the people weak from hunger, but malarial mosquitoes breed and several other diseases are at their worst. All this comes at a time when a week of inaction means the loss of a fifth of the year's productive work. Farming land shrinks to a small area near the houses to save the effort of walking to work, and this greatly favors hookworm infestation. If matters go too far, the end may be famine and death for all. Or the village, like Keneba, may last for generations at a miserably low level of health. Until the Europeans and the Japanese began the study of tropical medicine, there was no hope of breaking out of the vicious circle.

All this makes the tropical dead-end more intelligible than ever. With the inertia and helplessness of individuals, there grew a terrible stagnation of society, which came to perpetuate and intensify the burden of sickness. The cruelty of tropical nature came to be reflected in a routine social cruelty. Most of the tropical tribal societies have (until modern education disrupts them) ceremonies of initiation, in which the fixed patterns of tribal behavior are stamped on teen-agers in an atmosphere of pain and terror, with especially cruel penalties for teen-agers liable to make innovations. Over the ages, the sick crushed the few healthy. The method of swidden farming remained the permanent hallmark of these societies. It worked for the simple reason that, except for the Mayas in their early home on the healthy uplands, the populations were too sick to increase. Only with modern medicine can we now see the stagnation of these societies begin to give way.

If disease set the seal on the tropical dead-end, it was no less disastrous in the dry belt. To begin with, the hydraulic societies had to cope with bilharziasis, a disease caused by worms of the genus *Schistosoma*. Like hookworms, they cause considerable loss of blood, pain, and permanent weakness and inertia. The worms spend part of their lives in water-snails, which live in canals. Perfect conditions for the disease are created by continuous irrigation projects. Hence in many places large-scale irrigation has brought this weakening disease upon the people who practice it. The introduction of continuous irrigation in the Aswan

Province of Egypt raised the incidence of bilharziasis in the farmers there from 5 per cent to 75 per cent between 1904 and 1926. The same development in the Gezira district of Sudan, Africa, raised the incidence from 1 per cent to 20 per cent in adults and 45 per cent in children between 1948 and 1962. Similar results have been observed in the Baghdad area of Iraq. Eggs of the bilharziasis parasite have been found in the kidneys of mummies, so it was already a plague of ancient Egypt. In 1947, it was estimated that 114 million people were suffering from the disease. Bilharziasis must undoubtedly have helped to keep the peasants of Near Eastern hydraulic societies hopeless and docile.

The story of malaria in the dry belt is more intricate. *Anopheles* mosquitoes of all species breed, as we saw, in stagnant water. In about 1910, the British medical scientist C. A. Bentley made a map of the incidence of malaria in Bengal, India. The many stagnant river channels and marshy lakes provided perfect conditions for *Anopheles* in the west of the provinces, where the disease was correspondingly widespread. In the east, vast areas were flooded every year and soaked with rain. Here there was too much water flow for the mosquitoes and therefore less malaria. The effect of irrigation on malaria thus depends on its effect on water flow.

The danger lies not in broad canals but in smaller channels choked with weeds, in seepage from canals, and in swamped fields. So, wherever the mosquitoes and the parasites can live, malaria is the inevitable outcome of even temporary neglect or destruction of extensive irrigation works. When wars became intense in the dry belt, or the attacks of the nomads catastrophic, malaria moved in and killed, crippled, or expelled people before they could recover and repair their irrigation canals. Bentley made another map of Bengal that showed all too clearly how population declined as malaria moved in. This grim ally, following the camps of the nomads, caused many of the *permanent* devastations of the western zone of the dry belt. Malaria from this cause is widespread in Iraq, Afghanistan, and Syria (see Chapter 7). In the north of Ceylon, great irrigation works, built in the Middle Ages, fell into decay, and vast areas became uninhabited until modern times. In Cambodia there arose and flourished in the Middle Ages the hydraulic civilization of the Khmers. Its matchless carvings reflect, in this distant jungle, the far-flung influence of Greek art. Chou Ta-Kuan, a Chinese diplomat of the Mongol Empire, has left us an account of this brilliant kingdom, where women received an advanced education and could rise to high administrative office. But even during his visit, the end was near. In the fifteenth century A.D., after a series of barbarian invasions, the

Darker areas on Bentley's map of Bengal, India, (above) show where malaria was most prevalent (1910). This corresponds to areas with much stagnant water. Light gray areas on map above right indicate decreasing population, and dark gray expanding population (1901–11).

Below: Facade of Angkor Wat, probably the largest religious edifice in the world, built in the first part of the 12th century A.D. by the Khmers. In the 15th century this great hydraulic civilization suffered several barbarian invasions. But malaria was probably the ultimate destroyer of their empire.

Khmers deserted their homeland, and today the forest surges around the fabulous ruins of Angkor. The last invader may well have been the malarial mosquito.

## The Dance of Death

When a parasite is always present in some members of a community, it is said to be *endemic*. When it is present in most of them (like malaria at Keneba), it is called *hyperendemic*; when in all of them, *holoendemic*. It is in these conditions that the population can acquire immunity against the diseases caused by at least some parasites. When infectious disease attacks many of the people in a community, we speak of an *epidemic*. This can happen in at least three ways. The parasite may be hyperendemic, and something happens (such as a famine) that breaks down the people's immunity, so that the parasites they are already harboring suddenly make them ill. Or the parasite may be normally endemic in only a few people, or may even infest members of the community only from time to time. In these conditions, the population probably has no immunity at all, but natural good health and good sanitary conditions prevent the parasite from spreading easily. Now, suppose something happens to make the disease more easily transmitted. Conditions arise that favor the vector; a new vector appears; sanitation breaks down, favoring the spread of diseases transmitted in human excrement. Or, finally, a new parasite, which the community has never experienced and against which it has no immunity, is suddenly introduced from outside. In all these circumstances epidemics can ravage a whole community, and even kill off most of its members. If a disease spreads in this way over whole continents, or even the whole world, then mankind experiences a *pandemic*, the most terrifying of all disasters.

With the rise of towns and trade—vital elements in the progress of civilization—epidemics and pandemics came into their own. In towns, people are concentrated in large numbers. Whereas a disease might spare most of them if they were spread out, it will sweep through all of them in a town. The greater the concentration of people, the more difficult sanitation becomes. Diseases that spread by contact, excrement, or vermin have been the natural scourges of the city. Where people are scattered in self-sufficient communities, epidemics are local. When trade becomes widespread, vectors and parasites are carried over larger areas, ultimately all over the world, and the epidemic becomes a pandemic. Again and again, diseases have been brought into regions hitherto free of them by trading fleets or caravans.

While infectious disease has helped to block the progress of the wet tropics and the dry belt, progress even in the favored societies of northwestern Europe has been slowed by epidemics and periodically halted by a pandemic. The history of civilization is punctuated by these catastrophes. Every time society recovered, towns grew, and trade flourished, the danger returned, on an ever-increasing scale.

Throughout civilized history, the supreme ally of infectious disease has been the breakdown of social life in revolution and war, more devastating with every larger integration of societies. Sieges and blockades and deliberate crop and herd devastations all engender famine and malnutrition, lowering the people's resistance. The demands and disturbances of war rapidly break down the hard-won benefits of sanitation. Among the ravaged communities, masses of men are carried all over the continents, in the worst possible conditions of camp and warship, to spread far and wide the parasites of infectious disease. Armies and navies were among the first communities to be studied in the dawn of public health research, not only because governments have always had a special interest in the condition of their fighting forces but also because conditions in them were so indescribably bad. Other human barbarities besides war have played a part in spreading disease. The slave trade between Africa and America, with its appalling conditions on the voyage, brought many diseases (possibly including yellow fever) from the Old World to the New.

Two of the chief killers have been *plague* and *typhus*. Plague is a very dangerous disease caused by the bacterium *Pasteurella pestis*. It is originally a disease of wild rodents, and has been observed in over 50 species. It is transmitted from one rodent to the other by fleas. In all parts of the world, people are occasionally bitten by the fleas and hence catch the disease, but usually it does not spread. Such diseases, occasionally caught in the countryside and not giving rise to epidemics, are called *sylvatic* diseases. The plot thickened when the fleas and the diseases passed to the black rat (*Rattus rattus*). Rats are the most tenacious of man's many unwelcome guests. They can live almost anywhere, on almost any diet, and have spread all over the the world in the wake of man, their mealticket. They eat practically everything man has, and are not above eating man himself. The black rat, which lives in human houses, was from early times man's most inseparable rat companion—traces of black rats have been found on a Neolithic site in Israel.

If large numbers of rats die of plague in a rat epidemic, their fleas look for another host species, and find one conveniently at hand—man. The result is a human epidemic, and since the black rat is a habitual stowaway on ships, this may turn into a pandemic. The two worst pandemics in history were caused in this way. As the

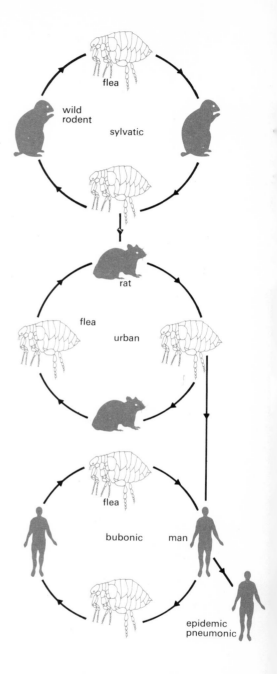

Diagram illustrates development of plague. Sylvatic plague occurs in rural areas among rodents and fleas, who may pass it to urban rats. Urban fleas thus infected may attack humans, who develop bubonic plague. When this invades human lungs (pneumonic plague) it spreads fast by droplet infection as well.

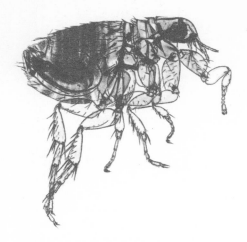

Above: The rat flea, main vector of bubonic plague. Below: The black rat, its usual host. Only when large numbers of such rats die of plague do fleas seek a new host—man.

Chinese poet Shih Tao-nan (1765–92) put it, before he died of plague himself: "Dead rats in the east, Dead rats in the west. . . . Few days following death of the rats, men pass away like falling walls. . . . There in the fields are crops, To be reaped by none; And the officials collect no tax!" What made the plague pandemics so murderous was one further step in the complicated sequence of transmission. The plague infection in man sometimes attacks the lungs, and it can then pass out in human breath and spread not only by fleas but by droplet infection. It is then called *pneumonic* plague, and sweeps like wildfire through a crowded community. An epidemic in Manchuria in 1910 actually started as a sylvatic disease from a local wild rodent, but became pneumonic and spread through slums to kill 42,302 people. The plague pandemics certainly must have involved both black rats and human lungs. Of the two supreme pandemics, that of the sixth century spared Britain,

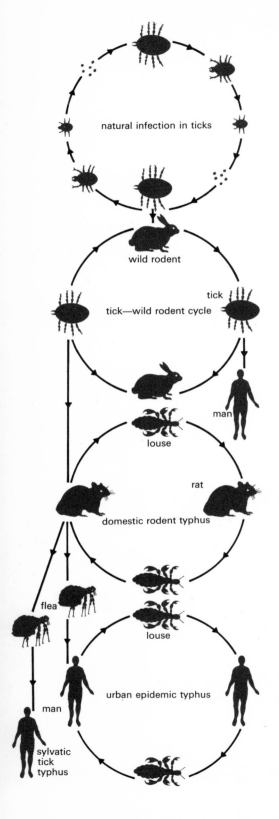

natural infection in ticks

wild rodent

tick—wild rodent cycle

tick

man

louse

rat

domestic rodent typhus

flea

louse

man

urban epidemic typhus

sylvatic
tick
typhus

which the black rat had not yet reached. When the Black Death came in the fourteenth century, returning Crusaders had already brought the rat to Britain, and this time Britain shared the fate of continental Europe.

The virus disease of smallpox (spread by contact) was probably already epidemic in the Indus valley cities of the third millennium B.C. Epidemic plague can also probably be traced back to the dawn of city life, although it cannot be recognized with certainty before a Near East outbreak in the second century A.D. A much more recent scourge is epidemic *typhus*, perhaps because it has an even more intricate history of changes in manner of transmission. The typhus rickettsia began as a parasite of ticks. But the ticks became sufficiently adapted to it not to suffer disease. From ticks, it began to pass into wild rodents, and occasionally even into human beings, causing the rare sylvatic disease, spotted fever. The next step was the transmission of the organism from rodent to rodent by means of lice, causing murine typhus. Rat-lice will not attack man, but rat-fleas will. Once the disease became established among wild rodents it could reach man in fleas and cause small local epidemics of murine typhus. This became more likely if the rodents affected were rats. This stage may have been reached in the Near East in the early Middle Ages. It seems to have caused its first European typhus epidemic in the monastery of La Cava, near Salerno, Italy, in 1083. A dangerous next step occurred when the disease began to pass between *human* lice, greatly favoring its spread in man. It is even more lethal to lice than to man, but before it dies an infected louse has time to move to another human being. This stage seems to have been reached in the fifteenth century, when typhus was brought by Spanish soldiers returning from Cyprus to the camp of Ferdinand and Isabella of Spain, in their campaign against the last Moorish stronghold of Granada. When the Spanish army was reviewed in 1490, according to Joaquin Villalba, "the generals noticed that 20,000 men were missing from the rolls, and of these 3,000 had been killed by the Moors and 17,000 had died of disease."

By the early sixteenth century, local typhus epidemics were beginning to spread over the continent. A new step was now being taken, the establishment of typhus as a disease of human lice, eliminating the rat-fleas altogether. The infection became localized in populations that had had time to acquire some immunity, and could pass it to others who had not. According to Hans Zinsser, the American medical scientist who pieced the whole story together, this stage was probably reached in Hungary, where Europe was fighting off the Ottoman Turks. It may have begun in 1456, when Hunyady was fighting Mohammed II, but it had almost certainly happened by 1542, when the Margrave

Diagram of development of typhus from natural infection in ticks via wild rodents to domestic rodents and then to man via fleas. Urban typhus, carried by human lice, causes serious epidemics.

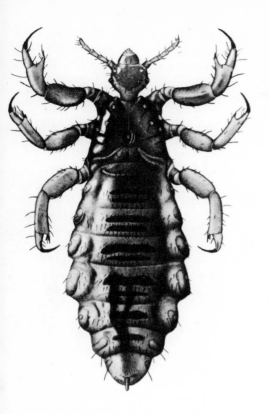

Above: Body louse (*Pediculus corporis*), which transmits urban typhus in man.

The network of Roman roads (map below) was an amazing feat of engineering that facilitated trade and communications. It also meant that when an epidemic broke out in one part of the Empire it spread in a way impossible before.

of Brandenburg brought a German army to Hungary's support. In this campaign, typhus killed few of the Hungarians and Turks, who had already gained a measure of immunity, but it killed 30,000 of the Margrave's soldiers, and Hungary was known as the graveyard of Germans. The survivors brought typhus back to Germany.

In 1566 the Emperor Maximilian II brought an army of assorted northwestern Europeans into Hungary. The resulting typhus epidemic wrecked his campaign, and this time the survivors carried typhus all over northwestern Europe. It had reached England by 1577. The infection of Europe was finally completed, in the seventeenth century, by the Thirty Years' War, which Zinsser has called "the most gigantic natural experiment in epidemiology to which mankind has ever been subjected." When it was over, no corner of the continent was left without its localized regions of infection. Armies, deserters, and refugees had roamed all over a Europe ridden by famine and disease. Since by now typhus was firmly united to the louse, its natural focal points from this time on were the most unsanitary and crowded places everywhere. It came to be called army fever, ship fever, jail fever, and, most appropriately of all, war fever.

In the first half of the first century B.C., the Roman poet Lucretius, greatest of all popularizers of science, was writing his poem *On the Nature of Things*. Part of the poem tells the epic story of the progress of human society. The poet describes the dawn of agriculture, the domestication of animals, the building of cities, the smelting of metals, and the emergence of civilized institutions. And then, suddenly, he ends with a grim picture of pestilence. Lucretius' version was modelled closely on the account by Thucydides (who caught it and recovered) of the pestilence of 430 B.C., that murdered the civilization of Athens. Lucretius seems to be saying that this is where human progress stops. However much we achieve, we shall always come up against this impenetrable barrier, the mysterious power of pestilence, which can wipe out in a year the patient work of centuries. The civilization of antiquity, sooner or later, was doomed. It was an astonishing poetic insight, for the ancient world had so far experienced only local epidemics and no pandemic. Yet this was indeed a critical factor that for so long interrupted the advance of even northwestern European civilization, breaking it into a jagged curve of dark ages and renaissances.

Lucretius was not immediately vindicated. The first century A.D. was not remarkable for pestilence. But the bomb was only waiting to be ignited. Trade on an unprecedented scale had made the whole Roman Empire one, and linked it with the civilizations of the distant East. The slums grew. The monarchy (a creation of big business)

made no attempt to improve the distribution of wealth, comfort, and education. The peasants remained a focus of bitter discontent, ready to explode (as army recruits) into the frightful revolution of the third century (p. 156). And along its splendid lines of communication the Empire had to dispatch troops all over Europe, the Mediterranean, and the Near East, to guard this frontier or that. All the conditions were there for pandemics, and in the second century they began to strike.

The first pandemic struck in the reign of Marcus Aurelius. It was said to have started from a chest looted in a Near Eastern temple, as if it really came out of Pandora's Box. It certainly started in the army of the Near East, in A.D. 165, and spread from Persia to the shores of the Rhine, infecting even German tribes across the frontier. The pandemic was probably a whole group of diseases, each reducing resistance to the others, but the chief killer may have been *smallpox*. It killed the emperor and an unknown number of his subjects. It went on till A.D. 180, paused, and returned in 189, killing 200 people a day in Rome itself. Throughout the third century, the peasants in the armies raged over the Empire, wrecking city life in a holocaust of revenge on the middle classes for their callous indifference to social welfare.

In A.D. 256 the next pandemic came, more extensive than before. It swept from Egypt to Scotland. St. Jerome said it had all but destroyed the human race, and that the earth was returning to deserts and forests. Nevertheless, much evidence (for instance the RAF survey of Italy, p. 161) suggests that the retreat of agriculture during these terrible centuries was limited and temporary, and that from the fourth century onward the population of the Empire continued to increase more than ever.

Then, in 540, there came the first of the two supreme pandemics, mainly *plague*. It lasted for nearly 60 years, and destroyed between one-third and one-half of the populations of the ancient Mediterranean world. After the year 565, Latin and classical Greek ceased to be living languages. The prophecy of Lucretius had come true: The ancient world was dead.

This time there was no doubt about the retreat in forest clearance (see Chapter 2). But, in northwestern Europe, the pandemics had removed some of the conditions that gave them birth. Towns and trade had dwindled. And so the early medieval monks and farmers and technologists were free of the dreadful menace that shadowed the Roman Empire. But as trade revived, there were danger signals. Venice paid a price for her trade supremacy: She had 63 plague epidemics in 600 years. But such disasters were still local hazards, and many people must have gone through life without experiencing an epidemic at all. It was in this

The first pandemic, perhaps mainly smallpox, struck in the reign of Marcus Aurelius (above), who died of it himself. In the reign of Justinian (below), the first pandemic of plague occurred.

period that the final steps were taken to make the technological breakthrough a certain prospect.

In the fourteenth century the rise in population sent everything wrong. Wars intensified, sanitation and morale began to crack. Above all, shortage of protein was reducing the resistance of the people to disease. The northern Dutch, who remained stockraisers and continued to eat meat, were remarkably immune to epidemics. This shows that malnutrition was a crucial factor in what followed. Meanwhile, trade had linked up the whole continent. The population was already going down, and agriculture already retreating. Epidemics were growing more frequent. The way was prepared for the King of Terrors, and in 1347, the Dance of Death began. Plague, the greatest killer of all, appeared in an army of Mongols in the Crimea. The black

Map shows how the plague swept across Europe in the 14th century. Lines indicate how far infection had spread at specific dates. In December 1347 the plague had only a small foothold in Mediterranean Europe, where it had arrived from the Near East. In three years it had engulfed all Europe.

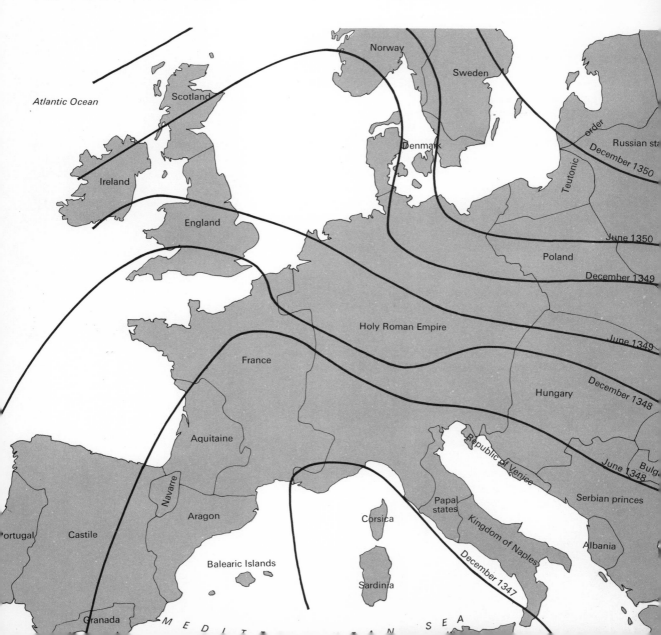

rat again carried it all over the civilized world, in the second supreme pandemic, known to history as the Black Death. *In five years, it destroyed between one third and one half of the population of Europe.* Pope Clement VI ordered statistics to be drawn up: The death-roll came to 42,836,486.

Unlike the ancient world, which was rotting when the pandemics struck, medieval civilization had passed a threshold of progress and was now certain to make the breakthrough. Recovery was therefore extremely rapid, and science and technology forged ahead with movable-type printing and the Italian Renaissance of the fifteenth century. By the end of the second century A.D., the people of the Roman Empire had felt that things could only go on getting worse. Medieval Europe, on the other hand, saw the end of the Black Death with unbounded joy, and settled down to another bout of progress. People gathered at gay parties to exchange plague stories, as they were later to exchange tales of the guillotine or the London blitz. The fashion world had its own renaissance: Women's dresses were slinky and low-cut, and (despite endless adult grumbling) teenagers of both sexes *would* wear pointed shoes. But in one respect the result of the second great pandemic was like that of the first. The end of the Black Death ushered in a new world, and the new national languages of Europe began to take their final shape.

Indeed, from the early Middle Ages onward, European history has a curiously two-fold aspect. On the one hand, there was a surge of progress such as had never occurred elsewhere. On the other, recurrent population crises gave rise to seemingly endless miseries and horrors, in which infectious diseases played a large part. The next three centuries were distinguished by an endless succession of epidemics making the rounds of Europe. In the bigger cities they could be devastating, like the London outbreak of plague in 1665. The new pattern of epidemics was firmly established by the end of the Thirty Years' War. The endless wars that followed gave Europe little chance to shake it off until the battle of Waterloo (1815). From then on, however, systematic improvements in public health began to take effect, and rising standards of living began to make people healthier and disease less lethal. Danger lay, however, in the swelling slums of the new big industrial cities, and a new disease took its place on the world stage. *Cholera* is a bacterial disease spread when people are crowded and their excrement gets mixed up with their drinking-water. In 1816 it broke out of its endemic home in India and China, causing four successive pandemics, three of which devastated Europe and North America. After 1875 it began to retreat again, somewhat mysteriously, although improved drainage must have helped. By the twentieth

Europeans celebrated the end of the Black Death joyfully. Above: At a feast a more sober guest treads on the long pointed shoes of another. Not all approved the exaggerated new fashions.

Right: Spread of cholera, 1816–1923. Before 1816 India was home of the disease. In mid-century, pandemics spread across Europe and America. Retreat of the disease in early 20th century was perhaps encouraged by improved drainage systems, but it still affected much of the East.

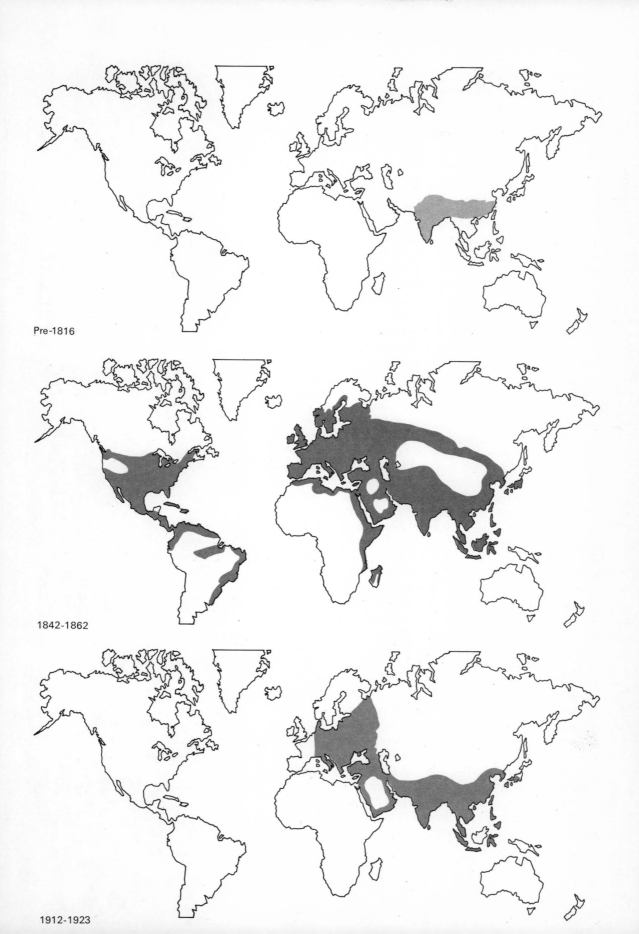

Pre-1816

1842-1862

1912-1923

century it was shrinking back to its homelands. The last cholera epidemic in Europe occurred in 1923.

World War I plunged the whole of eastern Europe into a nightmare. With tragic irony, this blow followed on the heels of the discovery in 1909 that typhus was carried by lice. In this new horror, typhus was supported by a coalition of other diseases. The principal sufferer was Russia. According to the heroic Russian physician Tarassewitch, there were probably more than 25 million cases of typhus in Soviet territories between 1917 and 1921, with almost three million deaths. The war must also have affected the health of northwestern Europe. It was almost certainly responsible for the last of the pandemics, the influenza outbreak of 1917-9. In the weakened war survivors, the disease was unusually lethal, and about 20 million people died. In Europe, previous epidemics had conferred some immunity; India fared worse. But if this influenza had been as lethal in Europe as the Black Death plague, one billion people might have died.

Epidemics and pandemics do more than reduce the population. The testimony of observers (Thucydides, medieval writers, Daniel Defoe) is unanimous: Pestilence has devastating effects on human behavior and human society. Distortions of family life are bound to outlast the generation of the pestilence. In general, people become less sociable and more aggressive. Thucydides noted that pestilence destroyed that feeling for law and cooperation on which Athenian democracy was based, and it is easy to trace the degeneration of Athenian politics after 430 B.C. From Athens, the "school of Greece" (as Pericles called her), the effect spread to the pupils: For the next generation, Greek war became more atrocious than ever before or after. War and pestilence are the two sides of a vicious spiral; each encourages the other. As for the Black Death, apart from evidence everywhere of the increase in crime, there is one outstandingly terrible example. Local *pogroms*—as organized massacres of the Jews are known—had begun at the time of the early Crusades, often during epidemics. Then a new kind of suspicion of "non-Europeans" began to play into the hands of a new and rising class of non-Jewish bankers. At first these had remained local. When the Black Death got under way, there occurred, all over Europe, a pogrom of pandemic proportions, the greatest before Hitler. Just as the Nazis accused Jews of fomenting the inflation and depression crises (contributing causes of the Nazi outbreak), so in the fourteenth century the Jews were accused of spreading the plague. As in the previous "epidemic" pogroms (and as in Nazi Germany), there was an obvious criminal motive on the part of the executioners, which some objective medieval chroniclers did not miss— the desire to eliminate prosperous Jewish communities.

The Black Death attacked people of all classes and ages—an idea strikingly expressed by these three groups (left), an early 19th-century copy of a medieval dance of death from Basel, Switzerland. Top: Death takes a merchant. Middle: Death leads away an unwilling pope. Bottom: Death takes a court jester.

Anxious to find a scapegoat for the Black Death, many people accused the Jews of spreading the plague, and large numbers were killed and their property looted. Below: Illustration, from Schedel's *Chronicle*, of Jews being burned alive.

"The money of the Jews," wrote one chronicler, "was the poison which brought about their death." But none of the pogroms would have been possible without the conditions created by the Black Death.

We have considered the routine cruelty of tropical tribes, always a prey to sickness (p. 215). A similar routine cruelty, on a more sophisticated level, has characterized the disease-ridden hydraulic societies. Here initiation ceremonies were replaced by "deterrent" criminal penalties. Republican Romans recoiled in disgust at the cruel death penalties of the Near East—except those for slaves. Medieval Europeans were amazed at the contrast in China between the superlatively conscientious judicial procedures, in which no effort was spared to ensure fair trial, and the revolting nature of the penalties after conviction. But although European societies were the first to abolish torture, at the same time, Europeans have not shrunk from killing on a grand scale. The history of Europe is stained with appalling episodes of rampant cruelty, like the Thirty Years' War or the Nazi outbreak. The last few centuries have been especially confusing, with real progress interwoven with endless recurrences of cruelty and war. In the long run, the effects of modern medicine and public health, in overcoming the factor of epidemic disease, may be incalculable—unless it is replaced by the no less dangerous factor we shall consider in the final chapter of this book.

# 12  One More Problem

We have seen how new disease problems have arisen from seemingly unrelated changes, such as the rise of towns. So, too, disease problems have sometimes receded as a result of such events. Progress in other fields can bring unexpected health bonuses. Two examples are plague and malaria in Europe. Plagues had disappeared from all of Europe except Turkey by the end of the seventeenth century, and great plague epidemics never occurred again there. This retreat has never been fully explained, but some of the factors are clear enough. Nutrition improved again after its deterioration in the seventeenth century. Cotton, more easily washed than wool, replaced woolen garments on an increasing scale. Houses were more often built of stone. In at least the more prosperous houses, carpets from the expanding Eastern trade replaced the deplorably unsanitary straw floors of the Middle Ages in which layer upon layer of spittle and other filth accumulated.

It now became less easy for the black rat to hide in houses. This weighted the scales against it at the time when a new rival, the brown rat, was invading from Asia. The brown rat is a "mobster" among rodents. It not only competed with the black rat, but assembled in gangs and set about exterminating its enemy. From man's point of view, this was eminently satisfactory, for the brown rat, although it can also carry plague, lives in less intimate contact with man than the black one. It inhabits his sewers. On land, the result was an unqualified victory for the brown rat. Only on shipboard did the black rat, better at climbing cables, keep its advantage. So today, as maps demonstrate, plague is a slum disease of the world's great ports, especially in the least sanitary coastal regions.

Malaria has not always been essentially a tropical disease; it has played its part in the history of Europe. This is especially clear in the Romagna, the area around Rome. Malaria appeared here about 200 B.C., after the second and biggest war with Carthage, when invading troops from North Africa had been in the neighborhood of Rome. It became really serious in the fourth century A.D., and remained so for about 400 years. This first wave coincided with a pronounced retreat in the agriculture of the Romagna (somewhat ahead of the general European retreat) and a low ebb in the political importance of Rome. Europe has been favored even in its malarial mosquitoes. Unlike *Anopheles gambiae*, they have not had a preference for man, or sought out his dwellings. European malaria is

As early as the 5th century B.C., scientists had noted the prevalence of malaria near marshy areas. When Empedocles drained a swamp near Selinus, Sicily, he reduced outbreaks of the disease, and a coin (above) was struck in his honor.

Murine plague is transmitted by black rats, which flourish in unsanitary conditions and often infest ships. Inevitably ports are infected, as can be seen on this map, marking areas of Africa affected by the disease in the first half of the 20th century.

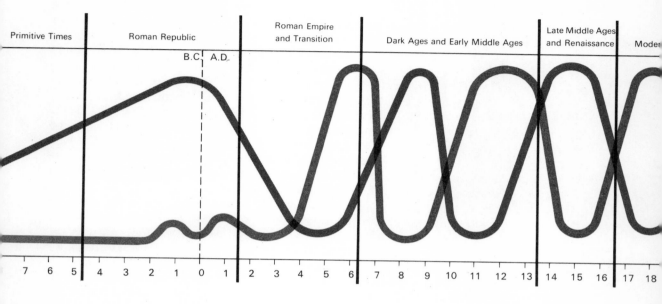

Primitive Times | Roman Republic | Roman Empire and Transition | Dark Ages and Early Middle Ages | Late Middle Ages and Renaissance | Modern

B.C. | A.D.

7 6 5 4 3 2 1 0 1 2 3 4 5 6 7 8 9 10 11 12 13 14 15 16 17 18

(as Hippocrates noticed in the fifth century B.C.) a disease of marsh areas. The Romagna is naturally marshy, but in ancient Roman times it was kept well drained, sometimes by extensive projects. As farming receded, the land returned to marsh and the mosquitoes flourished. As malaria increased, the farmers that survived either became weak and slovenly or left the area. In the seventh century, agriculture here began to recover as part of the general recovery of northwestern Europe, and malaria suddenly declined, presumably because of marsh reclamation. Rome took a new lease on life, and the papacy was at the height of its powers, creating in 800 the Holy Roman Empire. In the tenth century, agriculture declined again and malaria returned; Rome had an increasingly stormy history, which ended when the papacy was forced to move to Avignon in France. In the fourteenth century, the tide turned again. The papacy returned to Rome, and the city played a memorable part in the Italian Renaissance. Malaria declined again during this period. Finally—after the sack of Rome in 1527 and the Spanish domination of Italy— declining agriculture, rising malaria, and a phenomenal crime wave combined to keep Rome insignificant until the nineteenth century. At every retreat, malaria had made matters worse. At every recovery, its suppression by marsh reclamation had made matters better.

When agriculture (green line) was at a low ebb in the Italian Romagna, malaria (black line) was widespread. Recovery of farming led to reclamation of marshes, reducing malaria. Diagram shows interaction of farming and the disease.

Above: Miniature from a 14th-century English manuscript of an early surgical operation. The surgeon, holding his patient down, is suturing, or sewing up, a head wound with a large needle.

Above: Medieval forerunner of a modern clinic. Physician, left, dresses a wound, while other patients wait for attention. (Belgian MS, 15th century.)

During the last two centuries, long before the World Health Organization (WHO) of the United Nations began its campaign, malaria has been disappearing from northwestern Europe. It was gone from England as an endemic disease by 1887, although in 1918 malarious soldiers returning from the war were able to start an epidemic in the counties of Kent and Essex. It seems that two main factors have been involved in this improvement. As part of the new advance in agriculture, extensive drainage operations were carried out, thereby reducing the marshy areas in which the mosquitoes breed. Meanwhile, as a consequence of the new farming systems more cattle were kept indoors through the winter (p. 183). The mosquitoes (especially the most northerly ones, which like shelter) moved from house to barn, and bit cattle instead of man. It appears that these factors, unaided by deliberate control measures, were enough to eradicate malaria in several northwestern European countries.

But if we relied on such uncontrolled changes alone, we should probably only be exchanging new diseases for old. The crucial event of the last two centuries has been the advance, thanks to the technological breakthrough, of medicine and public health science. The medical researchers of the ancient Near East, of Greece and Rome, of Islam, and of the European Renaissance made impressive progress in diagnosis and treatment of disease in the individual. The greatest step forward was taken by Hippocrates and his colleagues in Greece during the fifth century B.C. The ancient Greeks (and Hebrews) had their suspicions of rats and Hippocrates could notice the connection of malaria with marshes. But the level of early knowledge of biology was far too low to permit any hope of controlling disease in populations, either epidemic or pandemic. So much and such varied knowledge was needed that this is hardly surprising. Only the work of biologists of the sixteenth to nineteenth centuries laid the necessary foundations and only at the end of the eighteenth century could the real advance in "death control" begin. Lucretius was right in feeling that man in his own day had no control over pestilence. It was reserved for peoples of the modern Western world and Japan to tackle the problems of public health, epidemic control, and tropical medicine.

## The Turning Point

Sanitary practices are not in themselves new. Nothing could be more hygienic than the palaces of Minoan Crete (2nd millennium B.C.) and much of the Mosaic Law was admirably sound. Agamemnon according to Homer, ordered all refuse removed from the Greek camp, because it had offended the gods and thus started a pestilence.

Many reasonable observations about public health were made by ancient and medieval scientists. But what was needed was an understanding of the individual diseases, of exactly how they spread, of how to combat vectors, and of how to take advantage of the development of immunity in the body. Man's first major success was in this last area although it was achieved by trial and error long before the facts were understood. The first great killer to be tackled was one of the oldest, smallpox. The trick here was to make the body produce antibodies by deliberately inducing a mild infection. Preparations used for this purpose are called *vaccines*. They may be live disease parasites modified by growing them in animals or cultures where they lose their special virulence for man. Or vaccines may be dead germs that still contain the substances necessary to stimulate antibody production. Ideally, they should produce little or no illness while making the body resistant to natural infection in the future. Protection against smallpox (with secretions from smallpox sores) had been practiced in China and Turkey for some time before it began in Europe. One of the first European "guinea-pigs" was Catherine the Great (1762–96), who summoned Dr. Dimsdale of Hertford, England, to Russia for the purpose. In 1796, Edward Jenner improved the technique by discovering that the related organism of cowpox (relatively

In 1796 Edward Jenner discovered that the organism of cowpox could be used to produce immunity against smallpox. Below: Jenner performing his first vaccination on a small boy. (From a painting by Melingue.)

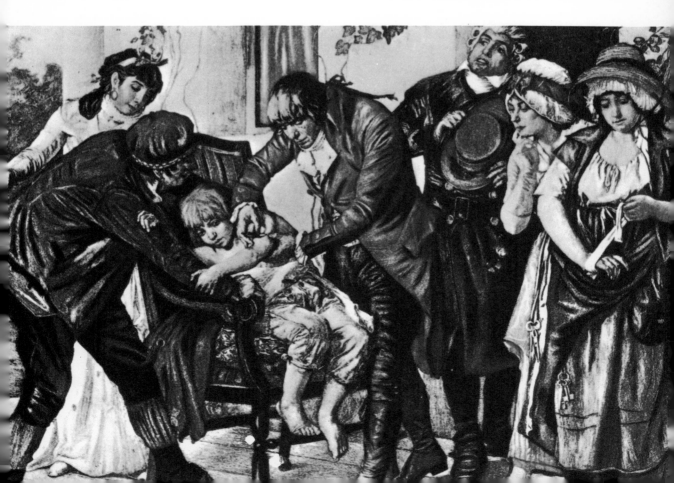

harmless to man) confers immunity against smallpox. Cowpox is called *vaccinia* (from Latin *vacca*, meaning a cow), and thus we have the word "vaccine."

Vaccination became more prevalent in the nineteenth century and smallpox at last vanished from the roll of great killers. Its elimination in Britain has been almost too successful. Vaccination is on the decline as it ceases to seem necessary, and some think there is again danger of smallpox epidemics. Meanwhile, Pasteur and Koch, in the 1860's and 1870's, began to discover the secrets of infectious disease and its microscopic agents. The principle of vaccination was extended to many other diseases (to some by Pasteur himself). These new discoveries have been invaluable, for instance, against tuberculosis.

By rendering many or most people in a community artificially immune, vaccination greatly reduces the danger of epidemics. Another approach has been the development of quarantine regulations, as a means of preventing spread of diseases, especially from immune to nonimmune parts of the world. This began on commonsense lines. The pioneer state was the Republic of Venice, which had every

German scientist Robert Koch traveled widely to study infectious diseases. Below left: Center figure, he holds a postmortem on an ox at Kimberley, Australia (1900). Below: Louis Pasteur, the French scientist who developed innoculations against anthrax, hydrophobia, and other diseases.

The ancient Minoans had a highly efficient drainage system in the palace at Knossos, Crete. Above: Minoan clay waterpipe (about 1800 B.C.). Below: It was not until 19th century that London fully realized the importance of good sanitation and built proper sewers that did not contaminate drinking-water.

reason to fear plague introduction from abroad (p. 222). In 1127 a law was enacted that anyone coming from the Levant had to remain in a building called the House of St. Lazarus for 40 days before entering the city. (The word "quarantine" comes from the Italian *quaranta*—forty.) However, quarantine (always liable to break down in war) remained rather ineffective until modern times, for more precise information was needed about each disease. Its rational development has been largely accomplished in the twentieth century, and owes most to the work of the League of Nations agencies and the World Health Organization of UNO.

Meanwhile, substantial changes began to take place in systematic public sanitation. It has been said that the great sewers of Roman and Greek cities were essentially storm drains, designed to prevent floods. Certainly nobody but the rich had domestic plumbing. In modern Europe there was, for a long time, a definite prejudice against putting human excrement into drains. Until 1815 the discharge of any refuse except kitchen slops into London drains was prohibited by law. In Paris this policy lasted till 1880.

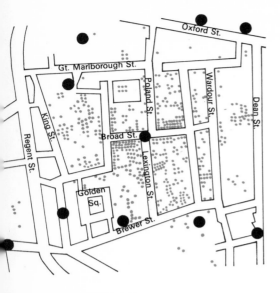

Above: Map of Soho drawn up by Dr. John Snow marking houses where cases of cholera occurred in outbreak of 1848. Circles mark drinking-water pumps. When pump in Broad Street was put out of use, the epidemic ended, thus confirming his suspicions of its contaminated water.

Below: American army officials using powder sprays to delouse inhabitants of Naples in typhus epidemic in January 1944. This attack on the vectors of the disease swiftly brought the epidemic to an end.

What spurred the authorities to investigate the problem and change their policy was the succession of cholera outbreaks.

In 1848 Dr. John Snow of Soho, London, made a large-scale map of his practice and marked on it the houses of the 500 cholera victims in the area. These clustered around a hand-pump in what was then Broad Street, and Snow deduced that cholera was spread by contaminated drinking-water. From the mid-nineteenth century, human excrement was systematically passed to the drains, and steps taken to dispose of it. This one reform must have been enormously important for all diseases spread by excrement. Other improvements were on the way. Hospitals, formerly a natural focus for epidemics, were reformed by the colossal energy of one tough and self-assured woman. Anyone who doubts the influence of individuals on human history may examine the casualty figures of the armies in the Crimea in 1854–6. The French lost 51 per cent of their wounded, the English 27 per cent. The French lost 25 per cent of their sick, the English 12 per cent. The only factor that the English had and the French had not was Florence Nightingale.

By the twentieth century the work of Pasteur and Koch had laid the foundations of the science of infectious diseases. The work of Manson, Laveran, Ross, and others had begun to unravel the complexity of life-cycles and vectors. Large-scale systematic assaults on disease problems began. Work on the Panama Canal was at first halted by disease, especially yellow fever. The builders mounted a vigorous research campaign that (at the cost of several European and Japanese scientists, who took too many risks) ended by identifying yellow jack and its vector, *Aedes aegypti*. Finally, the first grand public health and quarantine operation was mounted during World War I by, of all people, the Kaiser's General Staff. These generals realized that if the typhus outbreak of Eastern Europe spread westward into Germany, the war was lost. We owe it to their Prussian efficiency that not only Germany but the whole of northwestern Europe was spared the fate of Russia.

With the coming of the international agencies—first of the League of Nations, then of the United Nations—man's campaigns against infectious disease became world-wide and ever more effective, thanks to the fundamental knowledge now available and to the constant search for more. Even the tropics could begin at last to draw breath. Most spectacular has been the campaign that has totally eradicated malaria from vast areas of the earth, and aims at its eradication everywhere. In the control of vector-borne diseases, insecticides have played a great part. Spraying the walls of houses is a crucial part of the World

Health Organization (WHO) campaign against malarial mosquitoes. The new knowledge and techniques even enabled man to come through World War II without the catastrophic disease outbreaks of World War I. Of course, as always, this war came to the rescue of some diseases. It even reintroduced malaria into central Europe, because the deaths of large numbers of cattle drove the mosquitoes back to man. But the typhus epidemic in war-torn Naples in 1943 was quelled promptly by delousing the population with the insecticide DDT.

As always, there are continual new problems, but dealing with them is no longer a matter of centuries or millennia. Poliomyelitis is an old disease, as is clear from at least one ancient Egyptian portrait, but it has only recently become a common illness. It is, in fact, an epidemic disease that breaks out because of *good* sanitation. In unsanitary communities, more than 80 per cent of the children acquire natural immunity before they are four years old. As sanitation improves, people no longer become immune and polio epidemics can occur. They began to be serious as drainage improved in nineteenth-century Europe, and are appearing in the developing countries as their sanitation improves. Man is coping with this loss of natural immunity by artificial immunization. Thanks to virus research, when polio became a real threat it took relatively few years to produce the Salk vaccine.

In another respect, the danger of pandemics is greater now than it ever was before. The speed of air transport gives terrifying opportunities for the spread of diseases

Above: Limestone monument from Egypt (about 2000 B.C.) showing the priest Ruma who had an atrophied limb—the result of an attack of poliomyelitis.

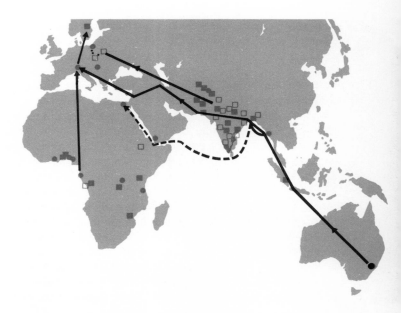

Map shows how smallpox epidemic spread by aircraft from Australia and Africa to Europe in 1963. Dots mark small outbreaks, squares large outbreaks. Significantly, large outbreaks occurred along air routes (solid lines). Broken lines mark shipping routes, and dotted line marks bus or train routes.

between world regions. Experts in the field are haunted by the possibility of yellow fever (always confined to the two sides of the Atlantic) reaching the vast, nonimmune populations of Asia. Of 80,716 airplanes inspected in the United States between 1937 and 1947, 28,852 were found to contain insects and related animals. The nightmare became real in 1930, when ships and probably airplanes carried *Anopheles gambiae* from Dakar to Brazil, where malaria killed thousands. Swift action by a team of experts eradicated the mosquito by 1940. But this sort of thing shows what could happen if the ever-more-stringent quarantine precautions of the world broke down—for instance, as a result of war. The 1964 malaria report of WHO shows clearly that the greatest concern of the malaria campaign now is to prevent reintroduction of the disease into countries from which it has been eradicated.

In February 1957 a new influenza virus was isolated on the Chinese mainland. In May, the first notification was made to WHO, from Singapore. Within a few months a new vaccine was ready for use—just too late. The pandemic of Asian flu had meanwhile hit Britain, making seven and one-half million people ill in England and Wales. The death-rate was fortunately extremely low. Otherwise a disease with such an attack rate might have been another Black Death. Notifications in February would have given time for vaccine production, but no routine machinery existed for Communist China to give this notification, for she was not a member of the United Nations. It is clear that we exclude any country from the work of the international agencies at our own risk. Fortunately, Communist China is now already a member of several international scientific organizations. For the impartial organisms and vectors of disease, the world is one, and mankind is a common host. The lesson is gradually being learned. It is probably true to say that infectious disease (including disease of crops and herds) is doing more than anything else to force mankind to think and work in terms of international integration.

With all the dangers, old and new, there is no doubt that infectious disease is under control as never before in the history of man. We have passed the germ barrier of Lucretius. Even the tropics are beginning to benefit on a grand scale. In England, average life expectancy at birth in 1550 was 8.5 years. It is now very nearly the biblical three-score years and ten. In such countries as Britain and the United States, the causes of death have changed completely. The dramatic decline of diphtheria and tuberculosis in the twentieth century is especially noteworthy. Infectious diseases are no longer at all prominent. Their places are taken by cancer and "diseases of old age"—for instance, diseases of the blood-vessel system. These last illnesses are

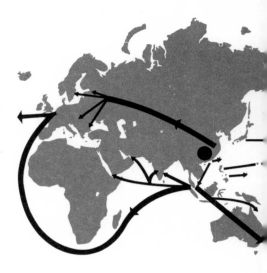

This map shows routes by which Asian flu epidemic of 1957 spread. Probably originating in southeast Asia (black dot), it spread across central Asia to eastern Europe but arrived in Britain by sea. It was then passed on to America.

Below: Causes of death in Britain in 1907 and 1963. Deaths from infectious diseases (dark gray) have declined dramatically, while deaths from diseases of heart and blood vessels (dark green) have trebled. Total of deaths from all other diseases (gray) has fallen slightly.

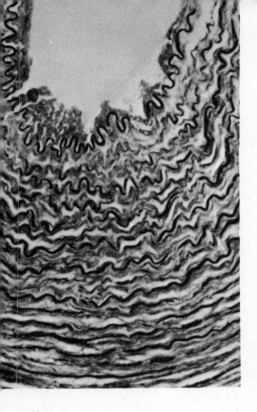

Today, hardening of the arteries is a disease often attributed to the stress of modern life. But evidence of it has also been found in Egyptian mummies, as in this magnified section across an artery of a male mummy.

Below: Growth of the world's population (in approximate figures) from 10,000 B.C. to A.D. 1950. Note slow steady climb to 750 million and then, after Industrial Revolution and advances in agriculture and medicine, sharp rise to 2476 million by 1950.

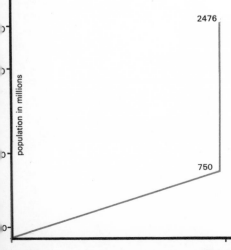

not new reactions to the strains of modern life, as some suppose—hardening of the arteries attacked at least two Egyptian Pharaohs, Mereneptah and Rameses II. It can actually be diagnosed in tissue sections from mummies. It is simply that most of us, and not just pampered Pharaohs, can now live long enough to die of such diseases. The problems of longevity and cancer are the ones that now lie before biological science. Infectious disease will present continual new problems, and eternal vigilance is the price of public health.

But this is a problem of the past. What more is there to withhold mankind from continuous progress toward happiness and creative activity? What is left in Pandora's Box? There is, indeed, still another problem, and by a supreme irony this has appeared as a result of the achievement of modern medicine. It is the problem of population.

## A Question of Numbers

At the Brussels International Exhibition of 1958, the British Pavilion contained perhaps the most terrifying exhibit ever put on show. It was a little device like the mileage gauge on a car dashboard, showing the growing population of the British Commonwealth. As the gadget ticked on and the number steadily increased, mankind's latest problem was presented with startling effect.

Population is a complicated subject, but the rise or fall of a population depends fundamentally on the difference between birth-rate and death-rate, both usually calculated as numbers per hundred (or per thousand) per year. If the death-rate is higher, the population falls. If the birth-rate is higher, the population rises. The trouble is that any rise is by compound interest, since the more people there are, the more they can breed. If a population increases by the same percentage every year, it increases by a constantly greater absolute number. If it rises by two per cent per year, for instance, it more than doubles every generation. A calculation has been made that shows the fantastic implications of all this. Suppose mankind had sprung from a single couple living about 12,000 years ago (shortly before the coming of agriculture), and suppose there had been one more birth than deaths per hundred per year (a one per cent increase every year). Then today the world population would form a sphere of flesh many thousand light-years in diameter, expanding with a velocity many times faster than light.

From the ages at death of fossil remains of Paleolithic populations, it has been shown that the death-rate was very high. But since man survived, it is assumed that the birth-rate was even higher. About the agricultural civilizations we know even more than this. Evidence from many sources shows that they generally had very high birth-rates

237

Sharply rising populations in small developed countries like Britain are a very real problem. Above: Liverpool Street station, London, in the rush hour with commuters pouring off the trains.

A feature of rising populations is the increased proportion of people living in towns. The two maps shown below illustrate the spectacular spread of London in the 19th century.

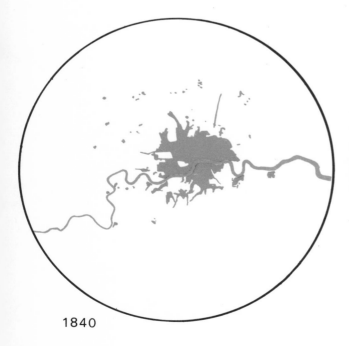

1840

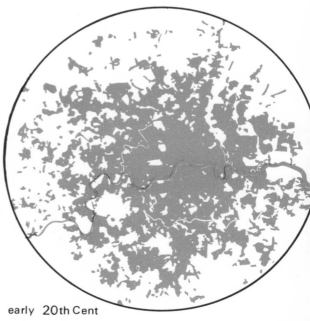

early 20th Cent

of 3.5–5 per cent, and death-rates also high but normally lower, 3–4 per cent. The populations therefore increased by 0.5–1 per cent per year. They did not end up as an expanding sphere of flesh because every so often they were cut down by a catastrophic death-rate of 15–50 per cent.

The agents of death were war, famine, malnutrition, and infectious disease. Hence world population grew relatively slowly. It may have been 2–20 millions in 10,000 B.C., and it has been estimated as 650–850 millions in A.D. 1750.

The technological breakthrough and the Industrial Revolution brought with them a mastery of food production and infectious disease control that reduced the normal death-rate to below 1.5 per cent. Even more important, man's material progress reduced the periodic catastrophic death-rates from famine and pestilence. The birth-rate in the developed countries eventually came down to a little above the death-rate, but only after a considerable lag. Thus in England and Wales the death-rate was falling steeply before 1820, while the birth-rate began to fall steeply only after 1870. Since, in any case, the periodic catastrophes were under control, the European population rocketed.

In the developing countries, events were still more spectacular. At a time when they still had the high "agricultural" birth-rate, the coming of modern famine- and disease-control suddenly removed their catastrophic death-rates and cut their normal death-rates. Between 1891 and 1921, the population of India rose by only a total of 5 per cent. Between 1921 and 1951, when famines and epidemics were under considerable control, it rose by more than 1 per cent *per year*. In Ceylon, the DDT campaign by WHO against malarial mosquitoes lowered the normal death-rate from 2 to 1.4 per cent in the single year 1946–7. The birth-rate remained over 4 per cent. Hence the annual population increase of Ceylon, which was 0.46 per cent in 1871–80 and 1.71 per cent in 1941–5, rose to 2.74 per cent in 1948. Annual increases of over 2 per cent appeared about the same time in India, China, Central and South America, and other developing areas. Africa, where food and disease problems are tougher, has taken longer to reach this point. In January 1966, however, a new drug, Ambilihar, was announced for use in the cure of bilharziasis. It is said to effect a cure in as little as a week, and may be used by the millions of bilharziasis sufferers in Africa as soon as supplies are available. If bilharziasis is conquered, vast areas of the African dry belt will be opened up by modern irrigation schemes without fear of the consequences. As a result, we can expect a sensational rise in the African populations.

To crown all this, since World War II the birth-rate in developed countries has begun to rise again. In January 1964, the British Minister of Health announced that the

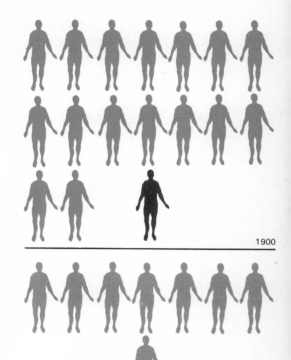

1900

1800

Diagram shows increase in population of Europe in the 19th century. Each figure represents 25 million people. The one colored gray represents the Europeans who had emigrated by 1900.

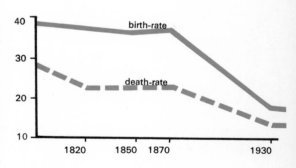

Above: Birth- and death-rates per 1000 in England and Wales, 1750–1950. The graphs show the lag between the fall of the death-rate and that of birth-rate. This lag explains the population increase.

"birth-rate in Britain has risen more sharply than any expert could possibly have forecast." It was calculated that births in 1965 would probably reach the figure that experts, a few years earlier, had predicted for 1975.

The minister's experts were not the only people to be taken by surprise. One of the most alarming things about the present rise in world population is the way it outstrips the predictions of experts. The rate of increase itself is continually rising. For India, it was still about 2 per cent in 1960, and 2.8 per cent by 1964. In 1950, Sir Julian Huxley was considered an alarmist when he suggested the world population might reach 3 billion by the year 2000. United Nations estimates prepared in 1951 predicted more than 3 billion by 1980. According to FAO's 1964 Production Yearbook (published in 1965), the world population was in fact 3.22 billion in 1963. Recent estimates suggest (at the present rate) a world population of 22 billion by the year 2040.

In publications by scientists concerned with food production, one often reads now of a "race" to feed the growing population, and sometimes there is a suggestion that we can win the race. As a result of a fantastic scientific and technological effort, with sharply increasing use of agricultural chemicals, world food production was increased by 10 per cent between 1958 and 1963—a staggering achievement. Yet world food production *per head of population* (and therefore the amount of food per person) was the same in both years, because the population had increased just as much. "Now *here*, you see," said the Red Queen to Alice in *Through the Looking Glass*, "it takes all the running you can do, to keep in the same place." In the Far East and Latin America, food production per head in 1963–4 was actually lower than before World War II. Even at the level of supply we are struggling to preserve, more than half the people in the world are not getting an adequate diet. Moreover, the increase of food production on land is approaching a limit beyond which all our technology cannot push it. Even with the full harvest of the oceans added, we could hardly expect to feed the 22 billion people expected by 2040. In any case, if population increase simply remained at its present rate (let alone became faster), it would sooner or later become that expanding sphere of flesh. Obviously, in real life, one of two things must happen: Either the birth-rate will come down or the death-rate will go up.

This does not mean that the heroic labors of the food-producers should be slackened. The real race is to "keep in the same place" until the birth-rate can be lowered. Nor is food the only aspect of the problem. At present the population increase is especially disturbing in the developing countries and in small developed countries like Britain,

Above: Photo of Golcar, England (background), with its industrial and domestic buildings gradually encroaching on the land around. This exemplifies a dangerous development in a country that already has too little agricultural land to grow food for its population.

Dotted line on graph (right) shows that world production of food has risen steeply in the years 1954–65. But so has population (black line), so that production per head is in fact decreasing slightly. In 1965–66, production per head dropped by about two per cent. (All figures exclude Red China.)

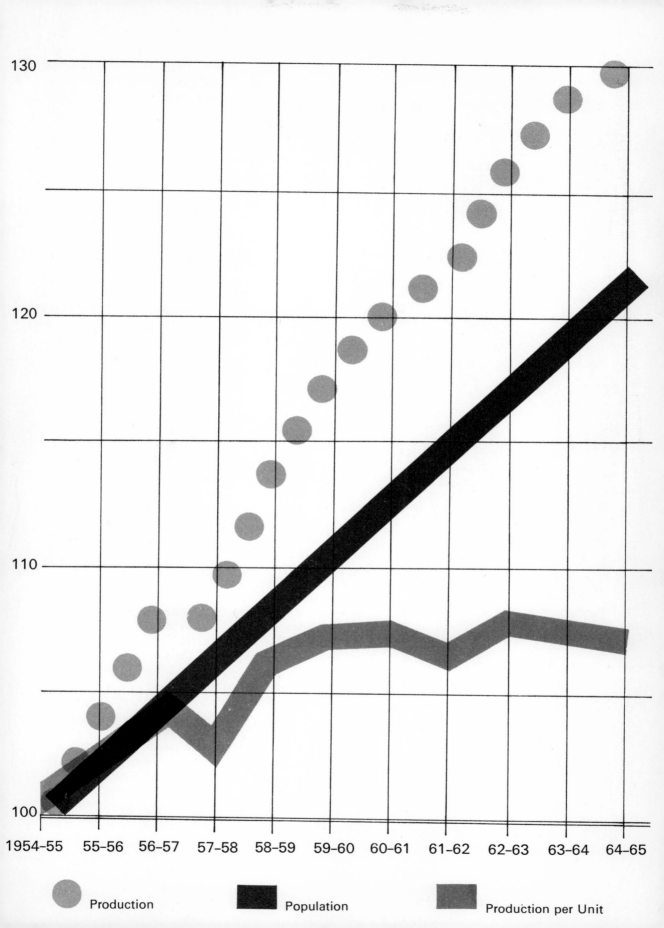

130

120

110

100

1954–55   55–56   56–57   57–58   58–59   59–60   60–61   61–62   62–63   63–64   64–65

● Production          ■ Population          ■ Production per Unit

Priests tearing the hearts from live human sacrifices to the Aztec God of War. Nuclear weapons offer a similar solution to the problem of matching population and resources. Can we find a different solution?

the Netherlands, and Japan—although the Japanese in recent years have taken steps to hold down their increase. The British and Dutch already had only half an acre of farmland per head in 1961, and by 1965 the British Government was talking of building on farmland. The larger developed countries, like the U.S.A. and U.S.S.R., will feel the pinch in due course. Already California has a serious water-shortage problem.

All those problems of man's relations with nature that we considered earlier are now trivial if the population is stabilized even at its present level. All are insoluble if it goes on rising much longer. In that case, much evidence suggests that, long before we run completely out of food, tensions due to crowding will erupt in violence and ultimately in wars far worse than those of the fourteenth and even the twentieth centuries. War, followed by famine and pestilence as our vulnerable machinery for food production and public health breaks down, will end in a more catastrophic death-rate than those of the two supreme pandemics, and will throw man's progress back untold centuries. On the other hand, if the population can soon be stabilized or reduced, the prospects for man are golden. Then the work of the food producers will bring rich rewards. Up until now, only a tiny minority of people have ever been able to enjoy comfort, leisure, and education, supported by the surplus produced by all the rest. Now, for the first time, modern technology and automation could bring these things within the reach of all mankind.

One of the last problems facing man, therefore, is to reduce the human birth-rate. Population control methods, brutal and painful, have appeared in many human societies, enforced by cruel economic pressure or tribal or state tyranny. The mainland ancient Greeks killed surplus infants by exposure. The Incas made a proportion of women compulsory virgins for life. Shaka, the Zulu dictator of the nineteenth century, made his young warriors remain celibate until middle age. Many tribal societies practice surgical mutilation on their members. We cannot afford to reduce the birth-rate by tyrannies worse than those that blocked the progress of the empires of the dry belt. The problem is, therefore, to discover what makes human beings breed less of their own free will.

The initially falling birth-rate of developed nations suggests one factor: hope. When people expect things to improve, they want the best for their children, and so have fewer. The renewed rise in birth-rate in these same countries may mean that things no longer seem to be improving so fast. This is a powerful argument for making all-out efforts to develop the emerging nations faster and for increasing the opportunities of the underprivileged in the developed ones. A related factor emerges from some very encouraging recent events in Japan. Between 1950 and 1951, a group of Japanese newspapers asked a cross-section of the population: "Do you expect to depend on your children in your old age?" In 1950 more than 55 per cent answered: "Definitely, yes." The proportion giving this answer declined steadily, reaching 27 per cent by 1961, presumably owing to increasing confidence in social services for old people. Now, during this same period the Japanese birth-rate actually *fell*, from 2.8 to 1.7 per cent.

There is some hope, therefore, that the birth-rate *can* be reduced in time, if we devote all our research resources to obtaining a general solution of the fundamental problem. After all he has achieved in controlling nature, it would be sad and strange if man proved incapable of this. In any event, we have now reached the most exciting and critical stage in the story of man, and this or the next generation may see the creation of paradise or hell on earth. Which will it be? The question remains an open one, as it was for the poet Sophocles, who wrote these words in his play *Antigone*, produced in Athens about 2400 years ago :

*There are many remarkable things, and nothing more remarkable than man; he crosses the sea in the troughs of great waves through the stormy winds of winter; he grinds away the indestructible unwearied earth, eldest of the gods, as his mule-drawn plows drive back and forth, year after year.*

*In the coils of his nets he takes the careless birds and the wild beasts and the beings of the sea; by his devices he tames the shaggy-maned horse and the oxen of the mountains.*

*He has learned speech and wind-swift thought, and how to live in cities, and to shelter from the bite of frost and the lash of sleet, the all-providing one; baffled by no emergency, only death he cannot escape; but he has found means to avoid diseases hard to control.*

*Possessing by his skill resources beyond belief, sometimes he comes to harm, sometimes to prosperity.*

If we can solve the population problem humanely, the peaceful use of our resources, symbolized by this nuclear power-station, could bring about a paradise on earth.

# Index

# Credits